Seminars in Basic Neurosciences

College Seminars Series

Series Editors

Professor Hugh Freeman, Honorary Professor, University of Salford, and Honorary Consultant Psychiatrist, Salford Health Authority

Dr Ian Pullen, Consultant Psychiatrist, Dingleton Hospital, Melrose, Roxburghshire

Dr George Stein, Consultant Psychiatrist, Farnborough Hospital, and King's College Hospital

Professor Greg Wilkinson, Editor, *British Journal of Psychiatry*, and Professor of Liaison Psychiatry, University of Liverpool

Other books in the series

Seminars in Alcohol and Drug Misuse. Edited by Jonathan Chick & Roch Cantwell

Seminars in Child and Adolescent Psychiatry. Edited by Dora Black & David Cottrell

Seminars in Clinical Psychopharmacology. Edited by David King

Seminars in Liaison Psychiatry. Edited by Elspeth Guthrie & Francis Creed

Seminars in Practical Forensic Psychiatry. Edited by Derek Chiswick & Rosemarie Cope

Seminars in Psychiatric Genetics. By Peter McGuffin, Michael J. Owen, Michael C. O'Donovan, Anita Thapar & Irving Gottesman

Seminars in the Psychiatry of Learning Disabilities. Edited by Oliver Russell

Seminars in Psychology and the Social Sciences. Edited by Digby Tantam & Max Birchwood

Seminars in General Adult Psychiatry. Edited by George Stein & Greg Wilkinson

Forthcoming titles

Seminars in Psychiatry for the Elderly. Edited by Brice Pitt & Mohsen Naguib

Seminars in Psychotherapy. Edited by Sandra Grant & Jane Naismith

Seminars in
Basic Neurosciences

Edited by
Gethin Morgan & Stuart Butler

GASKELL

British Library Cataloguing-in-Publication Data

Seminars in Basic Neurosciences.–
(College Seminars Series)
  I. Morgan, Gethin II. Butler, Stuart
  III. Series
  612.8

ISBN 0 902241 61 3

Distributed in North America
by American Psychiatric Press, Inc.
ISBN 0 88048 625 2

Gaskell is an imprint of the Royal College of Psychiatrists,
17 Belgrave Square, London SW1X 8PG.
The Royal College of Psychiatrists is a registered charity, number 228636.

The views presented in this book do not necessarily reflect those
of the Royal College of Psychiatrists, and the publishers are not
responsible for any error of omission or fact. College Seminars are
produced by the Publications Department of the College; they
should in no way be construed as providing a syllabus or other
material for any College examination.

Phototypeset by Dobbie Typesetting Limited, Tavistock, Devon
Printed in Great Britain by Bell and Bain Ltd, Glasgow

Contents

Contributors

Dr Ken Barrett, Consultant Neuropsychiatrist/Senior Lecturer, Department of Psychiatry, School of Postgraduate Medicine, Keele University, Stoke on Trent ST4 7QB

Dr John Bradshaw, Consultant Radiologist, Department of Neuroradiology, Frenchay Hospital, Frenchay, Bristol BS16 1LE

Dr Stuart Butler, Scientific Director, Burden Neurological Institute, Stoke Lane, Stapleton, Bristol BS16 1QT

Dr Stephen Gilbey, Consultant Physician, Department of Endocrinology, Hammersmith Hospital, Ducane Road, London W12 0HS

Dr Stephen Hallett, Consultant Clinical Neuropsychologist, Coventry Consulting Rooms, 11 Dalton Road, Earlsdon, Coventry CV5 6PB

Dr Timothy Lewis, Consultant Radiologist, Department of Neuroradiology, Frenchay Hospital, Frenchay, Bristol BS16 1LE

Dr Steve Logan, Senior Lecturer, Department of Physiology, The Medical School, University of Birmingham, Birmingham B15 2TT

Dr Philip Luthert, Senior Lecturer in Neuropathology and Honorary Consultant Neuropathologist, Department of Neuropathology, Institute of Psychiatry, De Crespigny Park, Denmark Hill, London SE5 8AF

Dr Alexander Macrae, MRC Training Fellow, Molecular Genetics Unit, Department of Medicine, Addenbrooke's Hospital, Cambridge CB2 2QQ

Professor Gethin Morgan, Professor of Mental Health, University of Bristol, 41 St Michael's Hill, Bristol BS2 8DZ

Dr Hilary Morgan, Consultant Clinical Neurophysiologist, Burden Neurological Hospital, Stoke Lane, Stapleton, Bristol BS16 1QT

Dr David Nutt, Director, Psychopharmacology Unit, School of Medical Sciences, University Walk, Bristol BS8 1TD

Foreword
Series Editors

The publication of *College Seminars*, a series of textbooks covering the breadth of psychiatry, represents a new venture for the Royal College of Psychiatrists. At the same time, it is very much in line with the College's established role in education and in setting professional standards.

College Seminars are intended to help junior doctors during their training years. We hope that trainees will find these books useful, on the ward as well as in preparation for the MRCPsych examination. Separate volumes will cover clinical psychiatry, each of its subspecialties, and also the relevant non-clinical academic disciplines of psychology and sociology.

College Seminars will also make a contribution to the continuing medical education of established clinicians.

Psychiatry is concerned primarily with people, and to a lesser extent with disease processes and pathology. The core of the subject is rich in ideas and schools of thought, and no single approach or solution can embrace the variety of problems a psychiatrist meets. For this reason, we have endeavoured to adopt an eclectic approach to practical management throughout the series.

The College can draw on the collective wisdom of many individuals in clinical and academic psychiatry. More than a hundred people have contributed to this series; this reflects how diverse and complex psychiatry has become.

Frequent new editions of books appearing in the series are envisaged, which should allow *College Seminars* to be responsive to readers' suggestions and needs.

Hugh Freeman
Ian Pullen
George Stein
Greg Wilkinson

Preface

Trainees in psychiatry need to acquire a thorough knowledge of the basic neurosciences. As things are at present, they are liable to experience several problems in trying to do so. They often find it difficult to decide exactly how far they should explore topics which may not have been addressed since they were undergraduates, and perhaps no more than superficially at that time. Furthermore, totally new fields of knowledge may have appeared, ones which are complex and not easy to understand. Access to relevant texts and identification of appropriate key original sources may also be difficult, with the result that trainees fear that they have not covered essential areas in their reading.

In preparing this volume we have tried to address such problems which have long been voiced. Relevant postgraduate examinations do not specify a detailed syllabus and it is necessary to use good judgement in deciding exactly how much detailed knowledge is required. We have dealt with this problem by ensuring that our contributors are experienced as teachers of clinical trainees. We do not claim to have comprehensively defined a basic neurosciences curriculum, nor do we have any formal remit to do so, but we do believe that included in the present volume are the key topics which are likely to be encountered in postgraduate examinations in psychiatry. Bringing them together under a single cover should help by making access to relevant information easier, as will the recommendations for selective further reading. The chapter concerned with examination of the nervous system and neurological syndromes rounds off the total picture. It emphasises the close relationships which psychiatry has with both basic and clinical neurosciences, and reminds trainees that they are expected to be able to carry out a competent and thorough examination of the nervous system.

We hope that the text which is presented here will also allow psychiatrists, trainees or otherwise, to update their knowledge of the neurosciences and help them to feel confident that they are appropriately aware of the important topics in this complex and rapidly developing field.

Gethin Morgan
Stuart Butler

1 Functional neuroanatomy
Stuart Butler

Basic structures ● Sensory systems ● Motor systems ● Functional organisation of the forebrain

---

Why should psychiatrists study neuroanatomy? Unlike neurologists and neurosurgeons, their specialty does not deal directly with the structures of the nervous system.

The evidence suggests that the brain provides the physical substrate for the mind, and that malfunction of parts of the brain can lead to disorders of mental activity and behaviour. Organic approaches to psychiatry seek an understanding of mental illness in terms of dysfunction within the nervous system. For example, changes in social behaviour after head injury may result from damage to the frontal lobes; some of the symptoms of schizophrenia may be produced by disturbances in the temporal lobes; and the amnesia and dementia of Alzheimer's disease is due to the impairment of cholinergic transmission in the limbic system and cerebral cortex. Even though the psychiatrist does not deal directly with the brain, some knowledge of neuroanatomy is necessary to take advantage of biological explanations of this kind.

An understanding of sensory and motor pathways and their relationship to other structures within the central nervous system (CNS) is also required in order to interpret the findings of the neurological examination of a patient in terms of organic disorder.

Looking to the future, it is clear that therapeutic advances in psychopharmacology will depend on targeting neuroanatomical pathways with increasing specificity. Studies of the functional organisation of the cerebral cortex and limbic system are beginning to provide an understanding of physical mechanisms which underlie psychological processes.

All of these issues require a knowledge of the structure of the nervous system, of how information is relayed from one place to another, and of how different functions are represented in the brain.

This chapter first provides a synopsis of aspects of neuroanatomy which the psychiatrist will have studied in preclinical courses. It then deals with the organisation of the cerebral cortex and the limbic system; although the treatment is didactic, it goes beyond descriptive morphology to consider the functional aspects of these systems in more detail than is usually attempted before specialisation. However, neurohistology, neuroembryology and other aspects of neuroanatomy which do not directly support psychiatry or the neurological examination are not dealt with here. The bibliography includes a list of textbooks which provide a more detailed treatment of the subject than is possible in this volume.

Basic structures

Subdivisions and major surface features of the brain

The brainstem links the forebrain with the spinal cord. It is divided into three sections: the medulla, the pons, and the midbrain (Fig. 1.1). Each section contains the nuclei of a number of cranial nerves and provides passage for ascending and descending pathways. The medulla contains the cardiovascular and respiratory centres. The tectum forms the roof of the midbrain and contains important visual and auditory reflex centres - the superior and inferior colliculi respectively. Together, the brainstem and cerebellum are known as the hindbrain.

The cerebellum is attached to the brainstem by peduncles (literally 'stalks'). The superior, middle and inferior cerebellar peduncles attach it to the midbrain, the pons and the medulla respectively.

The largest and most rostral enlargement of the neuraxis is the cerebrum, or forebrain, which is attached to the brainstem by the midbrain. The cerebral peduncles form the most ventral part of the midbrain. The region between the peduncles and the tectum is known as the tegmentum.

The surface of the cerebral hemispheres is deeply folded, forming fissures and sulci which divide the forebrain into hemispheres, lobes and gyri. The fissures are normally several centimetres deep. Sulci are lesser furrows casting the surface of the cerebrum into undulating convexities, the gyri. The folds enable a large area of cerebral cortex to be accommodated within the cranium.

The longitudinal (or saggital) fissure divides the cerebrum into left and right hemispheres. It extends inferiorly as far as the corpus callosum, a white-matter pathway of 600 million axons linking homotopic areas of cerebral cortex in opposite hemispheres.

The lateral (or Sylvian) fissure partly divides the cerebrum horizontally, separating the temporal and frontal lobes. These are named after the bones of the skull under which they lie. The occipital and parietal lobes are also named after plates of the skull but, for the most part, the divisions between them do not have clear anatomical boundaries. By convention, the border between frontal and parietal territories is delineated by the central sulcus (also called the Rolandic fissure), which runs from the vertex towards the midpoint of the lateral fissure. The banks of the central sulcus, the precentral and postcentral gyri, comprise the motor and somatosensory cortex respectively (Fig 1.2). The border between the occipital and parietal cortex is marked on the medial surface of the hemisphere by the parieto-occipital sulcus. No such boundary is present on the lateral aspect of the hemisphere.

The patterns of cerebral gyri differ greatly between individuals and between hemispheres in the same person. The most constant features tend to be the primary sensory projection areas; that is, the regions receiving the majority of fibres from afferent pathways, and the motor cortex. Their locations are shown in Fig. 1.2. In practice even these areas weave a more undulating and variable course than is indicated schematically in the diagram. The uncus,

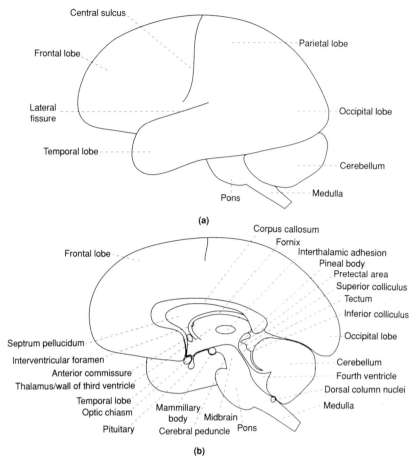

Fig. 1.1 The major surface features of (a) the lateral and (b) the medial surfaces of the brain.

a hooked extension of the parahippocampal gyrus, is a relatively constant landmark; it receives sensory information from the olfactory bulb. Heschl's gyrus runs horizontally across the surface of the temporal lobe (the planum temporale) and receives the major input from the auditory pathway; only a small area of the auditory cortex is therefore exposed on the lateral surface of the brain, midway along the superior temporal gyrus. Fig. 1.2 also shows the location of the angular, cingulate and parahippocampal gyri as well as Broca's speech area and the three temporal gyri. The sulcal patterns of the rest of the cortex are variable in appearance and are not illustrated.

The blood supply to the brain

Arterial blood reaches the brain via the vertebral arteries and the internal carotid arteries. Links between these four inputs produce an

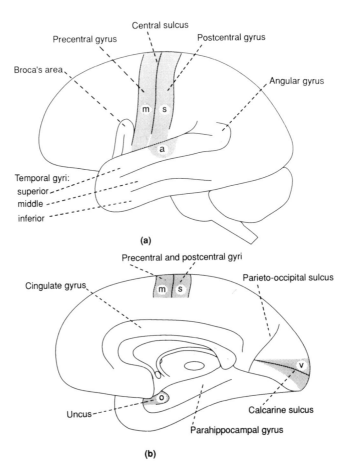

Fig. 1.2 The principal gyri and sulci with the location of the sensory and motor areas of (a) the lateral and (b) the medial cerebral cortex: a, auditory cortex Heschl's gyrus begins here and continues into the lateral fissure; m, motor cortex; v, visual cortex; s, somatosensory cortex; o, olfactory cortex.

anastomotic arterial network distributed across the basal surface of the brain (Fig. 1.3).

The vertebral arteries are situated on the ventrolateral aspect of the medulla. They converge to form the basilar artery, which runs along the midline of the pons. On reaching the midbrain, the basilar artery divides to form two pairs of vessels: the superior cerebellar and posterior cerebral arteries.

The cerebellum derives its blood supply from branches of the vertebral and basilar arteries: the posterior inferior, anterior inferior and superior cerebellar arteries. The medulla is supplied by branches of the posterior inferior cerebellar arteries and the anterior spinal arteries. The pons is supplied by circumferential branches of the basilar artery.

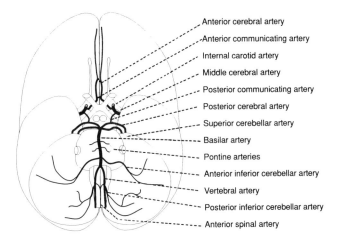

Anterior cerebral artery
Anterior communicating artery
Internal carotid artery
Middle cerebral artery
Posterior communicating artery
Posterior cerebral artery
Superior cerebellar artery
Basilar artery
Pontine arteries
Anterior inferior cerebellar artery
Vertebral artery
Posterior inferior cerebellar artery
Anterior spinal artery

Fig. 1.3   The arterial supply to the brain.

On each side of the optic chiasm, the internal carotid artery divides to form the middle cerebral and anterior cerebral arteries. An anastomosis exists between left and right anterior cerebral arteries – the anterior communicating artery. Anastomoses also exist between the middle and posterior cerebral arteries on each side – the posterior communicating arteries. The three communicating arteries complete an arterial circle with the cerebral arteries, known as the 'circle of Willis'.

When all its elements are present, this system may have the capacity to protect the brain against the failure of one or more of the major arterial inputs. However, the posterior communicating artery or the first segment of the posterior cerebral artery is often narrow or atrophic on one side. In practice therefore, the potential for rerouting the blood supply to the cerebrum may not be there.

The blood supply to the core structures of the cerebrum – the internal capsule, basal ganglia and limbic system (see below) – is provided by fine vessels which arise directly from the circle of Willis and from segments of the cerebral arteries just beyond the circle. These are known as the ganglionic or central branches of the circle of Willis.

The middle cerebral artery travels through the lateral fissure to emerge on the lateral surface of the hemisphere (Fig. 1.4). Its branches supply the entire lateral surface of the forebrain, except for a narrow territory close to the saggital fissure. This vessel therefore supplies the somatosensory and motor cortices (except for their representations of the foot, which are situated on the medial surface of the hemisphere) as well as Broca's and Wernicke's speech areas (see below). Obstruction or haemorrhage of the middle cerebral artery is therefore associated with hemiplegia and aphasic disorders. Infarction of its more posterior branches may lead to visual or somaesthetic agnosias.

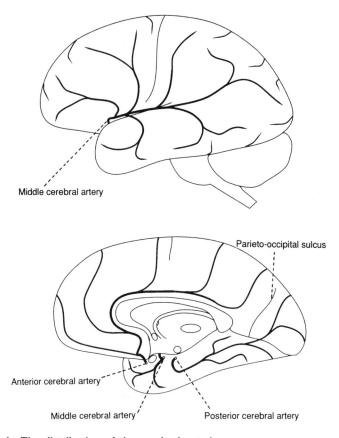

Fig. 1.4 The distribution of the cerebral arteries.

The posterior cerebral artery supplies the medial and inferior surface of the occipital and temporal lobes. Disruption of its supply is associated with scotomatous defects in the visual field and disorders of visual perception. If the branches which supply the medial parts of the temporal lobe are affected, there may be disorders of memory.

The anterior cerebral artery supplies the medial surface of the frontal and parietal lobes as far posteriorly as the parieto-occipital sulcus. The most conspicuous effects of occlusion are sensory loss and spastic paralysis of the foot.

Venous drainage

The cerebral veins drain through the dural sinuses. The basal ganglia and other core structures of the forebrain drain into the vein of Galen and into the straight sinus, which lies at the junction of two major sheets of dura: the tentorium cerebelli, which covers the cerebellum, and the falx cerebri, which lies in the saggital fissure. The superior surface of the forebrain drains into

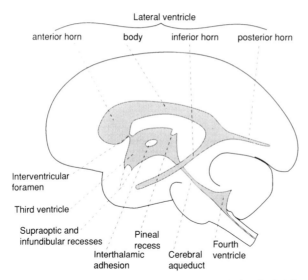

Fig. 1.5 The ventricles (the lateral ventricle is shown only for the left hemisphere).

the superior saggital sinus. This runs posteriorly along the margin of the longitudinal fissure to join the straight sinus at the posterior edge of the tentorium cerebelli. From this confluence, the transverse sinus runs laterally, left and right, around the margins of the tentorium to join the sigmoid sinus and then the internal jugular vein.

The ventricles

The ventricular system comprises a number of fluid-filled spaces within the cerebrum and hindbrain. Within each hemisphere is a large space, the lateral ventricle. Its body is situated immediately below the corpus callosum, with extensions into the frontal lobe (the anterior horn), the occipital lobe (the posterior horn) and the temporal lobe (the inferior horn). The two lateral ventricles are separated anteriorly by a thin membrane, the septum pellucidum (Fig. 1.1). They drain through the interventricular foramena (Figs 1.1, 1.5) into the third ventricle, a flat midline space between the thalamus and hypothalamus of each hemisphere. The fourth ventricle lies above the pons and below the cerebellum. It is connected to the third ventricle by the narrow cerebral aqueduct (the aqueduct of Sylvius), which is situated immediately below the tectum in the midbrain.

Choroid plexus is a highly vascular tissue which occupies part of the space within each ventricle. The choroid plexus secretes cerebrospinal fluid (CSF) into the ventricles at the rate of some 300 ml per day. The CSF is an almost protein-free filtrate of blood. It flows from the forebrain ventricles to the fourth ventricle via the aqueduct and passes out into the subarachnoid space via recesses of the fourth ventricle – the foramena of Luschka and Magendie.

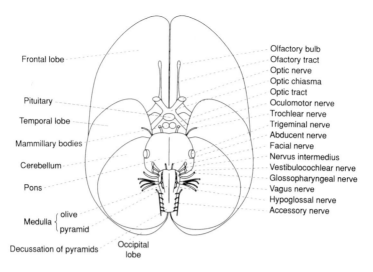

Fig. 1.6 The cranial nerves.

Its slight positive pressure forces the arachnoid covering of the brain against the dura, leaving a CSF-filled subarachnoid space between the pia and the arachnoid. The brain floats within this space, an arrangement which effectively protects it from impact with the skull under normal conditions. The CSF is actively transported back into the blood via granulations of the arachnoid which invaginate the superior saggital sinus.

Obstruction to this circulation most commonly occurs within the third or fourth ventricle, leading to a non-communicating hydrocephalus and consequent enlargement of the ventricular system. Obstruction can also occur over the surface of the brain and spinal cord (usually by fibrous adhesion following haemorrhage or infection), leading to a communicating hydrocephalus.

The cranial nerves

The cranial nerves convey information from the special senses and somatosensory receptors to the brain. They also supply skeletal muscle in the head and certain parts of the trunk. Their autonomic components provide parasympathetic innervation to smooth muscle and glands in the head and thorax. The sympathetic innervation of these areas is not provided by the cranial nerves but is derived from the upper thoracic sympathetic outflow. Fig. 1.6 shows the location of the nerves on the brainstem. Table 1.1 summarises their functions.

The cranial nerves arise or terminate on clusters of neurons within the brainstem known as the cranial nerve nuclei. A knowledge of the spatial relations between these nuclei and the major ascending and descending

Table 1.1 The function of the nerves on the brainstem

	Nerve	Component[1]	Main functions
I	Olfactory	S	Smell
II	Optic	S	Vision
III	Oculomotor	M	Vertical and medial eye movement Elevates eyelid
		A	Focusing and pupillary constriction
IV	Trochlear	M	Torsional eye movement correction
V	Trigeminal	S	Cutaneous sensation from the anterior part of the head, including teeth, cornea, air sinuses, meninges, mouth and anterior two-thirds of tongue
		M	Mastication and movement of part of soft palate
VI	Abducent	M	Lateral eye movement
VII	Facial	S	Taste on anterior two-thirds of tongue Sensation from back of external ear
		M	Facial expression. Elevates hyoid. Tenses stapes
		A	Lacrimation and salivation (sublingual and submandibular glands)
VIII	Vestibulo-cochlear	S	Detects orientation and acceleration Hearing
IX	Glosso-pharyngeal	S	Taste and general sensation from posterior tongue and upper larynx Information from carotid body and sinus
		M	Swallowing. Raises larynx, pharynx
		A	Salivation (parotid gland)
X	Vagus	S	Taste and general sensation from upper part of alimentary tract
		M	Swallowing and phonation
		A	Control of heart, stomach and other thoracic and abdominal viscera
XI	Accessory	M	Rotates head. Elevates shoulder
XII	Hypoglossal	M	Movement of the tongue

[1]S, sensory; A, autonomic; M, motor.

pathways makes it possible to deduce the location of lesions in the brainstem on the basis of the conjunction of signs and symptoms. These problems are frequently encountered in neurology. To master,the relevant anatomy it is necessary to study serial sections of the brainstem in more detail than the remit of the present chapter allows (see, for example, Snell, 1987; Barr, 1988).

Sensory systems

The conscious experience of sensation depends upon information reaching the primary projection areas of the cerebral cortex (Fig. 1.2). For all the modalities except olfaction, sensory information reaches the cortex in three stages. The first-order neuron receives information from the receptor and conveys it to a synaptic relay within the CNS. This neuron has its cell body outside the CNS, for example in the dorsal root ganglia or the trigeminal ganglion. The second-order neuron decussates (crosses from one side of the neuraxis to the other) and terminates in a nucleus of the thalamus. The third-order neuron travels from the thalamus to the primary projection area in the cortex.

Receptor fields are normally mapped onto the cortex in a spatially ordered manner. Thus the visual cortex is organised retinotopically, while the auditory cortex is arranged as a map of the basilar membrane of the cochlea. Registration at this level may be sufficient for simple awareness of stimulation, but higher levels of perception (e.g. recognition of the meaning or identity of the stimulus) depend on processes which take place in regions of cortex beyond the primary projection areas.

Somaesthesia

The somaesthetic (or somatosensory) system is concerned with cutaneous and deep-tissue sensations of touch (two-point discrimination and diffuse touch), pressure, vibration, limb position, pain, and temperature. Pain differs from the other modalities in that the registration of tissue damage is accompanied by affective experience of a strongly aversive kind.

Receptors

Somaesthesia depends upon input from a variety of different receptors. Free nerve endings are probably important in the registration of pain since these are the only receptors present in tooth pulp and in the cornea. The flower-spray and annulospiral endings in muscle spindle organs respond to stretch, as do the neurotendinous spindles and Golgi tendon organs. These receptors are probably important in the appreciation of limb position. This is in addition to their role in the proprioceptive mechanisms responsible for the control of posture and muscle tone. Pacinian corpuscles appear to be sensitive to deformation and may therefore contribute to the detection of pressure. There are other types of detector whose specificities are less well understood, including Meissner's corpuscles, Merkel's discs, and the corpuscles of Krause and Ruffini.

It is unlikely that individual modalities of somaesthetic sensation are provided by separate classes of receptor. Physiological evidence suggests that the character of experience is dependent on the pattern of excitation across a number of different types of receptor.

Dermatomes

The cutaneous distribution of a spinal nerve is known as its dermatome. The dermatomes are arranged as a succession of bands encircling the trunk in a manner which reflects the segmentation of the spinal cord. For example, sensation from a band through the nipples is conveyed by the fourth thoracic spinal nerve (T4), while that from the umbilicus is relayed by T10. The spinal nerves are mapped equally clearly onto the limbs, although the segmental pattern is more complex than it is on the thorax and abdomen.

The dermatomes do not correspond with the distribution of peripheral nerves. The axillary nerve, for example, collects sensory information from only lateral parts of the C4, C5 and C6 dermatomes on the upper arm. Before reaching the spinal cord, each peripheral nerve enters one of a number of plexuses (e.g. brachial, lumbar, or sacral plexuses). Here nerve fibres are re-grouped to produce spinal nerves containing axons from individual dermatomes.

The distribution of cutaneous sensory deficits provides valuable information about the locus of the causative lesions. If the sensory loss corresponds to the distribution of one or more peripheral nerves, the problem is distal to the plexus. If the deficit affects a single dermatome, the damage affects a spinal nerve. If sensation is lost over a number of segments below the border of a dermatome, the problem lies within the spinal cord. Sensory deficits which follow neither dermatomal nor peripheral nerve distributions may have a disseminated or psychogenic origin.

The dorsal columns and medial lemniscus: pathways for two-point discrimination, limb position and vibration sense

These modalities of sensation reach the spinal cord via fast-conducting, myelinated axons which have their cell bodies in the dorsal root ganglia and enter the cord just medial to the dorsal horn. The axons branch, sending collaterals to the dorsal horn, the ventral horn and into the dorsal columns. The branches to the dorsal horn contribute to pain gating (see p. 13) and to polysynaptic reflexes. Those which go to the ventral horn comprise the afferent limb of monosynaptic reflexes. Only the branches which enter the dorsal columns (Fig. 1.7) contribute directly to the conscious experience of touch and vibration and awareness of the position of the limbs.

The dorsal columns comprise two fibre tracts on each side of the cord: the gracile and cuneate columns. Axons from lumbar and sacral regions enter the gracile columns situated in the most dorsal part of the cord adjacent to the midline. Axons from thoracic and cervical levels form the cuneate column, which lies immediately lateral to the gracile column. These tracts ascend to the upper part of the medulla, where they synapse for the first time in the dorsal column nuclei. The second-order fibres cross the midline in the upper medulla where they are known as the internal arcuate fibres. After decussating, the pathways form a block of axons called the medial lemniscus. It ascends through the pons and the midbrain to relay in the lateral part of the

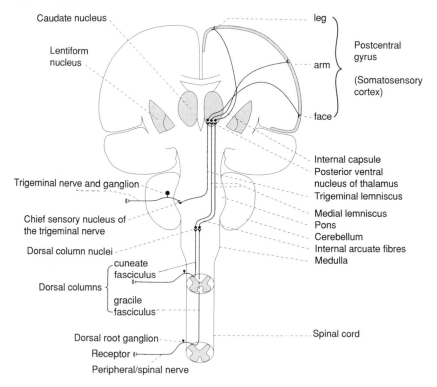

Caudate nucleus

Lentiform
nucleus

leg

Postcentral
gyrus

arm

(Somatosensory
cortex)

face

Internal capsule
Posterior ventral
nucleus of thalamus
Trigeminal lemniscus

Trigeminal nerve and ganglion

Chief sensory nucleus of
the trigeminal nerve

Medial lemniscus
Pons
Cerebellum
Internal arcuate fibres
Medulla

Dorsal column nuclei

cuneate
fasciculus

Dorsal columns

gracile
fasciculus

Dorsal root ganglion

Spinal cord

Receptor
Peripheral/spinal nerve

Fig. 1.7 The dorsal column/medial lemniscus pathway.

ventroposterior nucleus of the thalamus. The third-order stage of the pathway
then travels through the internal capsule and the corona radiata to the
somatosensory cortex (see Fig. 1.2). The body is mapped somatotopically on
the postcentral gyrus. The leg is represented on the medial surface of the
hemisphere; the rest of the body is mapped in an inverted fashion on the
lateral aspect of the hemisphere.

   Somaesthetic sensation from the head and upper alimentary tract reaches
the CNS from the trigeminal, facial, glossopharyngeal and vagus nerves. The
trigeminal is the most important of these, particularly with regard to tactile
and position senses. The axons which convey these modalities have their cell
bodies in the ganglia outside the brainstem, and relay in the chief sensory
nucleus of the trigeminal within the pons (irrespective of the cranial nerve
through which they arrive). Second-order fibres cross the midline to form a
block of fibres, the trigeminal lemniscus, lying next to the medial lemniscus.
They ascend to synapse in the medial part of the ventroposterior nucleus of
the thalamus. The third-order fibres make their way to the somatosensory
cortex at the inferior end of the postcentral gyrus. The face is mapped on the
lateral convexity of the hemisphere, close to the lateral fissure. The oral cavity
and upper parts of the alimentary tract are mapped onto an extension of the
postcentral gyrus which continues inside the lateral fissure across its upper bank.

The spinothalamic tracts: pathways for diffuse touch,
pressure, pain, and temperature

Information from receptors serving these modalities reaches the spinal cord
via slow-conducting (C and A delta) fibres whose cell bodies lie in the dorsal
root ganglia. The axons enter the tract of Lissauer, which lies immediately
above the grey matter of the dorsal horn. Here they arborise, and their branches
enter the dorsal horn of several adjacent segments.

Within the dorsal horn, synaptic interactions occur between these inputs
and collaterals of the dorsal column system. The process compares the activity
in the two sets of afferents, blocking the relay of information from C and A
delta fibres when their activity is accompanied by input from mechanoreceptors
of the skin and deep structures. When tissue damage causes the discharge
of free nerve endings to exceed that from tactile and other mechanical
receptors, signals are allowed to pass to the brain which are interpreted as
pain. This is known as 'pain gating', and ensures that tissue damage is not
confused with other conditions in which C and A delta fibres are activated.

The small fibre afferents also relay information about pressure and diffuse
touch. The evidence that this system mediates a form of touch is based upon
the fact that an awareness of tactile stimulation is retained when the dorsal

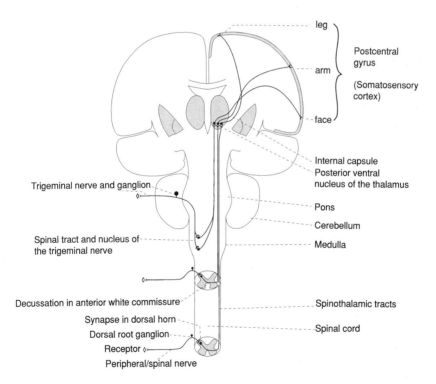

Fig. 1.8 The spinothalamic tracts.

columns are transected. However, the system has poor spatial resolution: the patient is unable to localise the place of cutaneous stimulation accurately.

The second-order neurons of the spinothalamic pathway (Fig. 1.8) cross the midline soon after leaving the dorsal horn, passing below the spinal canal to occupy a position in the white matter close to the ventral horn. The axons which convey information about pain and temperature travel in the lateral spinothalamic tract, which lies lateral to the ventral horn. Those concerned with touch and pressure take a more ventral route, in the anterior spinothalamic tract. The pathways ascend without further synapses until they reach the lateral division of the posterior ventral nucleus of the thalamus, where they converge with the terminals of the medial lemniscus. The third-order neuron travels with those serving dorsal column sensation to a common registration in the somatosensory cortex.

The sensations of pain, temperature, diffuse touch and pressure arising in the head and upper part of the alimentary tract depend on small fibre afferents in the trigeminal, facial, glossopharyngeal and vagus nerves. All four cranial nerves contribute to a column of fibres somewhat confusingly termed the 'spinal tract of the trigeminal nerve', which runs from the mid-pons to the upper segments of the spinal cord. The associated 'spinal nucleus' provides second-order fibres which cross the midline, join the trigeminal lemniscus, and ascend to the medial division of the posterior ventral nucleus of the thalamus. The third-order neurons follow the same course as those bringing two-point discrimination for the face and terminate in the same area of somatosensory cortex.

The appreciation of pain, that is, the affective concomitant of tissue damage, is not dependent upon the somatosensory cortex. It involves a relay from the thalamus to the limbic system, possibly in the anterior cingulate gyrus.

Dissociation of sensation

The spinothalamic and dorsal column systems diverge at the dorsal horn and reconverge at the thalamus. The spinothalamic tracts decussate a little above their segment of origin in the spinal cord. The dorsal column pathway does not cross until the medulla. Pressure, pain and temperature therefore ascend on the opposite side of the cord from two-point discrimination and limb position sense. Lesions within the spinal cord may therefore affect pain and temperature sensation while sparing two-point discrimination and limb position sense. Extensive damage in one half of the spinal cord can therefore give rise to loss of pain and temperature in dermatomes below and contralateral to the lesion, but to loss of two-point discrimination ipsilaterally (Brown–Séquard syndrome).

When sensory loss affects spinothalamic and dorsal column sensation equally, the lesion is likely to be outside the CNS or above the thalamus.

Vision

The visual fields

The areas of vision to the left and right of the point of fixation are referred to as the visual half-fields (or, more simply, the left and right visual fields, but these terms must not be confused with the visual fields of left and right eyes). Since the system is bilaterally symmetrical it is often convenient to distinguish nasal and temporal half-fields.

The cornea and the lens of the eye bring the image of the external world into focus on the retina. The refraction produces a real image which is laterally and vertically inverted. The right half-fields are therefore registered on the left half of each retina, and vice versa.

The retina

The retina contains the photosensitive receptors and also a neural network which is responsible for the initial steps in the analysis of the visual input.

The outermost layer of the retina is formed by the pigment epithelium, whose function is to prevent internal reflection of light within the eye.

Immediately adjacent to the pigment epithelium lie the receptors, the rods and cones. The rods outnumber the cones except in the fovea, the part of the retina which serves the central $2°$ of the visual field. The rods are more sensitive than the cones and are responsible for night (scotopic) vision. All rods contain the same photosensitive pigment and do not discriminate between light of different colours (though their sensitivity is maximal in the green region of the spectrum). The detector mechanism of the rods is saturated in bright light and they make little contribution to vision in daylight.

The cones are less sensitive than rods. The three types of cone contain pigments which afford maximal sensitivity in orange, green and blue regions of the spectrum. The experience of colour depends initially on the differential stimulation of these three classes of cone.

The neural network of the retina lies in front of the receptors. Light must pass through it and through the retinal blood vessels to reach the rods and cones. The receptors synapse with bipolar cells whose cell bodies occupy the central layer of the retina. In their turn, the bipolar cells synapse with the ganglion cells which form the innermost layer of nerve cell bodies in the retina. Their axons travel across the surface of the retina to the optic disc, where they leave the eye to form the optic nerves. A number of additional cell types exist among the bipolar cells which provide lateral inhibition and facilitation at the synaptic interfaces between receptors and bipolar cells, and between bipolar cells and the ganglion cells.

The retina and subsequent stages of the visual pathway have been intensively investigated in recent years in an effort to understand the neural mechanisms underlying perception. The retinal network is responsible for a number of important steps in the initial analysis of visual information. It controls the sensitivity of the retina, enabling scenes of very different brightness to be encoded without exceeding the range of action-potential frequencies which the optic nerve can transmit. In bright light, it effectively sharpens the encoded image to compensate for errors of diffraction and refraction. It converts the trichromatic coding of hue by the receptors into a red-green, yellow-blue and black-white colour-opponent code for transmission in the nervous system. It removes stationary images from the encoded signal, enabling the system to disregard the shadows of the blood vessels and neurons in front of the receptors. Finally it segregates information relevant to the detection of movement into separate and faster channels than those which serve the perception of form and colour.

The visual pathway

The ganglion cells of the retina are the second-order neurons of the visual pathway. Like the second-order neurons of other sensory modalities, their axons decussate and terminate in the thalamus. However, the decussation is complete only in vertebrates in which the eyes are situated on the side of the head. In man, the eyes look forward, providing overlapping fields as part of the adaptation for stereoscopic vision, and the decussation of the visual pathway is only partial.

Axons which originate in the nasal half of each retina (and which therefore serve the temporal visual fields) cross the midline in the optic chiasm (Fig. 1.9). Those which originate in the temporal half of each retina (serving the nasal visual fields) remain in a lateral position in the chiasm and do not cross. The result is that the fibres in the retrochiasmal sections of the visual pathway receive information exclusively from the contralateral visual half-field. The partial decussation therefore conserves the principle that left and right halves of sensory space (in this case of visual space) are registered in the contralateral hemisphere.

The optic tracts pass lateral to the cerebral peduncles and terminate in the lateral geniculate body (LGB), an outlying nucleus of the thalamus. The third-order fibres travel to the visual cortex through the optic radiations, part of the corona radiata. Fibres serving the lower field pass posteriorly from the LGB, skirting the posterior horn of the lateral ventricle, and terminate on the superior bank of the calcarine sulcus. Those which convey information from the upper half of the visual fields take a somewhat longer route, which takes them through the temporal lobe, around the inferior horn of the lateral ventricle, before ending in the inferior bank of the lateral fissure. The passage of this part of the optic radiation is known as Meyer's loop.

Lesions within the visual pathway lead to field defects, which may vary in extent from small areas of blindness, known as scotomata (singular scotoma), to hemianopia, in which vision is lost in an entire half-field. Damage to an optic nerve causes partial or total blindness in the ipsilateral eye. Lesions affecting the midline of the optic chiasm (e.g. some pituitary and hypothalamic

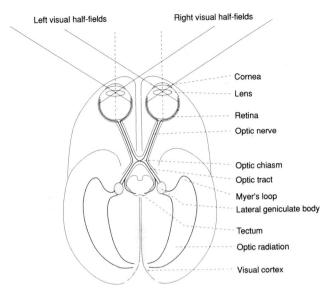

Left visual half-fields   Right visual half-fields

Cornea

Lens

Retina

Optic nerve

Optic chiasm

Optic tract

Myer's loop

Lateral geniculate body

Tectum

Optic radiation

Visual cortex

Fig. 1.9 The visual pathway.

tumours) are associated with scotomata or even hemianopia affecting the temporal fields. Lesions behind the chiasm affect equivalent parts of the field of both eyes; such defects are said to be homonymous. When the lesion involves Meyer's loop, only the upper part of the contralateral field is affected. Thus homonymous field defects in an upper quadrant of the visual field may provide an early indication of disorder in the contralateral temporal lobe.

The visual cortex

The visual fields are mapped retinotopically on the cortex. The upper half of each visual field is represented on the lower bank of the calcarine sulcus, the lower visual field on its upper bank. As a result of the partial decussation in the optic chiasma, the visual cortex of each hemisphere maps the contralateral half of the visual field. The macula, the central part of the visual field serving the area of fixation, is mapped at the occipital pole. The peripheral field is mapped more anteriorly along the calcarine sulcus.

The visual cortex is also referred to as the 'striate cortex', because the myelinated axons of the optic radiations arriving in cortical layer IV are responsible for the appearance of a thin white stripe part way through its thickness. This is one of the cytoarchitectural features which distinguishes the visual cortex as Brodmann's cortical area 17. Physiologists refer to the visual cortex as V1, to denote that it provides the first major relay for visual information within the cerebral cortex.

The loss of sensation caused by lesions of the striate cortex or optic radiations is in marked contrast to the perceptual deficits which result from lesions in the supplementary visual areas surrounding V1 (Table 1.4, p. 30).

Although conscious awareness of stimulation is lost within a scotoma, patients appear to be able to detect movement of flux change within the blind area when forced to do so. The phenomenon is known as 'blindsight'. It is believed to be mediated by pathways reaching the cerebral cortex indirectly via the tectum and perhaps the pulvinar of the thalamus, or reaching visual association areas directly from the lateral geniculate bodies, bypassing V1.

Visual reflexes mediated by the tectum

Each optic tract gives off a small branch (the brachium of the superior colliculus) which bypasses the lateral geniculate body and relays in the superior colliculus of the ipsilateral tectum and in the pretectal area of the rostral midbrain (Fig. 1.1).

The input to the superior colliculus serves as the afferent limb for the visual avoidance reflexes. These are the blinks and postural movements evoked by sudden changes in brightness or by approaching visual stimuli. The tectobulbar and tectospinal tracts effect the link to motor neurons in the cranial nerves and spinal cord which provide the efferent limb of these reflexes.

The fibres which relay in the pretectal area mediate the pupillary light reflex. Axons pass from the pretectal area to the parasympathetic Edinger–Westphal nucleus of each oculomotor nerve. Parasympathetic fibres of the oculomotor nerve innervate the constrictor pupillae within the eye. The reflex arc causes the pupils to constrict in bright light. When illumination is provided to one eye, constriction of the ipsilateral pupil is known as the 'direct light reflex'. Constriction of the contralateral pupil is known as the 'consensual response', and relies on the projection of the pretectal area to the contralateral Edinger–Westphal nucleus. Examination of the direct and consensual light reflexes

Table 1.2 Localising the significance of direct and consensual light reflexes

| Pupillary constriction in: | Illuminated eye | | Nerve damaged |
	right	left	
Right eye	Yes	Yes	Left oculomotor nerve
Left eye	No	No	
Right eye	No	No	Right oculomotor nerve
Left eye	Yes	Yes	
Right eye	Yes	No	Left optic nerve
Left eye	Yes	No	
Right eye	No	Yes	Right optic nerve
Left eye	No	Yes	

makes it possible to distinguish damage to optic and oculomotor motor nerves in injuries affecting the orbit and basal skull (Table 1.2).

The pretectal area is situated at the rostral end of the midbrain, where it is particularly sensitive to the effects of coning (i.e. movement of the brain through the hiatus in the tentorium cerebelli). The light reflex may therefore indicate the depth of coma caused by raised intracranial pressure.

The pretectal area also contributes fibres to the dorsal longitudinal fasciculus, and so sends information to the thoracic sympathetic outflow. From here, sympathetic fibres travel via the superior cervical ganglion to reach the dilator pupillae, causing the pupil to enlarge when illumination falls. Damage to this pathway results in Horner's syndrome, one of whose features is a fixed constricted pupil due to the unopposed action of the oculomotor nerve.

Eye movement

Vertical and horizontal eye movements are effected by the four rectus muscles under the control of the oculomotor and abducent nerves (Table 1.1). Since these muscles operate at an angle to the anteroposterior axis of the skull, they also exert torsional forces on the eye when the gaze is directed forwards. To counter this unwanted axial rotation of the eye, correction forces are applied by the superior and inferior oblique muscles, under the control of the trochlear and oculomotor nerves respectively. Conjugate deviation of gaze therefore requires the coordination of the six muscles of each eye, under the control of six cranial nerve nuclei, three on each side of the brainstem. This coordination depends upon commissural connections linking the three pairs of cranial nerve nuclei, and a paired fibre tract, the medial longitudinal fasciculus, which connects the three pairs of nuclei with one another.

Fixation on a moving target depends on a pathway from occipital association areas which reaches the medial longitudinal fasciculus without involvement of the frontal cortex. Tracking of this type is regarded as a visual reflex because it does not involve individual voluntary movements of the eyes. It occurs in optokinetic nystagmus, also known (somewhat more poetically) as 'railway carriage' nystagmus. This is a normal phenomenon, elicited when a pattern drifts continuously across the visual fields, requiring periodic shifts of fixation. Advantage may be taken of it to assess the state of the visual system when frontal eye fields are damaged.

By contrast, saccadic eye movements are successive fixations under voluntary control. They are the normal movements of visual search. This type of eye movement relies on a pathway, the occipitofrontal bundle, from occipitoparietal cortex to the eye fields of the frontal cortex (Brodmann's area 8, see Fig. 1.13, p. 29). The eye fields control fixation by a corticobulbar pathway, which reaches the medial longitudinal fasciculus via a relay in the para-abducens nucleus of gaze, a region of reticular formation in the lower pons. Damage to the frontal eye fields or their projection to the para-abducens nucleus may result in the head and eyes being involuntarily turned towards the side of the lesion. This contrasts with the effect of damage to the parietal source

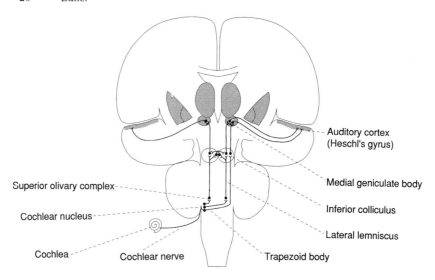

Auditory cortex
(Heschl's gyrus)

Medial geniculate body

Superior olivary complex

Inferior colliculus

Cochlear nucleus

Lateral lemniscus

Cochlea

Cochlear nerve

Trapezoid body

Fig. 1.10   The auditory pathway.

of the parietofrontal bundle, which manifests itself more subtly in neglect of the contralateral visual half-field.

Both voluntary and reflex eye movements are usually accompanied by head or even shoulder movements. These reduce the amplitude of eye movement when the gaze is redirected through a large angle. These postural changes also depend on the medial longitudinal fasciculus, which continues below the level of the abducens to reach upper cervical levels, that is, the spinal segments which innervate the shoulders and the upper part of the trunk.

Hearing

Auditory information reaches the brainstem via the cochlear division of the eighth nerve. The pathway first synapses in the superior and inferior cochlear nuclei, which are situated around the inferior cerebellar peduncle at the junction between pons and medulla. The pathway involves a complex network of connections within the brainstem, much simplified in Fig. 1.10. The projection to the auditory cortex involves a second-order neuron which crosses the midline in the trapezoid body and ascends as the lateral lemniscus to relay in the medial geniculate body of the thalamus. Many of the fibres in this section of the pathway relay in the inferior colliculus. The third-order neuron projects through the white matter of the temporal lobe to the auditory cortex, Heschl's gyrus, within the lateral fissure.

The auditory pathway is not entirely crossed. The lateral lemniscus also receives fibres from the ipsilateral cochlear nucleus and from relays in the superior olivary complex in the upper medulla and lower pons. This means that each auditory cortex receives information from both ears. Unilateral lesions of Heschl's gyrus are therefore not accompanied by unilateral deafness.

The predominance of the crossed pathway can be demonstrated by a procedure involving competitive stimulation of the ears ('dichotic listening'): since the speech areas are normally situated in the left hemisphere, words presented to the right ear are more accurately reported than those presented simultaneously to the left ear.

The complex connections of the pathway within the brainstem provide two quite different mechanisms for the spatial perception of sound. Low-frequency sounds can be localised only by comparing the time of arrival or phase of the sound pressure waves reaching opposite ears. For this it is necessary to resolve time differences of tens of microseconds. This is achieved by relays in the superior olivary complex. Their position within a few synapses of the cochlea ensures that the timing of the inputs is preserved. Sound whose frequency is greater than 2000 Hz cannot be located in this way because phase differences between the ears become meaningless when the wavelength is shorter than the width of the head. However, high frequencies give rise to a 'sound shadow' on the side of the head away from the source. Its direction can therefore be determined by comparing the loudness of the sound in the two ears. This comparison is dependent on the relay in the inferior colliculi.

As a result of the bilateral projection to the cortex focal lesions seldom give rise to auditory signs to aid localisation of the lesion. However, activity in the various brainstem relays gives rise to electrophysiological signals which are revealed in the brainstem auditory evoked response (BSAER). Abnormalities in the individual components of the BSAER are therefore of value in locating lesions in the brainstem.

Sudden loud sounds evoke postural reflexes which may involve avoidance or orientation towards the source. The inferior colliculus is the origin of tectospinal and tectobulbar pathways which elicit the necessary responses in motor neurons. The mechanism is equivalent to the visual reflexes mediated by the superior colliculus.

Olfaction

Unlike the other sensory pathways, the olfactory projection does not involve the thalamus or neocortex. This is because the olfactory pathway derives from chemosensory systems which were present early in the evolution of the vertebrates, before the development of those structures.

The olfactory receptors in the nasal mucosa communicate with the olfactory bulb through the cribriform plate of the ethmoid bone. The neural connections to the olfactory bulb are fragile and anosmia is therefore a frequent consequence of head injury.

The olfactory tracts pass posteriorly and divide into medial and lateral striae as they approach the anterior perforated substance on the orbital surface of the frontal lobes. The lateral striae terminate in the three-layered allocortex of the uncus. The representation in the uncus is responsible for olfactory experience. Epileptogenic foci in the medial temporal lobe may activate cells of the uncus, giving rise to the olfactory auras which characterise uncinate fits.

The medial olfactory striae project through the anterior commissure to the contralateral olfactory bulb. Their function in man is unknown. In other vertebrates they possibly assist the detection of olfactory gradients when tracking scents.

Motor systems

Upper and lower motor neurons

Skeletal muscle is innervated by neurons which have their cell bodies in the ventral horns of the spinal cord and in the motor nuclei of the cranial nerves. All movement is controlled by these neurons, which act as the final common pathway to the muscle. This final common pathway is referred to as the lower motor neuron (LMN). The neural systems of the brain and spinal cord which converge upon it are known collectively as the upper motor neuron (UMN). They include the motor cortex, the basal ganglia, the reticular formation, the tectum, vestibular and olivary nuclei, and their associated pathways. The concept of the UMN therefore embraces systems which have a wide variety of different functions. Nevertheless, the distinction between LMN and UMN is clinically useful.

Damage to the LMN deprives muscle of its input and so causes flaccid paralysis, hypotonia, and hyporeflexia. There is wasting due to disuse. The cell membrane of muscle fibres becomes excitable over its entire surface, a change which enables a new neuromuscular junction to be established wherever contact is made with the growth cone of a regenerating axon. While in this state, individual muscle fibres undergo frequent spontaneous contractions known as fibrillation. This is difficult to see through the skin, although it is sometimes visible in the tongue. Progressive degeneration of the LMN may be accompanied by a random spontaneous discharge of action potentials. These cause the contractions of entire motor units (a motor unit comprises all the muscle fibres innervated by the terminals of a single axon). The effect is fasciculation, a tremor whose amplitude is greater than that of fibrillation. (The terms are frequently but erroneously interchanged.)

In theory, damage to systems which converge on the LMN can produce a wide variety of effects. However, lesions seldom damage individual UMN systems or their descending pathways selectively. Whether the damage is in the forebrain, the brainstem or the spinal cord, the outcome usually includes the withdrawal of descending inhibition from spinal reflexes. This is because the majority of supraspinal motor systems control movement indirectly, by modifying the sensitivity of stretch reflex arcs through their action on the gamma efferents of the ventral horn. The pyramidal tracts are an important exception, as they exert a direct and excitatory action on alpha motor neurons.

Table 1.3 Effects of damage to upper and lower motor neurons

Lower motor neuron lesion	Upper motor neuron lesion
Flaccid paralysis	Spastic paralysis
Hypotonia	Hypertonia
Hyporeflexia	Hyperactive stretch reflexes
Wasting	Absent superficial reflexes
Fibrillation	Babinski sign
Fasciculation	

The over-riding effect of damage to the UMN is therefore a withdrawal of inhibition from spinal reflexes. The result is hyper-reflexia and hypertonia. Since the voluntary movements brought about by the modulation of spinal reflexes are also lost, the overall result is spastic paralysis.

The superficial reflexes (cremasteric, abdominal, plantar) are evoked by stroking the skin. They are somewhat dependent on the subject's perception of the social context of the stimulation, since they represent the normal response to stroking and tickling. They may therefore be more difficult than the stretch reflexes to demonstrate under clinical conditions. The element of perception means that they involve a path through the cerebral cortex and are therefore known as 'long-loop' reflexes. If UMN lesions interrupt this path, the superficial reflexes are abolished – unlike the stretch reflexes.

The normal plantar reflex to stroking the sole causes the foot to arch and the toes to flex. When this superficial reflex is abolished by an UMN lesion, the Babinski sign is unmasked. In this spinal reflex, the toes are splayed in extension. The effects of UMN and LMN lesions are summarised in Table 1.3.

Corticospinal and corticobulbar tracts

The corticospinal tracts (pyramidal tracts) (Fig. 1.11) originate largely but by no means exclusively in the motor context. The majority of fibres terminate on LMNs, although some end on nearby interneurons. The tracts are composed of large-diameter, fast-conducting axons which connect the cortex to the ventral horns of the spinal cord without intervening synapses. This high-speed system is adapted to control fast, precise voluntary actions such as manipulation by the fingers. The corticobulbar tracts provide the corresponding pathway to the cranial nerve nuclei.

The motor cortex (see Fig. 1.2) is so named because electrical or chemical stimulation of the area evokes movement. It is somatotopically organised in the same fashion as the adjacent somatosensory cortex. Epileptic discharges arising in the precentral gyrus produce localised muscle twitching or myoclonic jerking, which is usually localised to one side of the body and one limb but may spread along the motor cortex to involve the whole of that side (Jacksonian epilepsy). Transient paralysis may follow such a seizure (Todd's paralysis).

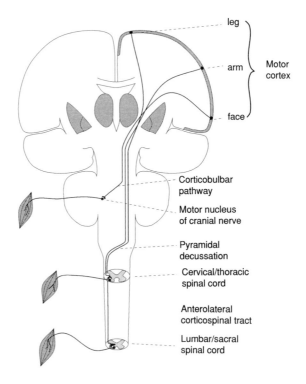

leg
arm } Motor
cortex
face

Corticobulbar
pathway

Motor nucleus
of cranial nerve

Pyramidal
decussation

Cervical/thoracic
spinal cord

Anterolateral
corticospinal tract

Lumbar/sacral
spinal cord

Fig. 1.11 The corticospinal and corticobulbar tracts.

The axons from the motor cortex, and from other areas which contribute to the corticospinal tracts, descend through the corona radiata and the internal capsule and pass through the ventral part of the midbrain in the cerebral peduncles. The pathway makes its way as a number of separate bundles through the pons. They come together as a single column of fibres, the pyramid, on each side of the midline in the ventral medulla. The pyramids are so called because they are triangular in cross-section – the 'pyramidal' tracts take their name from this section of the pathway. The tracts decussate in the ventral medulla and travel down the spinal cord in the white matter which lies between the dorsal and ventral horns. The corticobulbar tracts follow a comparable course but decussate within the brainstem before terminating in the respective cranial nerve nuclei.

The function of the corticospinal and corticobulbar tracts is to provide fast, fine control of the distal extremities, particularly prehensile parts such as the fingers. Their influence on LMNs is chiefly facilitatory. In animal experiments, lesions of the pyramidal tracts cause a loss of dexterous movement in the distal extremities without significant change in postural tone. Accordingly, damage to these pathways does not contribute to the spasticity associated with UMN lesions. However, the corticospinal tracts lie close to other structures involved in the control of movement throughout most of their length. The effect of

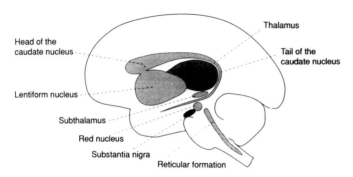

Fig. 1.12 The basal ganglia and brainstem nuclei which contribute to the control of movement.

selective damage to the pyramidal tracts is therefore seldom seen in clinical practice. If it were, it would take the form of clumsiness in manipulating things with the fingers and tongue while postural tone and the control of proximal muscles remained unaffected.

In the older neurological literature, the terms 'upper motor neuron' and 'pyramidal tract' were used almost interchangeably. Patients with spastic hemiplegia caused by stroke, or by lesions in the internal capsule or brainstem, were described as having pyramidal tract signs. Although the pyramidal tracts may indeed be damaged by such lesions, the spastic hemiplegia is clearly due to effects on other parts of the UMN. This confusing and inaccurate usage of the terminology should eventually disappear.

Extrapyramidal systems

Subcortical structures play an important part in the control of posture and movement. The basal ganglia receive connections from wide areas of the cerebral cortex and influence LMNs through relays in brainstem nuclei which give rise to the rubrospinal and reticulospinal tracts.

Figure 1.12 shows the principal basal ganglia and brainstem nuclei. Only structures of the left hemisphere are depicted. The corpus striatum is comprised of the lentiform nucleus and the head of the caudate nucleus. The head of the caudate nucleus is situated in the floor of the anterior horn of the lateral ventricle. Its tail runs posteriorly at first, curving around to lie in the roof of the inferior horn of the lateral ventricle in the temporal lobe. The lentiform nucleus lies lateral to both the caudate nucleus and the thalamus. The space between them is occupied by the internal capsule. The lentiform nucleus is almost triangular in cross-section (see Fig. 1.7); it is divided into the globus pallidus medially and the putamen laterally. The caudate and lentiform nuclei are joined anteriorly. This region of the striatum is known as the nucleus accumbens. The nucleus accumbens receives numerous inputs from the limbic system in addition to its connections with motor systems and the rest of the frontal lobe.

Lesions of the basal ganglia give rise to a group of movement disorders known as the dyskinesias. These are characterised by changes in muscle tone, difficulty in the initiation of movement, and the release of unwanted sequences of stereotyped movements. Athetosis, Huntington's chorea, and certain forms of dystonia are associated with lesions in the corpus striatum. In hemiballismus the damage normally involves the subthalamus. Degenerative changes in the substantia nigra lead to Parkinson's disease, apparently by depriving the striatum of dopamine which is supplied to the lentiform and caudate nuclei by axonal transport through the nigrostriatal tract.

The contribution of the basal ganglia to the control of movement is not well understood. The release phenomena of the dyskinesias suggest that these structures may automate common sequences of muscle activity. This would enable the cerebral cortex to control complex patterns of behaviour by selecting sequences of movements from a large repertoire of relatively simple, preprogrammed actions.

The red nuclei receive information from the cerebral cortex, the cerebellum, and the basal ganglia. They give rise to the rubrospinal tracts, which complement the pyramidal tracts in the control of voluntary movement. They are concerned chiefly with the control of the proximal musculature.

The reticular formation of the brainstem receives information from the cerebral cortex and from many of the basal ganglia. It is important in the regulation of muscle tone and the postural background to voluntary movement. The spasticity caused by UMN lesions is largely due to the withdrawal of the normal influences of the reticular formation on gamma motor efferents. Gamma motor efferents regulate the sensitivity of muscle stretch receptors as part of the normal stretch reflex. When descending influences from the reticular formation are withdrawn, the effect is reflexes of unattenuated vigour, manifested as spasticity.

The regulation of movement

It is not sufficient simply to relay instructions to LMNs if the amplitude, velocity, and force of movement are to be precisely regulated. The motor cortex must receive feedback about the progress of movements to enable their progress to be continuously corrected. For this purpose the cerebellum compares intended action with the actual progress of the movement, and relays the difference between them to the motor cortex as an error signal (e.g. keep going, more to the left, grip harder).

To make this comparison, the cerebellum must receive information from both sensory and motor systems. Input from cutaneous and proprioceptive receptors is provided by the spinocerebellar tracts, whose fibres arise in the dorsal horn and also as collaterals of the dorsal column system. These pathways do not decussate, since each cerebellar hemisphere is concerned with events on its own side of the body. Information about the body's orientation and acceleration arrives from the vestibular nuclei. Orientation in visual space is signalled from the colliculi. Collaterals of the corticospinal and corticobulbar pathways synapse in the pontine nuclei, which provide information about intended movement via the middle cerebellar peduncle. Input relating to the activity of extrapyramidal systems is provided in a similar fashion by the olivary nuclei, whose axons enter the cerebellum via the inferior cerebellar peduncle.

The cerebellum computes the error signal from these sensory and motor inputs and relays it back to the motor cortex via its dentate nucleus, the red nucleus, and the ventrolateral nucleus of the thalamus.

Damage to this system deprives the motor cortex of appropriate feedback and results in an impairment in the coordination of voluntary movement. The cerebellum needs at least two of its major sensory inputs for the maintenance of normal posture. If sensory information from the spinal cord is impaired, as it is in tabes dorsalis or demyelinating disorders, for example, the patient will have difficulty maintaining an erect posture in the dark or with the eyes closed (Romberg's sign). Damage to the cerebellum itself or to its feedback pathway to the cerebral cortex leads to dysmetria, a failure accurately to regulate the amplitude and force of movement. This is revealed in ataxic gait, intention tremor, dysarthria, dysdiadochokinesia (an inability to execute rapidly alternating movements), nystagmus, and in tests of accurate movement, including past-pointing and the heel-shin test. These movement disorders are termed 'cerebellar syndrome'. Actions which are normally executed in a smooth succession of accurate movements are replaced by misplaced, mistimed and oscillatory responses. The impairment is sometimes described as 'tremor of movement' to distinguish it from 'tremor at rest' in the dyskinesias. (It should be noted that dysarthria and nystagmus are not invariably manifestations of dysmetria – they may also result from lesions elsewhere in the brain; for example, dysarthria may be caused by damage to the pathway from the motor cortex to the LMNs controlling phonation and articulation.)

Functional organisation of the forebrain

The cerebral cortex

The concept of localisation of function

The functions of the primary projection areas (Fig. 1.2) are dictated by their anatomical connections. Direct electrical stimulation confirms their specificity. Electrodes in the visual cortex evoke the experience of visual phosphenes (patches of light) whose apparent location in the visual field conforms to the retinotopic organisation of the striate area. Comparable phenomena have been obtained for the other sensory areas. The cortex of the precentral gyrus (the motor cortex) has an exceptionally large population of pyramidal cells in layer V which contribute to the pyramidal tracts and to motor systems of the basal ganglia and brainstem. The motor cortex is the only area of cortex where stimulation evokes short-latency muscle responses.

It has proved more difficult to define the functional specialisation of other regions of the neocortex, the so-called association areas. The excesses of the 19th-century phrenologists created a climate of opinion which was unreceptive to the idea of functional divisions within the cortex. By the 1950s Karl Lashley had developed the concepts of mass action and equipotentiality, according to which the cerebral cortex acted as a single integrated system, and areas of cortex could substitute for one another. During the 1960s such hypotheses received support from psychophysicists and psychophysiologists, who used an analogy with holography to suggest that the analysis of sensory images might be performed by parallel distributed processing. In their most extreme forms, holistic models of cerebral function regarded the association cortex as an uncommitted information processor, rather like a personal computer which can serve successively as a word processor, a mathematical spreadsheet and a database, without dedicated structures for these processes within it.

More recently, electrophysiological studies in laboratory animals have clearly demonstrated a patchwork of anatomically distinct areas which make different contributions to the processing of sensory information. Studies of the visual system during the 1970s and subsequently have been particularly important in revealing local specialisation within the cortex. Areas exist where the cells respond to visual stimuli in a highly selective fashion. In the cortex adjacent to V1, cells respond to the orientation or velocity of a stimulus or encode its spectral composition. Further away, in areas of posterior parietal and inferior temporal cortex, cells respond more selectively. Regions exist where neurons respond only to the radial movement of the hand in the visual field, or to faces, or to a specific object such as a flower, or in a manner which signals the colour that an object would have in white light even where the illumination is coloured. The areas of local specialisation occur within a well defined neural network, arranged partly serially, partly in parallel, and supplied by separate groups of cells in V1. These findings have led to the idea that 'supplementary' areas in occipital, posterior parietal and inferior temporal cortex separately analyse the form, colour and movement of a visual image. The system acts as a distributed processor in the sense that the three streams of information are analysed in parallel and at different locations. However, the specialisation of discrete areas for particular processes of image analysis is clearly at variance with the idea of the cerebral cortex as an uncommitted information processor.

In man, evidence for localisation of function within the cerebral cortex is provided by the changes in perception, cognition and behaviour which result from damage at particular locations. Sensation is lost after lesions in the primary visual and somatosensory cortex. Damage in the surrounding association areas gives rise to the agnosias, disturbances of perception in which the interpretation of sensory input is defective or absent. In visual object agnosia, for example, an article cannot be recognised by inspection even though perimetry may reveal no defect in the visual field. By contrast, damage to the frontal lobes leaves sensory and perceptual processes intact but social control and the ability to plan complicated strategies of behaviour may be severely impaired.

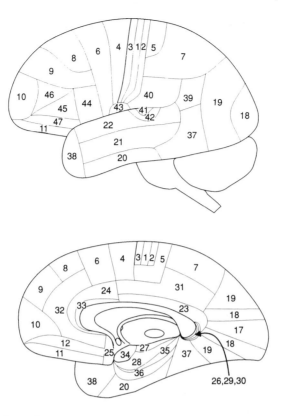

Fig. 1.13 Brodmann's areas.

Table 1.4 summarises some of the effects of lesions at different locations in the association cortex. The areas are denoted by their Brodmann numbers. At the turn of the century, Brodmann distinguished 47 regions of cerebral cortex on the basis of differences in their cellular architecture (Fig. 1.13). Many of these were subsequently identified as functional units, including the motor cortex (area 4), premotor cortex (6), frontal eye fields (8), visual cortex (17), auditory cortex (41, 42) and somatosensory cortex (1, 2, 3). For these systems at least, functional borders are defined by cytoarchitectural boundaries and not by gyri and sulci. Brodmann's areas therefore seem to provide the appropriate framework within which to consider localisation of function.

It is tempting to draw conclusions about the functional organisation of the neocortex from data such as those in Table 1.4. However, deficits caused by the ablation of a part of the nervous system may provide a misleading indication of its function. Removal of one component from such a complex system may do more than delete its intrinsic processes. The activity of areas with which it is normally connected may be disrupted, and behaviour may be released which has little to do with its normal function. Lesions may have excitatory effects through the withdrawal of inhibition from other areas or

Table 1.4   The effects of focal brain lesions on perception and cognitive function

	Brodmann's areas
Bilateral or unilateral lesions	
Astereognosia (tactile agnosia)	5, 7
Visual object agnosia	18, 19, 20
Auditory agnosia	42, 22
Loss of saccadic eye movement, impaired visual search	8, 9
Impulsive behaviour, perseveration	9, 10
Changes in personality, social and sexual behaviour	Dorsolateral and orbital frontal cortex
Left hemisphere lesions	
Colour anomia without aphasia	18, 19, 37
Gerstmann's syndrome	7, 40
Alexia without agraphia	18, 19 splenium
Alexia with agraphia	39, 40
Agraphia without alexia	6 (midlateral)
Broca's aphasia	6 (inferior)
Wernicke's aphasia	22
Acalculia	18, 19, 39, 40; frontal?
Right hemisphere lesions	
Constructional apraxia	7, 39, 40
Colour agnosia	18, 19
Achromatopsia (right or bilateral)	18, 19, 37
Prosopagnosia (right or bilateral)	19, 37, 20 + splenium
Contralateral neglect	7, 40
Anosognosia	5, 7
Autotopagnosia	7
Visual spatial agnosia	7, 40
Receptive amusia	42, 44

through the discharges of epileptogenic foci on their borders. Charting the effects of focal abnormalities (see Chapter 5) therefore provides only the starting point for models of the functional organisation of the cerebral cortex.

The reader who is interested in a comprehensive treatment of the cognitive impairments produced by focal cortical lesions is referred to Walsh (1987), Kolb & Wishaw (1990) and Lishman (1987), who provide detailed reviews.

Hemispheric specialisation

Differences in the perceptual and cognitive processes of left and right hemispheres have attracted a great deal of attention. The studies of focal abnormalities and disconnection syndromes by neurologists like Norman Geschwind and the neuropsychological investigations of commissurotomy patients by Roger Sperry and his colleagues have been largely responsible for this interest. The functional asymmetry was first recognised by the 19th-century neurologists who discovered an association between left hemisphere lesions and disorders of language – the aphasias. Paul Broca discovered that the ability to express ideas in speech was impaired by lesions affecting an area of the left frontal cortex. The region now referred to as Broca's area lies just anterior to the part of the motor cortex which controls the face, pharynx and larynx. Broca's aphasia is characterised by anomia, the utterance of unintended or repeated words or phonemes, difficulty in repeating heard sentences, and a reduction in the fluency of speech. In severe cases the patient may be mute. The condition is distinct from dysarthria, a disorder of articulation and phonation caused by damage to the motor cortex or to the pathway to the musculature involved in speech production.

Damage to the superior temporal gyrus causes Wernicke's aphasia. The most significant effect is the impairment of comprehension. Although speech remains fluent, its intelligibility is reduced by the intrusion of neologisms and the inappropriate use of words. The changes in spoken language seem to be secondary to an inability to monitor what is being said.

Broca's and Wernicke's aphasias are disorders of expression and reception respectively, a distinction which accords with the role of frontal cortex in the control of behaviour and of posterior areas in the analysis of sensory input. However, some disorders of language cannot be explained simply in terms of receptive and expressive processes. Perseverative, amnestic and syntactical aphasias have been described. In these forms, the deficit involves only the inappropriate repetition of words, anomia, or mistakes of grammar and sentence construction. The responsible lesions usually affect the superior temporal gyrus. Conduction aphasia is a rare condition in which the primary disorder is an inability to echo the speech of others word for word. Comprehension is intact and expressive language is otherwise normal. The lesion is said to disconnect the receptive and expressive speech areas.

Dysgraphia, an impairment of the ability to express ideas in writing, is associated with frontal lesions anterior to the hand area of the motor cortex. Acquired dyslexia is an impairment of the ability to read caused by disconnection of the visual cortex from the speech area of the temporal lobe, often by a lesion in the left angular gyrus. Acquired dyslexia is to be distinguished from developmental dyslexia, a problem in education whose neurological origins, if any, remain obscure.

An authoritative review of aphasia and its causative lesions has been provided by Damasio (1992).

Evidence from the effects of stroke in a large sample of adults who had no previous brain damage suggests that the neural mechanisms for language reside in the left hemisphere in at least 98% of normal individuals, irrespective of handedness (Kimura, 1983). Nevertheless, the brain displays a remarkable plasticity in its organisation for language. If the left hemisphere is injured early in life, language becomes dependent on the right half of the brain.

The localisation of the speech areas has been studied with the aid of unilateral anaesthesia induced by intracarotid injections of sodium amytal. This shows that language is represented in the right hemisphere of a significant proportion of individuals with congenital brain damage, or in whom epilepsy or neoplasm occurred in childhood. Children who undergo left hemispherectomy before two years of age may go on to develop language and intellectual skills within the normal range.

The importance of language for communication and thought and the prevalence of right handedness in the population led Hughlings Jackson to propose that the left hemisphere played a leading role in both cognitive and motor activity. The concept became known as 'cerebral dominance'.

Jackson was also aware that the right hemisphere had its own kind of specialisation, which he characterised as 'perceptive'. It has since become clear that many non-verbal skills are dependent upon this half of the brain. Lesions of the right hemisphere often produce selective decrements in performance IQ without affecting verbal IQ. Damage to the right parietal lobe produces disorders of body image, including anosognosia (failure to acknowledge illness), autopagnosia (failure to recognise parts of the body as self), neglect (failure to attend to appearance and hygiene) and dressing apraxis (in which garments are worn in the wrong place or wrong order). Right parietal lesions are also associated with difficulties in discriminating complex geometrical figures by touch (including Braille), as well as spatial disorientation. Damage to the right temporal areas reduces scores on the Seashore Musical Aptitude test and subjectively impairs the ability to appreciate music (receptive amusia). When the abnormality is situated in the right occipital lobe the patient may experience difficulty in distinguishing complex abstract shapes or in solving visual problems in three-dimensional space. Further evidence for asymmetry in cerebral function is summarised in Table 1.4.

Findings such as these have led to many attempts to characterise the 'duality of the brain'. The dichotomy is often expressed in terms of 'verbal' and 'visuospatial' processes. This distinction has proved useful as a form of shorthand but it is purely descriptive of behavioural impairment and has no explanatory value. It fails to accommodate the fact that the specialisation of the right hemisphere extends beyond the visual modality, or that acalculia can be caused by left hemisphere lesions outside the speech areas which do not impair verbal processes. Moreover there are a number of findings which run entirely counter to this specification of the functional asymmetry. Prosody (the emotional inflection of speech) is dependent on the right hemisphere. Conversely it is the left hemisphere which deciphers the visuospatially complex shapes of handwriting, while it is also apparently greatly impaired in the discrimination of simple line drawings of geometrical shapes.

The divergent specialisation of the cerebral hemispheres must confer some biological advantage on the individual. The effects of unilateral lesions suggest that opposite halves of the brain use different modes of imagery, one eidetic, the other symbolic, providing substrates for two quite different types of mental activity. Eidetic imagery enables the individual to think about the physical world by modelling it internally ('What would happen if I turned that handle?'). Symbolic imagery provides the mechanism for abstract thought, and thereby for language and mathematics also ('If $a=b$ and $b=c$, $a=c$'). It seems likely that the eidetic processes of the right hemisphere are phylogenetically the more primitive. The cognitive achievements which distinguish man from other animals depend upon language and the ability to manipulate abstract ideas. The capacity for abstract thought appears to be very limited in subhuman species, among which there is also little evidence for asymmetry of cerebral function.

The limbic system

Anatomy

The major components of the limbic system and their connections are shown schematically in Fig. 1.14. Their spatial relations are illustrated in Fig. 1.15.

Anatomically the hypothalamus, which forms the walls of the third ventricle, occupies a central position in the limbic system, and has direct connections with almost all of its component structures. It is connected to the amygdala via the stria terminalis and the amygdalofugal bundle, the hippocampus via

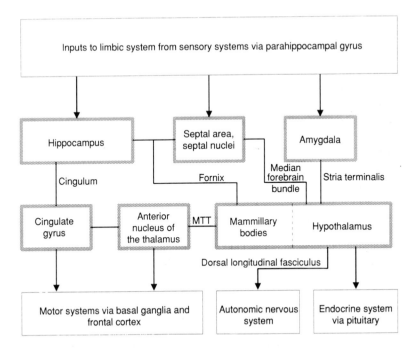

Fig. 1.14 The limbic system and its connections (MTT = mammillothalamic tract). Components of the limbic system are outlined in grey.

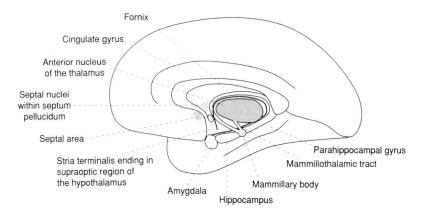

Fig. 1.15 Spatial relationships of the limbic system, looking into the right hemisphere from the midline.

the fornix, the septum via the medial forebrain bundle, and the anterior thalamus via the mammillothalamic tract.

The amygdala lies in the temporal lobe, medial to the uncus and anterior to both the hippocampus and the inferior horn of the lateral ventricle. The stria terminalis makes its way from the amygdala to the hypothalamus following the tail of the caudate nucleus around the posterior and superior aspects of the thalamus.

The septal area comprises grey matter immediately anterior to the genu of the corpus callosum and is functionally linked with the septal nuclei, which are clustered in the base of the septum pellucidum. In addition to their connection with the hypothalamus, the septal nuclei have reciprocal connections with the hippocampus via the fornix.

The mammillary bodies are part of the posterior hypothalamus, appearing as paired elevations in the interpeduncular fossa (see Fig. 1.6). They receive a large number of axons through the fornix, a fibre bundle which follows a helical path from the hippocampus. The hippocampus lies in the floor of the inferior horn of the lateral ventricle. Axons of the fornix gather over its superior surface, heading first posteriorly and then up into the body of the lateral ventricle. Here they are suspended beneath the corpus callosum and travel anteriorly until they reach the anterior margin of the thalamus. They then turn downwards, as the columns of the fornix, passing behind the anterior commissure and into the walls of the hypothalamus to reach the mammillary bodies.

The major output of the mammillary bodies to the rest of the limbic system is the mammillothalamic tract (the tract of Vicq d'Azyr) which projects to the anterior nucleus of the thalamus. From here a circuit is completed back to the hippocampus via the cingulate cortex, the gyrus immediately superior to the corpus callosum within the longitudinal fissure, and the white matter of the cingulum.

The limbic system receives information from all the sensory systems, including olfaction, via the parahippocampal gyrus. This gyrus traverses the medial edge of the inferior surface of the temporal lobe. The limbic system influences behaviour through its connections with basal ganglia and the frontal cortex. It exerts control over endocrine systems via the pituitary, and over both parasympathetic and sympathetic divisions of the autonomic nervous system via the dorsal longitudinal fasciculus, a pathway which extends through the brainstem and into the spinal cord.

Situated between the globus pallidus and the ventral surface of the brain is an area known as the substantia innominata. The substantia innominata contains two important clusters of large neurons: the basal nucleus of Meynert, and the nucleus of the diagonal band of Broca. Axons of the nucleus of Meynert project to the amygdala and to the cerebral cortex. The diagonal band projects to the hippocampus and the septum. These cholinergic pathways are important for the normal function of the limbic system and the cerebral cortex. They are the first to be affected in Alzheimer's disease, and probably play a central role in the disorder by depriving their targets of acetylcholine. Indeed, lesions of the basal nuclei in animals have been shown to deplete the cerebral cortex of 50% of its available acetylcholine.

Emotion and motivation

The limbic system is of importance in psychiatry because of the role which it is thought to play in emotion, motivation and memory. However, the understanding of its part in these processes in man is still fragmentary. The subject is more accessible if the evidence from animal studies is taken into account, and if it is viewed from a wider biological perspective than a purely anthropocentric one.

The hypothalamus acts as a control centre for the regulation of the internal environment. It operates on four major systems:

(1) nutrition, metabolism and energy supply
(2) water and electrolyte balance
(3) body temperature
(4) the reproductive system.

The first three require homeostatic control for the survival of the individual. Regulation of systems for reproduction is necessary for the survival of the species.

The hypothalamus exerts short-term control over these factors through autonomic and endocrine systems. These regulate the absorption of food from the gut, the distribution and storage of fats and glycogen, and the control of insulin and hence the availability of glucose. The hypothalamus controls basal metabolic rate indirectly through the pituitary's secretion of thyroid-stimulating hormone (TSH) and through the autonomic control of adrenaline secretion.

It regulates water and electrolyte balance through pituitary hormones which act on the adrenal cortex and the kidney. Temperature is regulated indirectly through the release of TSH and also through the autonomic control of piloerection, and vasodilation and vasoconstriction of vessels in the skin. The female reproductive cycle and male fertility are controlled by pituitary gonadotrophic hormones, while in coitus itself the autonomic nervous system controls erectile tissues and ejaculation. All these mechanisms depend upon elaborate feedback mechanisms which provide the hypothalamus with information about the current state of the internal environment.

However, endocrine and autonomic mechanisms alone cannot conserve the state of the internal environment indefinitely. Behaviour is necessary to ensure the survival of both the individual and the species. The organism must secure food, drink, shelter, and a mate. The limbic system provides the mechanisms which regulate these supporting behaviours.

The hypothalamus appears to contain centres which detect states of physiological need and trigger behaviours likely to correct them. Plasma glucose levels are detected by receptors in the lateral hypothalamus. When glucose levels fall below some limit, the activity of the receptors initiates foraging and eating. This area of the hypothalamus has been called a 'feeding centre'. The ventromedial hypothalamus receives information from the digestive tract and terminates feeding when appropriate amounts have been consumed. This 'satiety centre' appears to be necessary because plasma glucose levels do not rise until the food has been digested, possibly hours after eating. Similar mechanisms exist to initiate drinking when plasma tonicity changes. Likewise, hypothalamic receptors for circulating levels of oestrogen and testosterone control the sexual receptivity of the female, at least in laboratory animals. In humans, the action of these mechanisms is accompanied by the experience of specific appetites, such as hunger and thirst.

In animals, ablation of the feeding and satiety centres leads to aphagia and hyperphagia respectively. Adipsia and polydipsia can be induced in a similar fashion, while failure of temperature regulation is frequently a problem following surgical procedures which disturb the hypothalamus. Overeating and anorexia have both been observed in humans with hypothalamic lesions. It is not known whether the changes which take place in the hypothalamus following puberty interact with the psychological factors which dispose people to anorexia nervosa at this time.

Electrical stimulation of the hypothalamus in man may evoke an experience of profound well-being, akin to that which accompanies the satiation of appetites. The effects are so powerful that laboratory animals will work for the reward of hypothalamic stimulation to the exclusion of eating and drinking. There are also sites where stimulation is aversive. Animals will not repeat a response that was followed by stimulation at these loci. Humans experience fear or an overwhelming sense of foreboding. (Hypothalamic stimulation has been carried out in man both experimentally in exchange for remission of prison sentence and as a preliminary to psychosurgical procedures.) Stimulation of both the 'pleasure centres' and the aversive sites seems to correspond with reward and punishment, and is accompanied by a variety of autonomic responses, as might be expected given the control which the hypothalamus exerts over parasympathetic and sympathetic systems. Experiments with intracranial self-stimulation suggest that the hypothalamus is in some way involved not only in appetitive behaviour but in the emotional experience which accompanies it. Although emotional experience itself is not directly accessible to scientific study, it is often accompanied by autonomic activity: lacrimation, pallor, blushing, hot and cold sweats, 'butterflies' in the stomach, racing pulse, dilated or constricted pupils, or salivation. It is interesting that these autonomic phenomena are extensively used by writers of fiction to authenticate the emotions of their characters. They also provide psychophysiologists with objective markers of emotion and stress.

The appetitive behaviours triggered by the hypothalamus appear to be regulated by the amygdala and septal area. Patterns of eating, drinking and sexual activity are all modified by lesions of these structures. Although the understanding of these effects is still rudimentary, it is clear that the amygdala and septal area have important effects on the control of aggressive behaviour. If the cerebral hemispheres are surgically removed in the cat, leaving only the hypothalamus as a rostral extension of the brainstem, the animal displays a phenomenon known as 'sham rage'. Sensory stimuli trigger episodes of violent behaviour involving piloerection, vocalisation, biting and lashing movements of the limbs. The response differs from rage in two respects: it is evoked by low levels of stimulation and is short lasting. Responses of this kind can be produced in otherwise intact cats and monkeys by stimulation of the amygdala or ablation of the septal area. Conversely, ablation of the amygdala abolishes the normally aggressive behaviour of laboratory primates, not only towards humans but also towards members of their own species which were previously lower in the social hierarchy. The change towards a more docile disposition is seen in both humans and monkeys when surgical removals of the temporal lobe include the amygdala. If the visual association areas of the inferotemporal cortex are resected at the same time as the amygdala, the taming is accompanied by visual agnosia. The conjunction of signs is known as the Kluver–Bucy syndrome.

These observations suggest that the amygdala and septal area exert complementary effects on the expression of aggressive behaviour. The action of the amygdala is excitatory while that of the septal area is inhibitory. The biological significance of this is not clear. In the wild, aggressive behaviour is necessary for predation, and for the defence of territory within which to hunt and to drink and to establish a position in the social hierarchy, which gives access to potential mates. We may speculate that the amygdala and septal area support the appetitive functions of the hypothalamus through the regulation of aggressive and submissive behaviour.

The regulation of aggression in humans occurs in a social context more complicated even than that of our primate ancestors, but it may serve many of the same purposes. There is relatively little direct evidence of the operations of these mechanisms in man. However, in individuals prone to sudden outbursts of uncontrollable rage or aggression, recordings from intracerebral electrodes have revealed epileptic-like discharges in the amygdala immediately preceding the attack. Similarly, a marked reduction in irritability is one of the consequences of amygdalectomy in the surgical treatment of epilepsy.

The evidence for the role of the limbic system in emotion is chiefly concerned with pleasure and fear, submission, aggression and perhaps anger. Little is known about the anatomical or physiological mechanisms underlying happiness, sadness, and the other emotions that humans experience. Studies of the effects of cerebral lesions suggest that both the expression of emotion and the ability to detect it in others may depend more on the right hemisphere than the left. These processes involve cortical mechanisms in addition to any participation of the limbic system.

Memory

Figure 1.14 shows a circuit linking the hippocampus, the mammillary bodies, the anterior nucleus of the thalamus, and the cingulate gyrus. These associated structures play an important role in memory.

Degenerative changes in the cholinergic circuits of the hippocampus and in its projections from the substantia innominata are believed to be responsible for the loss of memory in Alzheimer's disease. Amnesia also occurs after surgical removal of the hippocampus when epilepsy is treated by temporal lobectomy. The surgery is normally carried out on one side, with the result that verbal or non-verbal memories are impaired selectively. The severity of the amnesia appears to be proportional to the extent of the resection. The amnesia has proved to be particularly severe after bilateral hippocampectomy or in cases where a unilateral ablation was performed when the hippocampus on the other side was already atrophic. The amnesia primarily affects episodic memory – the ability to recall personal experience. Motor learning, immediate memory (digit span) and semantic memory (memory for factual information) remain intact. The amnesia is chiefly anterograde: that is, old memories remain accessible but new ones are not formed after the hippocampus is damaged.

Lesions of the mammillary bodies, the mammillothalamic tract, or the anterior nucleus of the thalamus give rise to Korsakoff's disease. The most common cause is chronic alcohol abuse, but there have been cases of anterior thalamic damage in fencing accidents. Episodic memory is again affected, but in Korsakoff's disease the amnesia is both retrograde and anterograde; the patient has little insight into his disorder and confabulates to cover the impairment.

These effects raise the possibility that other parts of this circuit may be involved in memory. It is not clear whether damage to the fornix impairs episodic memory in humans, though it does so in other primates. The role of the cingulate gyrus remains to be established in humans and primates, although damage to its homologue in rats is known to impair avoidance learning.

Anatomically, the structures which are important in episodic memory are linked to limbic structures which control appetitive behaviour. The association between appetite and memory is not immediately obvious. For our mammalian ancestors at least, food, drink, shelter and sexual partners would not always have been immediately to hand. Survival of the individual and the species would have depended on the evolution of memory of personal experience, to make it possible to guess where to find them on the basis of previous encounters.

Arousal

A network of neurons with long processes known as the reticular formation extends throughout the brainstem. In the midbrain it appears as a core of grey matter surrounding the aqueduct of Silvius, the periaqueductal grey matter. The reticular formation receives collaterals from visual, auditory, vestibular and somatosensory pathways although not, apparently, from the dorsal column/medial lemniscal system. It projects rostrally to the intralaminar and reticular nuclei of the thalamus via the posterior hypothalamus, where it receives important inputs from the limbic system. Caudally, the reticulospinal tracts project to the gamma motor neurons of the spinal cord.

During sleep and relaxed wakefulness, these descending reticulospinal projections reduce the sensitivity of stretch reflex arcs and so reduce the tone of skeletal muscle. At the same time the intralaminar and reticular nuclei of the thalamus discharge rhythmically. Projections from these nuclei to large areas of the association cortex impose their electrical rhythms on the cerebral cortex, giving rise to characteristic waveforms in the electroencephalogram (EEG), including the alpha rhythm and the low-frequency, high-amplitude delta rhythm of slow-wave sleep. The repetitive synchronous discharge of cortical neurons prevents their participation in the information processing necessary for perception and cognitive processes, so one is unconscious during sleep.

Sensory inputs and limbic activity associated with hunger and thirst bring sleep to an end through their effects on the reticular formation. Descending inhibition of muscle is removed. Signals reach the thalamus from the reticular formation which change the pattern of firing in the intralaminar and reticular nuclei, blocking their rhythmic activity and freeing the cortex to take part in perceptual and cognitive processes. This mechanism is responsible for the fact that noise, bright light, physical discomfort, and heightened states of emotion and motivation all maintain arousal and prevent sleep. The reticular formation and its rostral connections with the thalamus have therefore been called the ascending reticular activating system (ARAS). Lesions of the midbrain periaqueductal grey matter interrupt the link between the brainstem and the thalamus which is necessary to bring about wakefulness. The coma caused by coning in raised intracranial pressure is due to this disconnection.

The collaterals to the reticular formation from afferent pathways provide a second but relatively non-specific route by which sensory information can influence the cerebral cortex (distinct from the pathways which relay in sensory-specific nuclei of the thalamus). The system has therefore been dubbed the diffuse thalamic projection system.

The ARAS was identified half a century ago through the electrophysiological studies of Morrison and Dempsey, Moruzzi and Magoun, Linsley and others. More recently a number of neurochemically specific pathways have been described which also project from the brainstem to the forebrain and influence behavioural arousal.

The locus coeruleus lies just beneath the floor of the fourth ventricle. The cells of this nucleus project via the ventral and dorsal noradrenergic bundles and the medial forebrain bundle to parts of the limbic system (particularly the hypothalamus, septal nuclei and septal area), to the thalamus and to much of the cerebral neocortex. Ablation and stimulation of the locus coeruleus have revealed that it plays an important part in the regulation of sleep and wakefulness, including the depression of muscle tone.

The raphe nuclei are situated in the midline of the pons and medulla. Their axons project diffusely to the thalamus, the basal ganglia, the limbic system and the cerebral cortex using the neurotransmitter 5-hydroyxtryptamine (5-HT, serotonin). They evidently contribute to the regulation of sleep because surgical lesions of the raphe nuclei cause insomnia, as do drugs which deplete central 5-HT.

It is likely that projections from the locus coeruleus and the raphe nuclei contribute to the ARAS, but there is no simple correspondence between these neurochemically and electrophysiologically identified systems. Understanding of the mechanisms which regulate sleep and wakefulness remains incomplete.

A dopaminergic system arises principally in the substantia nigra and projects to the corpus striatum via the nigrostriatal tract, to the limbic system and cerebral cortex. This is the system whose degeneration is responsible for the motor signs of Parkinsonism and eventually for the dementia which follows, because of the loss of dopamine from the cerebral cortex. A cholinergic pathway which projects to the limbic system and cerebral cortex from the ventral midbrain and pons has also been identified. Evidence from studies on animals, especially the rat, indicates that it too has tonic effects on arousal and attention.

An important feature of these pathways is that at least part of their role seems to be to supply parts of the forebrain with neurotransmitters. This contrasts with the traditional concepts of transmitters as chemical intermediaries in the communication of frequency-coded information between cells. Transplantation of cholinergic and dopaminergic tissue to the limbic system and striatum reverses many of the behavioural deficits which appear when they are experimentally depleted of neurotransmitters. Such transplants restore local levels of acetylcholine and dopamine but do not re-establish communication with the original sources in the brainstem. Accordingly, these pathways serve, at least in part, as neurochemical pipelines and their effect on behaviour must be exerted through non-specific modulation of the tone of forebrain systems.

References

Barr, M. L. (1988) *The Human Nervous System* (5th edn). New York: Lippincott.

Damasio, A. R. (1992) Aphasia. *New England Journal of Medicine,* **326**, 531–539.

Lishman, W. A. (1987) *Organic Psychiatry* (2nd edn). Oxford: Blackwell.

Kolb, B. & Wishaw, I. Q. (1990) *Fundamentals of Human Neuropsychology* (3rd edn). New York: Freeman.

Kimura, D. (1983) Speech representation in an unbiased sample of left handers. *Human Neurobiology,* **2**, 147–154.

Snell, R. S. (1987) *Clinical Neuroanatomy for Medical Students* (2nd edn). Boston: Little, Brown.

Walsh, K. W. (1987) *Neuropsychology: A Clinical Approach* (2nd edn). Edinburgh: Churchill Livingstone.

Recommended texts

Barr, M. L. (1988) *The Human Nervous System* (5th edn). New York: Lippincott.

Heimer, L. (1983) *The Human Brain and Spinal Cord.* New York: Springer-Verlag.

Snell, R. S. (1987) *Clinical Neuroanatomy for Medical Students* (2nd edn). Boston: Little, Brown.

Walton, J. (1987) *Introduction to Clinical Neuroscience* (2nd edn). London: Baillière.

2 Neurophysiology
Steve Logan

Cell excitability, ions and ion channels ● *Synapses* ● *Sensory receptors and signal transduction* ● *Reflexes and motor control* ● *Reflex responses to visual, vestibular, and auditory stimulation*

This chapter looks at the structure and functions of neurons, and their interconnections. Chapter 3 gives the details of the transmission of nerve impulses ('action potentials') between the neurons via the various neurotransmitters and receptors (Figs 3.1–3.5, pp. 72, 74, 78, 79, are of some relevance to the discussion below).

Cell excitability, ions and ion channels

Cell excitability in nerve cells (neurons), and indeed in all cells, is controlled by the behaviour of ion channels – proteins intrinsic to the plasma membrane. These channels govern the excitability of cells by permitting the flow of current carried by 10^7 to 10^9 ions per second through the membrane. Although, in addition, ions can be transported into and out of cells by specialised mechanisms that are essential for maintenance of ionic gradients, cell volume and pH, these latter mechanisms contribute very little to the electrical excitability of cells.

Ion channels, however, are more than just 'pores' in membranes, permitting unhindered passage of ions in an aqueous channel: these channels can be regulated, or 'gated', by a variety of factors, including membrane potential, neurotransmitters, and intracellular 'second messengers'. Moreover, these membrane ion channels can be modified by changes in their chemical nature and thus provide the basis for long-term alteration of cellular excitability.

The concomitant evolution of gene sequencing and structure-elucidation techniques in molecular biology and patch-clamp analysis of single ion channels in neurophysiology has made major contributions to our understanding of the roles of ion channels in cellular regulation. In neurons, ion-selective channels exist for each of the cations sodium, potassium and calcium, and also for the anion chloride.

The control of neuronal excitability is fundamental to brain function. Neurons have a potential difference between the outside of the cell and the inside of around -70 mV, and generate electrical signals (action potentials) of around 0.1 V. These two phenomena are controlled by the behaviour of ion channels.

The normal functioning of ion channels is involved in the electrical coding of events and the transfer of information from receptors (e.g. in the eye or in muscles) to brain areas where these stimuli are processed and 'perceived'.

Consequently, abnormalities in the behaviour of ion channels underly many aspects of central nervous dysfunction and are thus important targets for the development of therapeutic agents.

Membranes and ion distributions

The most common molecule in the body is H_2O, which accounts for 99% of all molecules; another 0.75% is accounted for by inorganic ions (e.g. Na^+, K^+, Cl^-) and the remainder is accounted for by organic molecules such as DNA, RNA, proteins, etc.

Water in the body can be divided into two compartments: intracellular fluid (ICF); and extracellular fluid (ECF), which comprises plasma and interstitial and transcellular fluids. A normal adult, weighing 70 kg, has approximately 40 litres H_2O, of which 16 litres (45%) is ECF and 25 litres (55%) is ICF. The 16 litres of ECF comprises 13 litres of interstitial fluid and 3 litres of plasma; the contribution from transcellular fluids is small (cerebrospinal fluid, synovial fluid, aqueous and vitreous humours, and digestive juices). There is a very different distribution of ions within these fluids. In particular, the concentrations of K^+, HPO_3^- and proteins is much higher inside the cells than in the ECF or plasma, while the reverse is true for Na^+ and Cl^- (Table 2.1). ECF and ICF are kept separate by plasma membrane, which has many common properties across cell types. In the electron microscope this structure looks like a double layer, 6-10 nm wide (average 7.5 nm). Biochemical experiments have determined that the principal components of cell membranes are phospholipids, steroids and proteins, arranged in the now accepted fluid mosaic model of Singer and Nicholson (Ganong, 1987).

Cell membranes have particular properties that are important in neurophysiology. They:

(1) are permeable to H_2O
(2) are permeable to lipophilic substances (e.g. some anaesthetics)

Table 2.1 The distribution of ions (mmol/l) in body fluids

	ICF	ECF	Plasma
Na^+	14	143	152
K^+	157	5	5
Cl^-	10	117	113
HCO_3^-	10	27	27
Protein (A^-)	74	–	16
Mg^{2+}	26	3	3
Ca^{2+}	0.1 μmol/l	5	5
HPO_4^{2-}	113	2	2

Modified from Ganong (1987).

(3) are impermeable to large molecules (e.g. proteins)
(4) behave as if there were 'pores' or 'holes' in the membrane
(5) are selectively permeable to ions (e.g. 50 times more to K^+ than Na^+).
    (NB Although K^+ is a larger ion than Na^+ (atomic weights 46 and 23
    respectively) – the shell of water molecules surrounding each ion (water
    of hydration) gives the sodium atoms a larger effective diameter.)

Resting membrane potential

The differential distribution of ions described above gives rise to an electrical
gradient (voltage difference) between the inside and outside of nerve cells.
This potential can be measured by fine glass microelectrodes (tip diameter
$<1 \mu m$) and arises because ions tend to diffuse down their concentration
gradients. However, since ions are charged they are also susceptible to the
effects of charge, and this too determines the flux of ions across the membrane.

Thus if potassium ions move down their concentration gradients (out of the
cell) they leave behind a negative charge which ultimately opposes further
movement of potassium. At equilibrium (no net movement of ions) the
electrical force (ΔE) preventing efflux of potassium ions is opposed by the
concentration gradient promoting efflux (ΔC). In terms of physical chemistry,
this relationship is given by the Nernst equation:

$$\Delta E = \Delta C = RT/zF \ \ln \ [\text{potassium}] \ \text{inside}/ [\text{potassium}] \text{outside}$$

where R, z and F are constants, and T is temperature (in this instance body
temperature), and the square brackets denote concentration (usually in
mmol/l). This equation simplifies to

$$\Delta E \ \text{or} \ E_K = -58 \log_{10} [\text{potassium}] \text{inside}/ [\text{potassium}] \text{outside}$$

E_K is known as the equilibrium potential for potassium, and is equal to
approximately -95 mV. This means that if the membrane were permeable
to only potassium ions, the membrane potential would equal -95 mV.
However, nerve cell membranes are permeable to Na^+ ($E_{Na} = +35$ mV) and
to Cl^- ($E_{Cl} = -65$ mV) at rest, and the resting membrane potential of most
neurons lies in the range -50 to -90 mV, which is a value determined by
the relative permeabilities of the ions and their equilibrium potentials.

Sodium channels

These channels have been purified from a variety of tissues by specific, high-
affinity binding to toxins such as tetrodotoxin (TTX), and most investigators
agree that the channel consists of a large glycosylated protein of approximately
1900 amino acids. This protein loops through the membrane several times with
four principal repeats (I–IV) which form the ion channel or pore (Hille, 1992).

Potassium channels

Potassium channels represent the most diverse set of ion channels and are key features in the control and modulation of cellular excitability.

These channels are voltage regulated, or calcium sensitive, or sensitive to extracellular signals (neurotransmitters) or to intracellular messengers, and as such allow complex modification of cellular behaviour. These channels contain six hydrophobic membrane-spanning regions and an arginine-rich (voltage-sensor) region, similar to the sodium channel and calcium channel.

Calcium channels

There are at least three types of calcium channel (L, T and N channels). The classification into subtypes is incomplete and precise differences between channels awaits confirmation. Calcium channels have a similar molecular form and membrane topology to sodium channels, with four internal repeats (of molecular weight around 200 kdaltons) and toxin-binding sites. Calcium channels are involved in synaptic transmission and rhythmic firing in neurons. L-type calcium-channel blockers have extensive clinical applications, especially in the treatment of hypertension and cardiac arrhythmias, and are used in the treatment of mania. Such drugs include verapamil (a phenalkylamine), nifedipine and nitrendipine (dihydropyridines).

The sodium pump

There is an active (energy-requiring) pump in cell membranes responsible for the maintenance of osmotic equilibrium. This Na/K adenosine triphosphatase uses the energy derived from the hydrolysis of the terminal phosphate of adenosine triphosphate to actively extrude Na^+ from the cell in exchange for K^+. The pump generally moves a larger number of Na^+ ions out of the cell in exchange for K^+ (usually in a ratio of 3:2), causing a small electrogenic effect and contributing around -5 mV to the resting membrane potential.

Resting membrane potentials therefore arise from ionic gradients which are maintained by active pumping.

Action potentials

Signalling in the nervous system is brought about by the rapid transfer of electrical signals. The fundamental process underlying this is the action potential. Action potentials represent a rapid change in the polarity of the voltage across the neuronal membrane, from around -60 mV to approximately $+35$ mV. This is brought about by a change in sodium permeability. Sodium permeability (pNa) or conductance (gNa $= 1/p$Na) is regulated by voltage-sensitive membrane channels that open in response to depolarisation of the

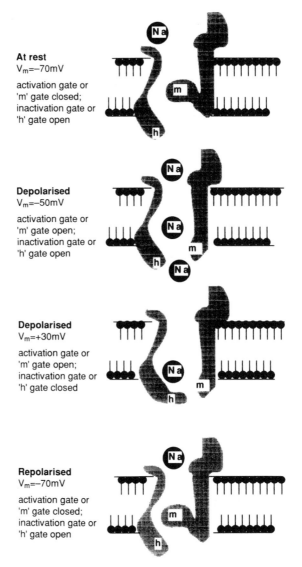

At rest
$V_m=-70mV$

activation gate or
'm' gate closed;
inactivation gate or
'h' gate open

Depolarised
$V_m=-50mV$

activation gate or
'm' gate open;
inactivation gate or
'h' gate open

Depolarised
$V_m=+30mV$

activation gate or
'm' gate open;
inactivation gate or
'h' gate closed

Repolarised
$V_m=-70mV$

activation gate or
'm' gate closed;
inactivation gate or
'h' gate open

Fig. 2.1 The mechanism of membrane depolarisation (V_m = membrane potential). The voltages shown for depolarisation are only approximate.

membrane (see Fig. 2.1 for details). This leads to the influx of Na^+ and further depolarisation. Repolarisation of the membrane is associated with the closing of the voltage-gated sodium channels and opening of voltage-gated potassium channels.

Refractory period
During the action potential, the neuronal membrane is usually completely refractory to further stimulation (i.e. no further action potentials can be

elicited, even with greatly increased stimuli). This is due to voltage-dependent inactivation of Na^+ channels, which cannot reach their 'closed' state until the membrane is repolarised, at which point they can be 'opened' in response to a stimulus (see Fig. 2.1).

During the last part of the action potential there is a relative refractory period, when increasing stimulus strength will produce an action potential. At this time some of the Na^+ channels are still voltage-inactivated and the K^+ channels are opened; this produces some membrane conductance (leakiness), but requiring a larger current (stimulus) to produce the same depolarisation (voltage).

Conduction of action potentials

Action potentials are conducted along axons (sometimes for distances greater than 1 m) without decrement. Local current flows by ions spreading to depolarise the adjacent areas of membrane, which reach threshold and initiate another action potential, which in turn starts the process of electrotonic spread again. The speed of electrotonic conduction is dependent on the resistance and capacitance of the membrane. In unmyelinated axons, the electrotonic spread is sufficient to depolarise immediately adjacent sections of axon; in myelinated

Table 2.2 Classification of nerve fibres

	Diameter: μm	Conduction velocity: ms^{-1}
(1) *Erlanger/Gasser*		
Aα Muscle spindle afferents	15	70-120
Aβ Cutaneous touch and pressure	8	30-70
Aγ Motor neurons to muscle spindle	5	15-30
Aδ Cutaneous temperature and pain afferents	13	12-30
B Sympathetic preganglionic neurons	3	3-15
C Pain/temperature afferents, sympathetic postganglionic neurons	1	0.5
(2) *Lloyd Hunt*		
I Ia Muscle spindle afferents Ib Tendon organs	13	70-120
II Cutaneous mechano-receptors	9	25-70
III Deep-pressure sensors in muscles	3	10-25
IV Unmyelinated pain fibres	1	1

axons, where axon diameter is increased (and thus resistance is lowered) and capacitance is reduced by the presence of insulating Schwann cells, the conduction velocities can be increased substantially (see Table 2.2).

Synapses

Neurons communicate with each other through specialised junctions called synapses. At a typical synapse the presynaptic (or afferent) axon forms a swelling called a bouton. On the postsynaptic side the membrane undergoes some structural changes, which usually consist of thickenings when viewed in the electron microscope. In the case of the neuromuscular junction, the surface area of the postsynaptic membrane is substantially increased by the presence of extensive invaginations in the postsynaptic membrane. In most cases there is a gap of around 20 nm between pre- and postsynaptic elements in the central nervous system. Presynaptic terminals contain synaptic vesicles – storage sites for neurotransmitters – and mitochondria. The arrival of an action potential triggers the opening of voltage-gated calcium channels, permitting the influx of Ca^{2+} into the terminal, which triggers the fusion of vesicles with the presynaptic membrane. The contents of the vesicles are emptied into the synaptic cleft, and the transmitters diffuse to bind to receptors.

Activation of receptors is associated with a variety of transduction mechanisms which can lead to excitation or inhibition in the postsynaptic neuron.

Synaptic integration

Neurons typically receive many thousands of synaptic inputs, and in the vast majority of these a single excitatory postsynaptic potential (EPSP) will be insufficient to reach threshold and induce an action potential in the receiving cell. Moreover, since many of the inputs may be inhibitory postsynaptic potentials (IPSPs), the neuron has to integrate the synaptic inputs before its output signal (i.e. discharge of action potentials) can be finalised. Neurons generally 'sum' the EPSPs and IPSPs to determine whether the final signal exceeds threshold and leads to action potential firing. Generally the area of the axon just as it leaves the soma (axon hillock) has the lowest threshold for action potential discharge, so the summation of electrical activity at this point determines whether firing will occur.

Postsynaptic potentials are electrotonic potentials; that is, they are conducted decrementally from their site of initiation. Thus synapses at distant parts of the dendrite are much less effective than those at proximal portions or those on the soma or axon hillock.

Spatial summation

The current produced by activation of synaptic inputs at different points in the dendritic field or on the soma if activated simultaneously can summate and thus increase the chances of reaching threshold. Moreover, repeated stimulation of a single synapse can lead to temporal summation, since individual EPSPs decay slowly, allowing a second and third EPSP to augment the effect of the preceding one. Thus the frequency of action potentials arriving at the presynaptic synapse is an important determinant of whether a postsynaptic cell will discharge or not (see "Sensory receptors and signal transduction", below).

Inhibitory synapses use neurotransmitters such as gamma-aminobutyric acid (GABA) and glycine, and often involve the opening of chloride channels. These synapses are often found close to the axon hillock or on the soma, where inhibitory mechanisms can exert more control over the discharge of action potentials. Other inhibitory mechanisms are linked to potassium channels, although these mechanisms act rather more slowly than the chloride mechanisms.

Presynaptic inhibition is a mechanism whereby certain neurotransmitters can decrease the amount of neurotransmitters released from a synaptic terminal through receptors that are located on the presynaptic element. There is certainly more than one mechanism involved in this process, including the phenomenon of primary afferent depolarisation in which the presynaptic inhibitory neurotransmitter (possibly GABA) depolarises the terminal, such that an arriving impulse is 'short circuited', so limiting the opening of voltage-gated calcium channels and thus reducing transmitter release. Other mechanisms, possibly employed by opiates and GABA acting at $GABA_B$ receptors, involve the selective reduction of the inward flux of calcium ions by a direct action on the channel.

Long-term changes in excitability

Repetitive stimulation at some synapses, particularly the neuromuscular junction, autonomic neurons and in the cerebellum, can modify the size of the postsynaptic potentials. If an incoming axon is stimulated at high frequency the EPSPs or end-plate potentials (EPPs) decline in size. Following cessation of the stimulus and recovery, the PSP returns to normal size. This is known as post-tetanic depression. If calcium influx is partially restricted during the stimulation period, the potentials get larger (post-tetanic facilitation) and at the end of the stimulus train there is a prolonged enhancement in the size of the response (post-tetanic potentiation).

The precise mechanisms underlying these changes are not yet fully understood, but depression involves a reduction in the number of vesicles released per impulse, whereas potentiation involves changes in intracellular calcium buffering, as well as alterations in the quantal release of neurotransmitter.

Long-term potentiation, learning and memory

In the mammalian hippocampus, following a brief tetanic stimulation to presynaptic axons impinging on pyramidal cells there is a prolonged increase in the size of unitary PSPs recorded in these cells, which can last for many hours. This is known as long-term potentiation (LTP). This phenomenon, which is believed to be an important neuronal mechanism underlying the processes of memory and learning, involves activation of at least two distinct receptors for the excitatory amino acid neurotransmitter l-glutamate, and involves changes in the postsynaptic cell as well as changes in the presynaptic terminal. Some form of retrograde messenger travelling from the postsynaptic cell back to the presynaptic terminal may be involved.

Sensory receptors and signal transduction

Awareness of events both inside and outside the body is a function of the nervous system. The nervous system must receive information in the form of trains of nerve impulses in afferent axons. It is the function of sensory receptors to convert aspects of physical events into repetitive discharges of action potentials in their axons. The perception of events depends in the first instance upon the properties of the receptors and the way in which they perform their transduction. If perception is to be accurate, the discharge of impulses in the afferent axons must relate precisely to the intensity and duration of the stimulus presented to the receptors.

Physical events perceived by the nervous system occur in four forms of energy: electromagnetic, mechanical, thermal, and chemical. The term 'modality' is used to refer to a class of more or less unique sensory experience. Some modalities of sensation can be related in a simple way to forms of energy: for example, vision to electromagnetic energy; hearing, touch, kinaesthesia, and vibration to mechanical energy; temperature to thermal energy; taste and olfaction to chemical energy; pain to mechanical, thermal, electrical and chemical energy.

Somatosensory mechanisms

In man, somatic sensation usually can be subdivided into four functional subdivisions: touch, proprioception, pain, and temperature.

Cutaneous receptors

A cutaneous receptor is the peripheral ending of an afferent nerve fibre. It may terminate in relation to specialised non-neural cells playing an important part in the sensory transduction process; in this case the whole structure is known as the receptor.

These receptors are not only specific to each modality, but in some cases they only respond to a limited part of the range of intensities encompassed within that modality. Furthermore they differ from each other in the way in which they respond to a continuous stimulus: they may be slowly adapting or quickly adapting.

Mechanoreceptors – touch and vibration   The stimulus is mechanical distortion of the nerve terminal.

Thermoreceptors – temperature   The natural stimulus is change in skin temperature. Cold receptors increase discharge on cooling and decrease discharge on warming; warm receptors increase to warming and decrease to cooling. Each afferent operates only over a small range of temperature, and the whole population of receptors is required to cover the range of perceived temperature change.

Nociceptors – pain   The natural stimulus is one that causes or threatens to cause tissue damage.

Receptive field   This is that spatial area within which a stimulus of sufficient intensity and proper quality will evoke a change in the discharge of impulses in the afferent axon. For a cutaneous afferent it is a particular area of the skin.

Threshold   This is the intensity of a stimulus that is just strong enough to produce a response in afferents. The threshold for excitation varies within the receptive field. The density of terminals is greatest towards the centre of a cutaneous receptive field, and here the threshold is lowest.

Peripheral innervation density   This is the number of innervating fibres per unit area of body surface. There is an inverse relation with size of the receptive field. Note the contrast between innervation density of fingers and lips as compared with trunks and arms.

Afferent fibres   Cutaneous sensibility is served by three groups of primary afferent fibres: myelinated $A\beta$ and $A\delta$ fibres, and unmyelinated C fibres. Cutaneous tactile sensation is carried by $A\beta$ and $A\delta$ fibres, temperature by $A\delta$ and C fibres, pain by $A\delta$ (pricking, first pain – see p. 55) and by C fibres (second pain – see p. 55). Note the differential blocking effects of local anaesthetics which act primarily on $A\delta$ and unmyelinated C fibres, whereas asphyxia affects the larger $A\beta$ fibres, resulting in quite different modifications of sensory capability in the affected area.

Morphology   The morphology of cutaneous receptors does not bear an obvious, simple relationship to their function in many cases. Several complex forms of cutaneous receptor have been described, classified into three groups:

free nerve endings; expanded nerve endings (e.g. Merkel's discs); encapsulated nerve endings (e.g. Pacinian corpuscle).

Signal transduction mechanism

The Pacinian corpuscle has been studied in great detail and can be used as an example to describe the underlying signal transduction mechanisms. Movement or pressure on the lamellar structure surrounding the Pacinian corpuscle axon distorts the axon terminal. This leads to the opening of mechanosensitive ion channels that are relatively non-selective for the ion species, thus allowing for an influx of Na^+ ions accompanied by a less significant, concomitant efflux of K^+ ions. This inward current leads to a generator or receptor potential. Local current flow to the first node of Ranvier, which is located within the lamellae, leads to production of action potentials. The size of the current, and therefore the depolarisation leading to the action potentials, is related to the magnitude of the stimulus. However, it is the frequency (f) of the action potentials that is responsible for the coding of the response. Current flow at the first node is translated into the delay between successive action potentials: the larger the current (or stimulus), the sooner a second or subsequent action potential can be generated. This is due to the refractoriness of the axon caused by open potassium channels (see earlier). Thus sensory mechanisms use a frequency-coded (or frequency-modulated, FM) signalling process but an amplitude-modulated (AM) transduction process.

Higher-order somatosensory processing

The anatomical substrates for somatosensory processing are described in Chapter 1, and comprise essentially an anterolateral pathway serving pain, temperature and crude touch and a dorsal column–medial lemniscus pathway serving proprioception and discriminative touch. These pathways consist of a series of relays or transfer nuclei in which the sensory signal is sequentially processed. In each relay nucleus, projection (or output) cells receive information from many afferent inputs; moreover, afferent inputs synapse with many relay cells. This extensive convergence and divergence of inputs is important in the generation of a new pattern of activity for higher processing. Inputs also terminate on inhibitory and excitatory interneurons, which further contribute to the signal-processing activities of the relay nucleus. In some cells in the dorsal column nuclei there is very little convergence, with often a single input being sufficient to cause the receiving cell to fire. This allows for signal transmission with high fidelity and without much integration of information, and is not common.

Lateral inhibition

Lateral inhibition is a mechanism to limit the spread of excitation between parallel inputs, thereby isolating cells that are anatomically adjacent. It is also

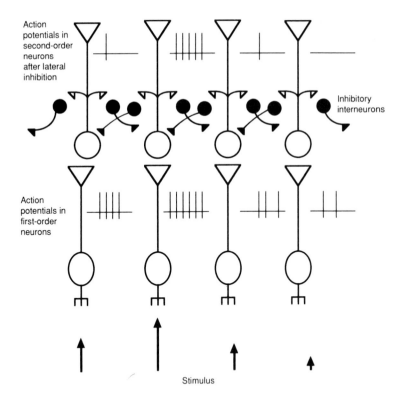

Action
potentials in
second-order
neurons
after lateral
inhibition

Inhibitory
interneurons

Action
potentials in
first-order
neurons

Stimulus

Fig. 2.2 The mechanism of lateral inhibition ($\longrightarrow\triangleleft$ excitatory synapse; $\blacktriangleleft$ inhibitory synapse; vertical bars indicate signal strength).

known as feed-forward or recurrent inhibition, and is a mechanism for producing contrast.

Lateral inhibition is illustrated in Fig. 2.2. Stimulation of first-order neurons leads to excitation of the second-order neurons in relation to the strength of the applied stimulus; this in turn leads to excitation of inhibitory interneurons (usually GABAergic). The most stimulated interneurons (i.e. those receiving an input from the most stimulated primary source) then exercise the greatest inhibition on the adjacent second-order neurons. This 'sharpens up' the response, as indicated in Fig. 2.2, since neurons in the 'main' pathway are still firing several action potentials, whereas those adjacent second-order neurons are substantially attenuated in their responses.

Receptive fields in second-order or third-order relay stations

With increasing anatomical convergence and divergence, plus lateral inhibition, the receptive field properties of neurons in relay nuclei assume more complex properties. For example, receptive fields for primary afferents are simply areas of skin which when stimulated produce action potential discharge. In contrast, in the thalamus or dorsal column nuclei the neurons have a centre-surround receptive field, which means that these cells are excited by a stimulus in the centre of the receptive field but inhibited by a stimulus in the region of skin surrounding the excitatory centre. At higher levels (e.g. somaesthetic cortex) the pattern of response required to activate neurons may be even more complex, with direction and velocity of stimulus application contributing to the features that are detected.

Modality and topography channels

In order for the central nervous system to recognise both the nature and the locality of a stimulus, there is little or no convergence between different modalities or from different somatotopic locations. The body surface is mapped onto the somaesthetic cortex with different amounts of cortical space devoted to those areas with different sensory function. A large peripheral innervation with extensive processing has a large cortical representation.

Modality-specific columns exist in the cortex; that is, single nerve cells respond to only one modality, with segregation between those that respond to light touch and hair movement, for example. Topographical organisation allows intracortical connections to be orderly and rapid.

Parallel pathways

Signals from the periphery reach the cortex via several parallel pathways. The information in each of these can be unique to the pathway or can duplicate information in other pathways. This means that lesions do not always result in complete abolition of sensation; for example, lesions of the medial lemniscus leave patients with the capacity for crude touch sensation through anterolateral pathways, while having lost fine or discriminative touch sensation. In addition, one pathway can project to more than one cortical area. There are at least ten representations of the body surface in the cortex (4 in S1, 1 in S2 and 5 in posterior parietal cortex). Although such a representation may appear to offer overelaboration and redundancy, it also offers some security in response to damage or disease; furthermore, parallel processing allows the nervous system to deal with the same information from the periphery in many different ways, thus endowing the whole process of sensory processing and therefore perception with a varied repertoire of meaning.

Pain sensation

At the most simple level, pain can be regarded as a sensation that derives from stimuli that cause or threaten to cause tissue damage. The nature of the experience may, however, vary considerably according to the circumstances giving rise to it.

Receptors

There is a distinct group of primary afferent nerve fibres that respond only to stimuli that are damaging and painful. These are probably free nerve endings. Some are 'polymodal' insofar as they respond to any stimulus producing tissue damage, whether mechanical, chemical or thermal, while others respond only to damaging mechanical stimuli (or rarely one of the others) and can be regarded as high-threshold mechanoreceptors, although it seems that some are activated by a chemical mediator produced by tissue damage.

Dual nature of pain

Classically the sensation of pain is subdivided into two compartments.

(1) First pain, a brightly prickly sensation, is well localised, and represents an input carried in small myelinated Aδ fibres.
(2) Second pain, a burning sensation, is poorly localised, and may continue as an 'after-image' following removal of the stimulus. This component is the one which is particularly difficult to endure. It is thought to be carried primarily by unmyelinated C fibres. Their discharge may outlast the stimulation.

The two qualities of pain reflect not only the dual nature of the input but also two sets of connections within the nervous system.

Large-fibre influence on pain sensation

The sensation of pain is not only dependent on an input from nociceptive afferents but also is significantly affected by the input from the large myelinated mechanoreceptive afferents (Aβ fibres). Activation of the large mechanoreceptive afferents can reduce or eliminate some types of pain. The common practice of rubbing the skin surface when one has been hurt serves to provide a powerful stimulus driving the cutaneous mechanoreceptors. Clinically, electrical stimulation of large myelinated afferents, either via cutaneous electrodes over peripheral nerves (transcutaneous stimulation) or by implanted dorsal column stimulators, has proved to be a successful means of treating certain pain states. Peripheral nerve neuropathies (e.g. herpetic neuralgia) where most of the large fibres are destroyed can result in chronic pain states where all types of stimuli, even light touch, will produce an unbearable pain.

Neural systems for pain sensation

Spinal cord   Spinal cord neurons relaying nociceptive inputs are found predominantly in superficial laminae of the dorsal grey matter (Rexed's

Large-fibre influence

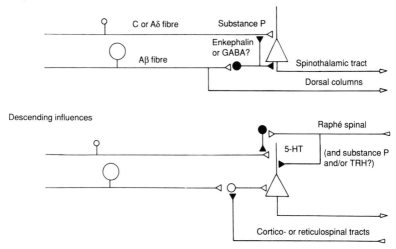

Fig. 2.3 Spinal mechanisms of analgesia (—◁ excitatory synapse; —◀ inhibitory synapse; 5-HT, 5-hydroxytryptamine; TRH, thyrotrophin-releasing hormone).

lamina 1 (marginal cells) and laminae IV–VI, but principally V). Fibres project to the thalamus in the contralateral anterolateral tract, although some fibres also travel ipsilaterally in the cord. Laminae 1 and 2 form a translucent cap over the dorsal horn of the spinal cord and are referred to as the substantia gelatinosa. Pain afferents entering the cord may travel some distance up and down the cord in Lissauer's tract before they synapse in the dorsal horn. The Aβ afferent cutaneous mechanoreceptors which are known to influence pain sensation terminate in lamina 3 and 4. The present view is that some cells in the substantia gelatinosa act as excitatory interneurons, relaying the C fibre input to the anterolateral tract cells in the deeper layers while others function as inhibitory interneurons controlling the flow of nociceptive information in the dorsal horn possibly by presynaptic inhibition (Fig. 2.3). The neuropeptide enkephalin and GABA are important inhibitory transmitters in this region. Descending fibres reach the substantia gelatinosa from Raphé nuclei and the reticular formation and the sensory cortex.

Thalamus   The ventroposterior nucleus of the thalamus is part of the topographically organised modality-specific pathway which provides the basis for the discriminating aspects of somaesthesia. It is important in the localisation and control of pain.

Reticular formation and non-specific thalamic nuclei   The connections here involve the brainstem reticular formation, mesencephalic reticular formation including the periaqueductal grey matter (PAG), the intralaminar nuclei of the thalamus, and the posterior thalamic nuclear group. The subsequent connections made by cells in these regions include hypothalamus, limbic system, and the frontal lobes. This set of connections in the nervous system is responsible for the aversive drive that pain stimuli generate, associated more with second pain than first pain. Note also that the limbic system and associated structures are also the neural substrate of aggressive, emotional, and sexual behaviour, together with that of more complex states. They should thus not simply be related to pain but represent the interface between emotion and pain.

Descending control of pain

There are important descending influences on the transmission of pain information at all levels, but of particular importance are those fibres modifying the processes of transmission in the dorsal horn (Fig. 2.3). A major descending pathway arises in the Raphé nuclei (especially the nucleus Raphé magnus) which themselves receive a powerful drive from the PAG. The PAG has a high density of opiate receptors and is innervated by fibres from the hypothalamus, containing the endogenous analgesic molecule β-endorphin. Electrical stimulation at the Raphé nuclei or PAG will produce a profound analgesia such that it is even possible to carry out surgery without anaesthetics. In humans, a few minutes of electrical stimulation of the PAG will produce relief from severe chronic pain which may last several hours.

Activation of the corticospinal fibres will block the input from low-threshold mechanoreceptors to what appear to be nociceptive relay neurons in the dorsal horn; without this descending control these cells would be activated by light mechanical stimuli. We know that such stimuli do elicit painful sensations in some pathological conditions. The corticospinal influence would depend on the nature of the input to the somaesthetic cortex and hence on the normal pattern of stimulation of the body regions concerned. It would be distorted if the input were abnormal (e.g. with the loss of large fibres in herpes infection).

Referred pain

Pain arising in the viscera is frequently perceived to occur in a region of the body surface innervated by the same spinal segment as the visceral region in question. Thus heart pain is often referred to the left arm. It seems that there is no ordered somatotopic representation of the viscera in the central nervous system, and thus no accurate means of localising pain sensation of visceral origin. Rather it seems that the visceral nociceptive input may converge on nociceptive neurons relating to the body surface, and hence be referred to the surface regions represented by the neurons in question. Thus, visceral referred pain can sometimes be exacerbated or reduced by modifying the pattern of input from the skin surface to the 'relay' neurons in question.

Congenital insensitivity to pain

There are two types of congenital insensitivity to pain. In one the peripheral input is normal; the subjects perceive the sensation but it does not produce an aversion drive. It is simply another quality of sensation like touch, temperature, or limb position. This suggests a lack of the proper connections at the level of the limbic system. In the second category, the subjects appear to lack the small-fibre groups in the peripheral nerve input.

*Effects of lesions to spinal cord and
central nervous system on pain sensation*

Transection of the anterolateral tract will cause a slight elevation of touch thresholds on the contralateral side of the body and a marked elevation of up to 50% or more in pain and temperature thresholds on the contralateral side (but recovery after 6 months, see below).

Lesions to somaesthetic cortex or ventroposterior nucleus cause a brief elevation of pain thresholds followed by hypersensitivity to painful stimuli which is presumably due to loss of descending control.

Transmitters involved in pain sensation

A proportion of C fibres in the dorsal horn contain the polypeptide substance P in their terminals. However, not all C fibres do so, and excitatory amino acids such as l-glutamate may also be important in the input pathway. The Raphé-spinal projection uses 5-hydroxytryptamine. Interneurons in the dorsal horn contain met-enkephalin or leu-enkephalin and/or GABA. Intravenous injection of the morphine antagonist naloxone blocks the analgesic effect of electrical stimulation of both the Raphé nuclei and PAG.

Reflexes and motor control

The division of the central nervous system's function into 'motor' and 'sensory' is artificial and for convenience only. Movement is used to improve sensory perception, and sensory inputs initiate or modify movements. The control of movements depends upon sensory receptors in muscles (muscle spindles and Golgi tendon organs) and in joints (several types of joint receptor) and probably upon many other sensory receptors elsewhere (e.g. skin touch receptors). There are many more afferent axons in muscle nerves than efferent (motor) axons.

Motor unit

Each motor neuron axon may divide many times within a muscle to innervate many muscle fibres. The axon with its muscle fibres is a functional unit, the 'motor unit'. All of the muscle fibres in a motor unit will contract together each time the motor neuron discharges an action potential. The innervation ratio (number of muscle fibres in muscle:number of efferent nerve axons innervating them) varies from 3–5 (extrinsic eye muscles) to 1500–2000 (back muscles). The degree of fine control exerted over the muscle by the nervous system is related to the number and the size of its constituent motor units. An increase in the contraction of a muscle is achieved firstly by recruitment of motor units and secondly by the increase in the rate of discharge of motor units after their recruitment.

Control of reflexes

A number of regions of the central nervous system are traditionally associated with motor function. These include: spinal cord, brainstem and vestibular organs, cerebellum, some thalamic nuclei, basal ganglia, and the cerebral cortex.

Spinal cord and brainstem

These contain the motor neurons which form the 'final common path' for all motor activity, and also the neurons involved in simple motor reflexes. Motor neurons may have at least 20 000 synapses impinging on them and are thus major sites of integration. The reflex may be considered as a basic unit of function. However, the basic reflex mechanisms are part of the overall pattern of central nervous function, and reflexes often depend upon activity (facilitation of inhibition) coming from other parts of the central nervous system. It is therefore artificial (but convenient) to describe reflexes in isolation.

Many motor reflexes have been described; of these, the stretch (tendon) reflex and the 'clasp-knife' response are particularly important.

Stretch reflex Muscle spindles (stretch receptors located in parallel with muscle fibres) are excited by muscle lengthening. Group 1a afferent axons (from primary or annulospiral endings) have an excitatory monosynaptic connection to motor neurons which cause the muscle to contract. The sensitivity of these reflexes is modulated by supraspinal mechanisms, with the result that they play an important part in the control of movement and posture (muscle tone). The stretch reflex is exaggerated in spastic paralysis.

'Clasp-knife' response This reflex is initiated following activation of Golgi tendon organs (located in series with muscle fibres) which respond to force of contraction in muscle. Group 1b afferent axons inhibit motor neurons through one or two inhibitory interneurons (di- or trisynaptic pathway), so preventing muscle contraction. This reflex is important in the regulation of muscle contraction, tension control and protective reflexes. The 'clasp-knife' response is the typical one in spastic paralysis.

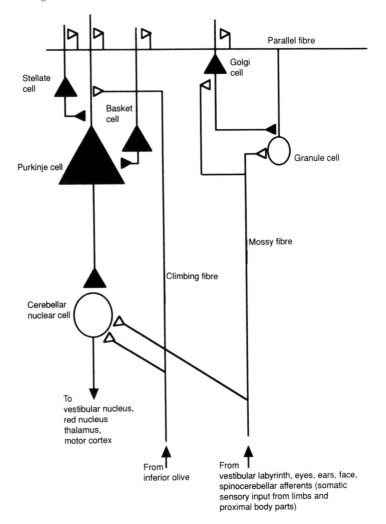

Fig. 2.4   Connections within the cerebellum (⊸◁ excitatory synapse; ⊸◀ inhibitory synapse).

Cerebellum

Cerebellum (literally, 'little brain') is the only area of the nervous system to span the midline of the body without interruption. This structure has increased in size substantially in humans, although its internal wiring is relatively similar to that found in lower vertebrates.

Much is known about the organisation of the neurons in the cerebellum (Fig. 2.4). There are two sets of neurons involved: those of the cerebellar cortex, and those of the cerebellar nuclei. The cerebellum receives two major input pathways: the mossy fibres and the climbing fibres. Both project to the cerebellar cortex, which in turn generates an output via Purkinje neurons to the cerebellar nuclei. The cerebellar nuclei receive collaterals from mossy and climbing fibres. The cerebellum receives afferents from all of the body via spinocerebellar and spino-olivo-cerebellar systems. Climbing fibres arise from the inferior olive, which receives inputs from spinal cord, brainstem, cerebellar nuclei, and the motor cortex. Mossy fibres originate from many brain areas. There is a particularly large input from the vestibular system and also from the cortex via the pontocerebellar pathway.

Outputs travel via the deep nuclei of cerebellum (nucleus fastigius, interpositus, dentate) to descending motor pathways. The vestibulospinal tract is served by the fastigial nucleus, and the rubrospinal tract by the dentate and interpositus nuclei. There is also an extensive output, via the dentate nucleus and thalamus (ventrolateral and anterior nuclei) which projects to the cerebral cortex.

The intrinsic neurons are the excitatory granule cells (whose axons give rise to parallel fibres and are the principal relays in a mossy fibre–granule cell – Purkinje cell pathway) and inhibitory interneurons called Golgi cells, basket cells, and stellate cells. Purkinje cells are also inhibitory neurons and, as with the majority of inhibitory interneurons in the cerebellum, use the neurotransmitter GABA (Kandel & Schwartz, 1985; Shepherd, 1990).

The cerebellum integrates information about movements over the whole body and provides feedback to the cerebral cortex about their progress, allowing coordination of motor tasks. Damage to the cerebellum causes ataxia, dysmetria, nystagmus, and tremor.

Basal ganglia

Situated within each cerebral hemisphere is a series of subcortical grey masses loosely called the basal ganglia or nuclei. The main nuclei are: caudate nucleus; lentiform nucleus, which comprises the putamen and the globus pallidus; subthalamic nucleus; and the substantia nigra. It is still not clear how these ganglia affect muscles or how information from muscles affects them. Most of the evidence that these nuclei are concerned with movements comes from the motor deficits which appear when the nuclei are damaged by vascular lesions, drug action, or disease. The neurophysiological and neurochemical basis of these effects is still rather unclear, but advances over the past 20 years have greatly increased our understanding of the role of the basal ganglia. The interconnections between the various ganglia are illustrated in Fig. 2.5. The main input structures are cerebral cortex, intralaminar thalamic nuclei, and the dorsal Raphé nuclei. The major output targets are the ventral nuclear group of the thalamus, the superior colliculus, and the habenula. There are important and sometimes reciprocal pathways interconnecting the constituent ganglia forming closed loops composed of powerful inhibitory interneurons.

Neurotransmitters   The major neurotransmitters used in these ganglia are:

(1) dopamine in the nigrostriatal pathway, which produces inhibitory postsynaptic potentials in neostriatal interneurons; this pathway becomes progressively impaired in Parkinson's disease
(2) GABA, which is found in many interneurons within the neostriatum and within neurons projecting from caudate and putamen to globus pallidus and to substantia nigra; often GABA may be co-localised with neuropeptides such as enkephalin or substance P
(3) acetylcholine (ACh), which is found within giant aspiny interneurons within the neostriatum, and which exerts a very powerful influence on the GABA-containing interneurons, so disinhibiting the circuit; in some neurons ACh may be co-localised with the peptide somatostatin (therapeutic interventions for Parkinson's disease and Huntington's chorea use cholinergic agents whose targets are on these neurons; there is a measurable deficiency in ACh and GABA in Huntington's chorea, where the motor deficits become explicable on the basis of loss of these neurons)
(4) excitatory amino acids; glutamate or aspartate are the most likely candidates for the input pathways from the cortex to the neostriatum
(5) 5-hydroxytryptamine (5-HT), which is a major transmitter in Raphé neurons (Shepherd, 1990).

Function   The major function of the basal ganglia may be in the preplanning stage of movement control. Signals from the premotor cortex are transmitted to the basal ganglia, where the overall programme of muscle movement is planned and projected to areas concerned with the modification of movement

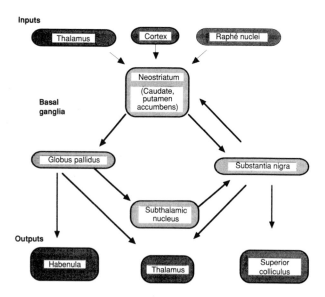

Fig. 2.5 Connections within the basal ganglia.

and thence back to the cortex from thalamocortical neurons. Evidence to support this notion comes from studies of the symptoms of Parkinson's disease, where patients find it difficult to initiate and execute willed movements. They also experience balance problems due to inadequate reflexes which are not normally troublesome. This produces rigid muscles and a tremor at rest when the system is out of balance. In chorea, the opposite is the case, with often endless movement of head and neck. Here the problem is not in initiating movement but with stopping it.

Thalamus

The thalamus plays a major role in the control of movement, mainly through inputs to ventrolateral and anterolateral nuclear groups. These areas also receive inputs from basal ganglia and cerebellum, and are thus principal relays of motor information *en route* to the cortex.

Cerebral cortex

The precentral gyrus and cingulate gyrus are closely connected with motor function. Both gyri are somatotopically organised. Activity in the precentral gyrus precedes activity in muscles, and is related to the force of movement. It is involved also in complex cortical 'reflex' responses, which may be 'set up' for different situations.

Damage to motor cortex leads to a loss of fine movements, especially of fingers on the contralateral side of the body. The direct corticospinal connection to the motor neurons of the forearm and hand muscles is important in the skilful use of hands and fingers.

Cortical output   The output from the cortex is via the internal capsule and cerebral penduncle, the site of many cerebrovascular accidents causing paralysis and spasticity. The output is often described in terms of pyramidal tracts and an extrapyramidal system. This division is anatomical and artificial, although it has some clinical value. Cortical output may be considered to comprise: the corticospinal tract (CST), which provides a direct connection to the lower motorneuron pool, often through interneurons in the spinal cord; and corticobulbar pathways, where the cortical signals relay through brainstem structures, which in turn give rise to descending pathways.

Corticospinal tracts   Descending axons arise from motor cortex (Brodmann's area 4), premotor cortex (area 6), and from somaesthetic cortex (postcentral gyrus areas 3, 1, 2, 5). These axons give off many collaterals, especially to ventrolateral thalamus, pontine nuclei and red nuclei. Ninety per cent of CST axons (arising from areas 6, 4, 1–3) decussate at the pyramids and descend in the lateral CST to spinal levels, where they synapse with interneurons, with sensory relay neurons, and with motorneurons innervating distal limb muscles, mainly on the side contralateral to the side of origin. The uncrossed portion (mainly from 4 and 6) projects bilaterally to motorneurons of axial and proximal muscles (Mandel & Schwartz, 1985).

Corticobulbar pathways These comprise two main descending systems: a ventromedial tract containing axons of the rubrospinal, tectospinal and vestibulospinal tracts; and a dorsolateral pathway containing axons of the rubrospinal tract. These tracts control different groups of motorneurons and muscles. The ventromedial tracts exert a larger influence on motorneurons located medially in the spinal cord (and thus proximal rather than distal muscle groups). The dorsolateral (rubrospinal) tract synapses mainly with laterally located motorneurons to influence chiefly the more distal muscles.

Complexity versus speed

The demands made on the motor system are complex and often conflicting. One such conflict is between speed and complexity of response. Fast responses are often crude; complex responses can incorporate corrections for errors but are slower. The nervous system contains a number of motor mechanisms of increasing complexity (Table 2.3).

It would seem that the higher levels of the motor system can modify the lower-level reflexes to give the best response to the sort of disturbances that the individual 'expects' to encounter. The responses of the lower levels are often stereotyped, and those of more complex mechanisms may be modified by learning. Many simple reflexes depend upon descending facilitation from higher structures, and cease to function for some weeks after the removal of this (e.g. in spinal shock following spinal transection) (Kandel & Schwartz, 1985).

Table 2.3 The speed and complexity of different motor mechanisms

	Speed	Complexity
Spinal reflexes	High	Low
Intersegmental reflexes		
Vestibular postural reflexes		
Cortical reflexes		
Conscious reactions	Low	High

Reflex responses to visual, vestibular, and auditory stimulation

Central visual pathways

The axons of ganglion cells (the final integrators of visual processing in the retina) exit the retina in the optic nerve (see Chapter 1, pp. 15–20). Axons from cells in the nasal hemiretinas cross over in the optic chiasm, whereas those arising from the temporal hemiretinas remain uncrossed. This means that at this stage of processing, the brain (or rather the lateral geniculate nucleus of the thalamus) is concerned with the contralateral hemifield of vision (Kandel & Schwartz, 1985; West, 1991).

Monocular vision

There is a small portion of the nasal hemiretina that receives only monocular vision since the nose interrupts the light path to the eye on the opposite side. This portion of the visual field is called the 'temporal crescent', and since there is no binocular overlap, vision is lost in the entire temporal crescent visual field if the retina is severely damaged.

Visual pathway

Retinal ganglion cells project to the lateral geniculate nucleus (LGN), a six-layered structure that receives inputs from the contralateral nasal retina to layers 1, 4 and 6 and from the ipsilateral temporal retina to layers 2, 3 and 5.

Projection neurons in the LGN send their axons to the visual cortex (striate cortex) in the occipital lobe.

Visual reflexes

Superior colliculus

The superior colliculus receives information from the retina and from the visual cortex. Superior colliculus neurons send their axons ipsilaterally to join the tectospinal tract, which is important in reflex control of head and neck movements. This nucleus coordinates visual inputs with eye movements and is involved in the saccadic eye movement system. This is responsible for directing the fovea to the visual target and consists of rapid (ballistic) movement of the eyes (up to 700° a second). It is controlled largely from the pontine gaze centre of the reticular formation. Once the fovea has located the target, a smooth-pursuit movement system operates to keep the image firmly on the fovea. The brain calculates the direction and speed of the image through a pathway involving the occipital cortex.

Vestibulo-oculomotor reflexes

The vestibulo-oculomotor system is concerned with maintaining visual fixation despite movement of the head. The sensory detectors for this lie in the semicircular canals of the inner ear, which detect head movements. Each semicircular canal detects angular acceleration through one axis of three-dimensional space. This information, in the form of action potential discharge (greater frequency with increased acceleration), is transmitted to vestibular nuclei, which integrate the information from each semicircular canal and then send an appropriate signal to cranial nuclei III, IV and VI, wherein lie the motorneurons projecting extraocular muscles.

Cortical eye fields

The frontal cortex directs saccadic movements and contributes to the initiation of voluntary gaze. A unilateral lesion in this area produces a sustained deviation of the eyes to the side of the lesion and an ability to redirect the gaze to the opposite side. Bilateral lesions result in an inability to direct the gaze laterally in either direction (Kandel & Schwartz, 1985).

Vestibular reflexes

The vestibular system detects both the position of the head in space and its motion. Vestibular sense organs are located in the inner ear and comprise: the three mutually perpendicular semicircular canals used to detect angular acceleration; and the otolith organs – saccule and utricle – for the detection of linear acceleration and the position of the head with respect to gravity. Information is transmitted via the vestibular ganglion in the VIII cranial nerve to the vestibular nuclei in the brainstem and to the floculonodular node of the cerebellum (West, 1991).

Vestibular nuclei

There are four vestibular nuclei located in the medulla – lateral (or Deiters'), medial, superior, and inferior nuclei – each having a distinct set of connections and roles in balance reflexes.

Lateral vestibular nucleus   Neurons in this nucleus receive inputs from the utricle (excitatory) and from the vermis of the cerebellum (inhibitory) and from proprioceptive afferents in the spinal cord. The nucleus gives rise to the lateral vestibulospinal tract, which projects to spinal motorneurons, providing a tonic excitatory drive to extensor muscles in the leg and flexor muscles in the arm (antigravity muscles), thus making a major contribution to the maintenance of an upright posture.

Medial and superior vestibular nuclei Neurons in these nuclei receive inputs from semicircular canals, and their axons project in the medial vestibulospinal tract, which terminates on neck motorneurons. Thus this pathway is important in the reflex control of head position. Other neurons in these nuclei are involved in vestibulo-oculomotor reflexes and participate in keeping the visual field in the central horizontal plane.

Inferior vestibular nucleus This nucleus receives inputs from the semicircular canals, saccule and utricle, and also from the vermis of the cerebellum. Efferents join the vestibulospinal and vestibuloreticular tracts and also project back to the cerebellum. Thus this nucleus plays a major role in the integration of vestibular input with cerebellar processing.

Vestibular nystagmus

This is a sequence of eye movements, involving vestibulo-ocular reflexes, which permits the direction of gaze to be preserved against a rotating head. The compensatory eye movement has two phases: a 'slow', tracking phase, up to the point where the eyes reach the limits of their movement, followed by a rapid or 'fast' snap back.

Nystagmography is a useful clinical tool for assessing vestibular function. This is usually done in a rotating chair; the subject is rotated at a constant velocity and then abruptly stopped. The nystagmus produced can be monitored providing the patient is prevented from fixating on objects and thus actively overcoming the vestibulo-ocular reflexes. This can be done by providing glasses with strong myopic lenses. Defects associated with the slow phase are associated with the vestibular system, whereas changes in the fast phase relate more to the reticular formation and occipital eye fields.

Auditory system

Auditory pathway

Primary afferent fibres from the cochlea project to the dorsal and ventral segments of the cochlear nucleus. Neurons of the ventral part project to the ipsilateral and contralateral olivary complexes. This area, particularly the accessory nucleus, is where the nervous system can analyse binaural inputs and thus compute the direction of the sound stimulus. Fibres from the dorsal cochlear nucleus cross to the opposite side and synapse with neurons in the lateral lemniscus nucleus, which also receives inputs from the olivary complex cells, permitting further integration of auditory signals. From the lateral lemniscus the auditory pathway proceeds via the inferior colliculus to the medial geniculate body and thence to the auditory cortex (West, 1991).

Auditory reflexes

These are important in the analysis of sound localisation and involve mainly the inferior colliculus which serves as a link between higher (cortical) and lower (cochlear nuclei and olive) centres. The inferior colliculus, which receives somaesthetic signals from spinothalamic tract and medial lemniscus axons, interchanges auditory and visual information with the superior colliculus. Both project to the midbrain reticular formation and periaqueductal grey matter, contributing to the mechanisms of arousal and attention. The inferior colliculus projects to the vermis of the cerebellum, where it integrates auditorially guided motor actions such as 'startle responses' or speech. The inferior colliculus also projects to other nuclei in the auditory pathway and provides feedback for the regulation of auditory signals.

Non-specific sensory responses and the reticular formation

Responses such as arousal from sleep and habituation may be provoked by most sensory inputs; that is, they are not specific to any one sensory modality. Correspondingly there are areas of the central nervous system containing neurons which respond to many different sensory inputs, and their functions are quite different from those of neurons in the specific sensory pathways, which are concerned with the detailed analysis of the external or internal environment. By contrast the non-specific sensory systems are concerned with sleep, wakefulness, and attention. The two systems interact, since the auditory system cannot function to analyse speech unless the individual is alert.

The reticular formation (RF) is the main region concerned with non-specific sensory responses. It is a large structure occupying the core of the brainstem from the caudal medulla to the rostral midbrain. Anatomically the RF receives sensory inputs from spinal cord and sensory nuclei, and other inputs from cerebellum, cerebral cortex, hypothalamus, thalamus, and so on. It also projects directly to most regions of the brain, except the cerebral cortex which, however, receives projections from RF relayed via the non-specific nuclei of the thalamus. These are situated medial to the specific sensory nuclei of the thalamus. As a group they receive an input from the reticular formation and project to the cerebral cortex.

Although the RF as a whole responds to almost all modalities of sensory input, each neuron responds to a limited number of sensory inputs. In the case of somatosensory stimulation, a neuron might respond, for example, to a tap or pinch over most or all of the body surface, although it might respond more rapidly and strongly to stimuli from certain areas. The most powerful inputs to the RF come from nociceptors.

Some reticular efferents have multiple projection sites – their axons may branch to innervate the spinal cord, hypothalamus, thalamus and other regions.

Functions of the reticular formation

The RF is phylogenetically a primitive part of the brain and is involved in primitive types of response, such as arousal, startle to novel stimuli, and habituation to repeated stimulation. Its descending pathways have an important role to play in motor control, by facilitating or inhibiting neurons in spinal reflex pathways and in responses to noxious stimuli.

Reticular activating system   In a classic experiment, Moruzzi & Magoun, in 1949, demonstrated that stimulation of the RF arouses a sleeping animal, as shown by behavioural signs and by changes in the electroencephalogram (EEG). Lesions in the classic sensory pathways did not disturb the sleep/waking cycle, but no animal with bilateral lesions of the midbrain RF became permanently comatose. Previously it had been thought that arousal was due to the direct effect of sensory input to the cerebral cortex. These experiments showed that arousal was due to sensory inputs into the RF, whose ascending projections relayed in non-specific thalamic nuclei and the hypothalamus. It is now thought that behavioural arousal can be related to hypothalamic activity, whereas EEG changes are due to the influence of certain thalamic nuclei on the cerebral cortex. (Thus, under certain conditions behavioural arousal and EEG changes can become dissociated.)

Habituation   This is the name given to certain characteristic effects which occur when a stimulus occurs repeatedly. The main change is a reduction in the amplitude of the response. This effect can be observed both in the response of single neurons in the RF and in behaviour (e.g. arousal to a tone becomes habituated on repetition of the same tone at regular intervals).

Novelty detection   This is complementary to habituation. A novel stimulus will produce behavioural arousal. Similarly, a reticular neuron will respond to a novel stimulus after it has become habituated and has ceased to respond to a frequently repeated stimulus.

The startle response   This is a primitive, and presumably protective, behavioural response. In humans it is the response of an awake subject to an unexpected and strong sensory stimulus. It has been studied using pistol shots, pin pricks, or a jet of cold water between the shoulder blades! The immediate response is predominantly flexor in all four limbs (towards a 'hunched' position), with a characteristic contraction of neck and facial muscles and blinking of eyelids. Exclamatory vocalisation may occur. Animal experiments show that this response is dependent on an intact RF. It occurs in a decerebrate animal, but not if a lesion is made in the RF. Thus it is presumably due to a strong activation of reticular neurons producing flexor contraction via the fast, descending reticulospinal pathway. The response is usually followed by other movements, which may take various forms.

The source of the input to the RF which evokes the startle response to visual or auditory stimuli appears to be the colliculi. The superior and inferior colliculi are phylogenetically old relays in the visual and auditory pathways respectively. There is evidence that the colliculi are concerned with organising the orientation of the head and eyes towards the source of the stimulus, which follows the immediate startle response.

Pain   Reticular neurons are particularly responsive to noxious inputs, and many are excited by pinching any point of the body surface. The RF relays noxious input to higher centres in the non-specific thalamic nuclei and elsewhere, and thus provides a relay on one of the pathways for nociception.

Stimulation in the RF leads to aversive behaviour – animals will take action to avoid such stimulation. In behavioural experiments, cats trained to jump over a barrier to avoid a noxious stimulus also jumped the barrier in response to stimulation in the RF at sites where neurons showed long-lasting excitation in response to the noxious stimulus.

Descending control of pain and sensation   The midline Raphé nuclei constitute a subdivision of the RF. Stimulation in nucleus Raphé magnus in the rostral medulla can produce analgesia by activation of descending Raphé spinal fibres. This descending projection travels mainly dorsolaterally in the white matter of the spinal cord and produces inhibition of the response of dorsal horn neurons to inputs from nociceptors. In this way the pain pathway can be controlled (gated) at the spinal level. Raphé neurons containing 5-hydroxytryptamine play an important part in this control system. Control of neuronal responses in pain pathways is the best documented example of sensory control. However, other sensory inputs can also be controlled by reticular neurons.

Effects of lesions

Damage to the descending systems of the RF may cause attenuations of movement ranging from enhanced tendon reflexes to spastic paralysis. Damage to ascending systems of the RF may lead to a permanently comatose state. Whatever the 'seat of consciousness', one can argue that an intact reticular formation is essential for consciousness and awareness.

References

Ganong, W. F. (1987) *Review of Medical Physiology* (13th edn). Norwalk, Connecticut: Appleton and Lange.

Hille, B. (1992) *Ionic Channels of Excitable Membranes* (2nd edn). Sunderland, Massachusetts: Sinauer Associates.

Kandel, E. R. & Schwartz, J. H. (1985) *Principles of Neural Science* (2nd edn). Amsterdam: Elsevier.

Shepherd, G. M. (1990) *The Synaptic Organisation of the Brain* (3rd edn). Oxford: Oxford University Press.

West, J. B. (1991) *Best & Taylor's Physiological Basis of Medical Practice* (12th edn). Baltimore: Williams and Wilkins.

3 Neurochemistry and neuropharmacology

David Nutt

*General features of neurotransmission ● Classification of receptors ●
Transduction mechanisms and second messengers ● Other features of
transmission ● Individual transmitters ● Peptides ● Conclusion*

Neurochemistry refers to the biochemistry of the brain and the peripheral nervous system, whereas neuropharmacology encompasses the effects of drugs on the biochemical and physiological processes underlying brain function. This chapter examines both areas since each is used to explore its relationship with the other. The related term 'psychopharmacology' is the study of the effect of drugs on behavioural and mental processes. This chapter presents a precis of the important concepts and facts that psychiatrists need to be aware of in order to appreciate the scientific basis of the pathophysiology of psychiatric disorder and its current drug therapy. It is in no way exhaustive, for although all the important non-peptide transmitters are covered, many peptides are not dealt with. For a less intensive perusal of the subject, one of the texts listed at the end is recommended.

The brain, the most complex organ, represents the highest point of evolution. It is characterised by a remarkable level of interactions between neurons. Neurons are so highly differentiated that they have little capacity for other functions, such as regeneration, and they rely to a large extent on other cells (the various types of glia) for metabolic support. They share the property of being able to conduct nerve impulses, or action potentials (Chapter 2), and form complex networks whose intercommunication is generally by means of chemical transmission across synapses.

The general organisation of a neuron is shown in Fig. 3.1. The cell body contains the nucleus and much of the synthetic material required for the production of transmitter synthetic enzymes and receptors. These are then transported down to the terminal processes. Transmitters are released as a result of depolarisation of the terminals, the influx of calcium ions and the subsequent exocytosis of transmitter-containing vesicles. This occurs from both axonal and dendritic terminals. The function of dendritic release is still unclear, although one possibility is that it may lead to autoinhibition (see later). Dendrites are fine, arborising processes that seem to be designed to receive information from other cells. This input is often onto specialised synaptic processes called spines. Loss of spines is seen in neurodegenerative conditions such as dementia and may contribute to the loss of mental plasticity and information storage.

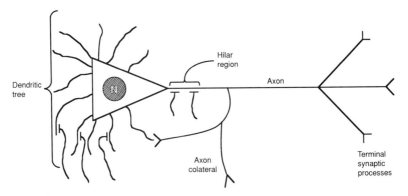

Fig. 3.1 Schematic diagram of a neuron. ⌐∿ synaptic inputs; N, nucleus.

The portion of the axon nearest the cell body is called the hilar region. It has a high density of incoming synaptic processes, which suggests it integrates the excitatory and inhibitory inputs to the cell which then determines whether an action potential is initiated. Neurons with long axons connecting to distant targets are in the minority in the brain. The most common type are the variety of interneurons, which modulate local excitatory inputs. Many of these contain the inhibitory transmitter gamma-aminobutyric acid (GABA) and so control the excitability of surrounding cells.

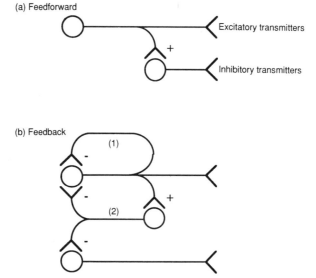

Fig. 3.2 Examples of the main types of inhibition found in the central nervous system. In (b), two sorts of feedback inhibition are shown: (1) is autoinhibition, the limitation of neuronal activity by feedback of its own transmitter; (2) represents feedback produced by activation of inhibitory interneurons. Both sorts limit the action of the active neuron and also its neighbours.

Two main types of inhibition are found in the brain: feedforward and feedback (Fig. 3.2). Both limit the magnitude or duration of neuronal transmission and both are important in normal and abnormal brain function. For instance, it has been suggested that the formation of memory is due to the failure of feedforward inhibition in the hippocampus, which leads to long-term potentiation by the excitatory amino acid glutamate. A failure of feedback inhibition has been postulated to underlie epilepsy, panic attacks, and alcohol withdrawal.

Supporting the neurons are glial cells of different types and presumed functions. These provide physical and metabolic support, assist in the clearance of overspilled transmitter, and help organise the differentiation of the brain. They can also directly augment the function of neurons, as in the case of the Schwann cell.

General features of neurotransmission

There are three types of chemical transmission, which can be distinguished in terms of speed and specificity of information transfer. The fastest is synaptic transmission, where the released transmitter is highly directed to the target cell across the synapse. Intermediate speed and specificity of transmission is obtained for transmitters released from varicosities dispersed along axonal processes, as is found with the monoamine transmitters such as noradrenaline and 5-hydroxytryptamine (5-HT). The third type of transmission is one of endocrine secretion (see Chapter 7); this has the lowest speed and specificity, since the transmitter diffuses to its target receptors through extracellular space, the vascular system (as in the case of anterior pituitary transmitters), or even the cerebrospinal fluid (CSF). Interestingly, the same transmitter can subserve several of these different roles. Thus glutamate can act as the very fast primary sensory transmitter and also, through a different set of receptors, have a metabolic action.

The general principles of neurotransmission are outlined in Fig. 3.3. Transmitter, released by terminal depolarisation, diffuses across the synapse and activates postsynaptic receptors. There may be several different receptors on the postsynaptic membrane, and they may interact either positively or negatively. Thus, in the pineal, the stimulatory actions of noradrenaline on β-adrenoceptors is augmented by concurrent α_1-adrenoceptor stimulation. Conversely, in some brain regions the coactivation of dopamine D_1 receptors reduces the effects of D_2 stimulation.

An important recent concept is that of autoinhibition (see Fig. 3.2). Many presynaptic processes contain receptors for their own transmitter, for example adrenoceptors in the case of noradrenaline. Usually, activation of these by the released transmitter leads to inhibition of further transmitter release and so can be considered a form of negative feedback that limits overactivation. In rare cases they may have a positive or stimulatory role; for example, in

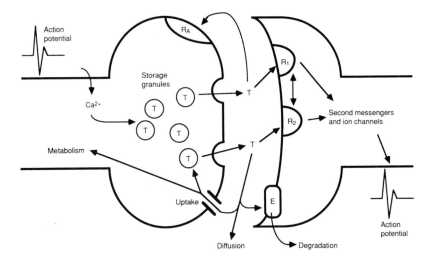

Fig. 3.3 General processes of synaptic transmission. T, transmitter; E, membrane-bound enzyme; R_1, R_2, postsynaptic receptors; R_A, autoreceptor.

some tissues stimulation of presynaptic β-adrenoceptors by noradrenaline can increase its own release.

An important feature of synaptic transmission is the active termination of transmitter effects. This occurs in two ways – the clearance of transmitter, and the modification of receptors. In general, transmitters are cleared by active uptake back into the presynaptic nerve terminal. Uptake carriers are very selective for the relevant transmitter, although those with similar chemical structures may also be transported; for example dopamine in cerebral cortex is probably taken up into noradrenaline terminals. Other uptake systems exist in glial cells; these have lower affinity but higher capacity than the neuronal ones. Uptake blockers increase the availability of transmitter in the synapse. Those which block uptake of the monoamines have proved an effective class of therapeutic agents, particularly for the treatment of depression. Since uptake blockade also results in increased activation of presynaptic autoreceptors it usually also decreases transmitter release as well. The delay in the therapeutic action of the tricyclic anti-depressants has been suggested to be due to the time it takes for tolerance to develop to the increased presynaptic inhibition and thus the elevation of synaptic levels of transmitter.

For some transmitters, such as acetylcholine and the peptides, the major mechanisms for the termination of trans-synaptic activity is by local enzymatic degradation. The duration of action of acetylcholine is limited by hydrolysis of the transmitter by an esterase enzyme that is specialised for the task – acetylcholinesterase. This is bound to the postsynaptic membrane and thus rapidly destroys transmitter that is not bound to receptor. Drugs have been discovered that antagonise acetylcholinesterase and increase the availability of acetylcholine. Some, such as neostigmine, are useful in the treatment of myasthenia gravis, a condition caused by autoantibodies to cholinergic receptors. However, others, particularly centrally acting ones such as 'nerve gases', can cause seizures and death owing to an excess of acetylcholine. There is hope that drugs can be developed with an optimal amount of central cholinesterase blockade for the treatment of conditions in which the cholinergic system is impaired, such as Alzheimer's disease. A good example of a peptide-degrading enzyme is enkephalinase, which metabolises released enkephalins. Agonists of this enzyme have analgesic actions.

The actions of transmitters can also be limited by adaptive changes in receptors. This is manifest as a reduction in agonist response that develops over time. Several processes underly this adaptation. Early changes (desensitisation) are thought to be due to the phosphorylation of receptors and a shift in the ratio of high-affinity (agonist-preferring) to low-affinity states. Later, the loss of receptors can occur by a process of internalisation and degradation (down-regulation). Genomic factors also come into play, with a reduced expression of messenger RNA (mRNA) for some receptors being seen on chronic treatment with agonists.

An interesting aspect of receptor adaptation is that the opposite sorts of phenomena occur if transmitter release is reduced, for example as a result of neurotoxins such as 6-hydroxy-dopamine or MPTP which deplete dopamine content, or following chronic blockade by antagonists. Thus increased receptor number and sensitivity can be observed (denervation supersensitivity). This may be of clinical relevance, such as the increase in dopamine receptors found after neuroleptic therapy, which may be linked to the production of dystonias and tardive dyskinesia.

Classification of receptors

The classification of receptors into different families according to their effector systems has become more justified by the new discoveries in the molecular biology of these systems. It appears that all the receptors working through one effector system may have originated from a single primitive receptor that has evolved in diversity up the phylogenic tree. The evidence for this is the observation that all ion-channel-linked receptors are made up of protein subunits that have four regions which span the cell membrane. Similarly, all G-protein-linked receptors have seven membrane-spanning regions and so can be considered to belong to a superfamily of receptors for which the prototype may be the light-sensitive protein rhodopsin.

Within each family of receptors and up the evolutionary tree there is often great similarity (conservation) of the amino acid structure of the membrane-spanning parts of the receptor, suggesting they are critical for its function. The most diverse amino-acid sections of all receptors appear to be the outer extracellular region, where the transmitter binding site is probably located.

This diversity of structure gives the specificity needed for discrimination between transmitters.

Ion-channel receptors also share the feature of being made up of four or five subunits that group together to form a doughnut shape, with a central pore that conducts the ion flow (e.g. the GABA$_A$/benzodiazepine receptor; see later and Fig. 3.8). The difference between anion and cation channels is determined by the charge of the amino acids lining this pore. Acidic ones predominate in cation channels, so their negative charge attracts the positively charged sodium or calcium ions, whereas the lining of anion channels has prominent basic residues that attract the negatively charged chloride ions. Another common feature of ion-channel receptors is the presence of a dicysteine loop in the extracellular domain that presumably is responsible for the all-or-none nature of channel opening.

It is possible to classify neurotransmitters in a number of different ways:

(1) by their chemical structure: amino acid, peptide, monoamine, etc.
(2) by the receptor(s) they activate: GABA$_A$ and GABA$_B$, α- and β-noradrenaline, etc.
(3) the second messengers that are influenced by the transmitter binding to the receptor: ion channel, G protein, phosphoinositol (PI), nuclear receptor (steroids)
(4) the protein structure of the receptor and its subunit composition: for example the α, β and γ subunits of the GABA$_A$ benzodiazepine receptor
(5) by the composition of the mRNA that codes for the receptor protein; this helps in the detection of receptor isoforms produced by splicing
(6) the genomic structure of the receptor protein; this defines it absolutely in terms of the nucleic acid constitution, number and position of gene components such as introns and exons.

Each approach has its own value depending on the nature of the question being asked. Although determining the composition of mRNA has the apparent virtue of being very precise, this is probably illusory since many other processes can alter the receptor protein once it is formed from the mRNA. Commonly receptors have carbohydrate groups added (glycosylation) and many are phosphorylated. Both processes of post-translational modification can markedly alter sensitivity and specificity to transmitters. For the purposes of clinical psychopharmacology, the most useful concept is still that of the receptor (sub)type as defined by the binding and activity of selective drugs (especially antagonists).

Transduction mechanisms and second messengers

These are the ways in which information is transferred into the recipient neuron following receptor activation. There are two main forms of information transduction: the activation of ion channels, and the modulation of membrane-bound enzymes. A list of the established transmitters that work by opening ion channels is given in Table 3.1.

Both anion and cation channels can be opened directly following the binding of the transmitter to its receptor. In general, the opening of cation channels permits the entry of sodium ions which depolarise the target neuron, so perpetuating action potentials. Anion channels allow chloride ions to move

Table 3.1 The major transmitters of the central nervous system and their receptors

Transmitter	Receptor	Effector
Fast (3-10 ms):ion-channel linked		
Glutamate	AMPA	$\uparrow Na^+$
	NMDA	$\uparrow Ca^{++}$
?Aspartate	Kainate	$\uparrow$Cations
GABA	$GABA_A$	$\uparrow Cl^-$
Glycine	Glycine (strychnine sensitive)	$\uparrow Cl^-$
Acetylcholine	Nicotinic	$\uparrow Na^+$
5-HT	$5\text{-}HT_3$	$\uparrow Na^+$
Moderate (10-100 ms):second-messenger linked		
GABA	$GABA_B$	$\uparrow$G
Acetylcholine	Muscarinic m_1, m_2	$\uparrow$PI
		$\downarrow$G
Noradrenaline	α_1	$\uparrow$PI
	α_2	$\downarrow$G $\uparrow K^+$
	β_{1-3}	$\uparrow$G
Dopamine	D_1	$\uparrow$G
	D_{2-4}	$\downarrow$G
5HT	$5\text{-}HT_{1a,b,d}$	$\downarrow$G
	$5\text{-}HT_{1c}$	$\uparrow$PI
	$5\text{-}HT_2$	$\uparrow$PI
	$5\text{-}HT_4$	$\uparrow$G
Adenosine	A_1	$\downarrow$G
	A_2	$\uparrow$G
Slow (100 ms and over): peptides		
Opioid type-enkephalins	μ/δ	$\downarrow$G $\uparrow K^+$
β-endorphins,	μ	$\downarrow$G
Dynorphin	κ	$?\downarrow K^+$
Cholecystokinin	CCK_A	?
	CCK_B	?
Corticotrophin-releasing hormone	CRH	?
Thyrotrophin-releasing hormone	TRH	$\uparrow$PI

$\uparrow$ indicates increase or stimulation; $\downarrow$ indicates decrease or inhibition. G, G protein; PI, phosphoinositol cycle.

across the cell membrane, and usually this results in an inward negative current that hyperpolarises the neuron and reduces excitability, thus inhibiting cell firing. Other ion channels include those conducting potassium and calcium. These are commonly linked to second-messenger processes and are opened or closed indirectly by transmitters. For instance, the ability of both opioids and α_2-adrenoceptor agonists to inhibit the firing of the noradrenergic cell bodies is due to a common action on second messengers. This leads to the opening of a potassium channel, the flow of potassium out of the cell, and an inhibitory hyperpolarisation.

'Second messenger' is a term encompassing a number of intracellular processes that mediate postsynaptic events. The major ones so far discovered are the G proteins and the phosphoinositol (PI) cycle. A brief sketch of their activity is given in Figs 3.4 and 3.5.

Many receptors are linked to G proteins (see Table 3.1). These are enzymes which are localised in membranes close to receptors and which catalyse the conversion of high-energy phosphate molecules (adenosine and guanosine triphosphate) to their cyclic derivatives. The binding of the transmitter to the

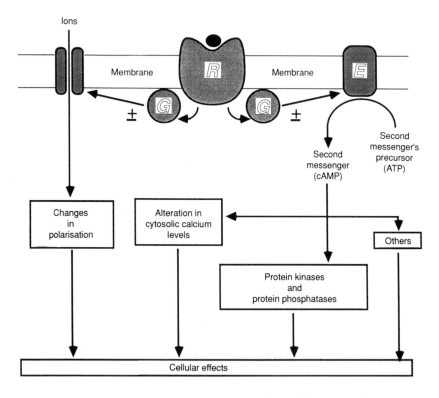

Fig. 3.4 A schematic diagram of how receptors (R) and G proteins (G) interact to alter ion flux or enzyme activity (E) following occupation of the receptor by the drug or transmitter (●).

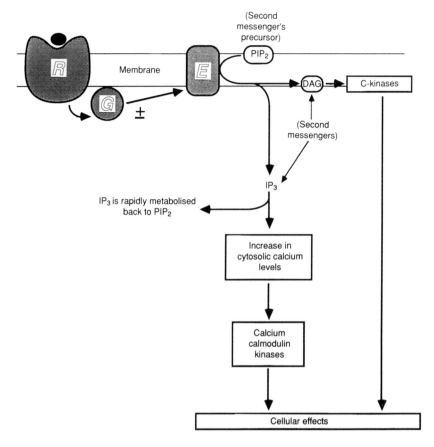

Fig. 3.5 Schematic diagram of how drug receptor interactions activate G proteins and then membrane-bound enzyme (E), which is phospholipase A2. This catalyses the conversion of precursor phospholipids to the active second messengers IP_3 and diacylglycerol (DG). These second messengers then produce further changes in enzymes such as kinases, which further alter cellular activity.

receptor then determines whether the stimulatory or inhibitory G protein subunits are engaged. If the stimulatory subunit is activated then enzymes (adenylate or guanylate cyclase) are 'turned on'. These catalyse the generation of either cyclic adenosine monophosphate (cAMP) or its close relative cyclic guanosine monophosphate (cGMP). These small molecules then initiate a number of other cellular processes such as the activation of calcium-binding proteins and other enzymes or the opening of ion channels, which in turn modify the activity of the neuron. Those receptors that link to the inhibitory subunit have the opposite action, reducing ongoing activity of the cyclase enzymes.

The PI cycle is a more recently discovered second-messenger system. Activation of receptors linked to it stimulates the enzyme phospholipase

A_2, which initiates the metabolism of the membrane-localised lipid PI. The two main products of this reaction are inositolphosphate-3 (IP_3) and diacylglycerol (DAG), both of which have the ability to promote further metabolic processes within cells (Fig. 3.5). It is likely that in neurons a balance exists between the actions of the G proteins and the PI system, and one theory of depression is that it is caused by a relative underproduction of cAMP or an excess of PI turnover. To some extent this is supported by the observation that antidepressant drugs may activate cAMP, for example imipramine acting to increase noradrenaline activity at β-adrenoceptors. A possible target for new antidepressants are drugs which directly increase cAMP, such as selective phosphodiesterase inhibitors.

Other features of transmission

The number of receptors in a given brain area is usually described in terms of the B_{max}, which is a measure of the density of receptors per unit of tissue (generally per mg protein). The other commonly used term to describe receptors is the K_d. This is a measure of the affinity with which the endogenous transmitter or drugs bind to the receptor. The lower the K_d, the better the binding, since the K_d is the concentration of drug or transmitter that occupies half the available receptors. The binding affinity of many transmitters is surprisingly weak, being in the low micromolar (10^{-6} mol/l) range as compared with the low nanomolar (10^{-9} mol/l) for reasonably potent synthetic antagonists. The term 'ligand' is used to refer to any molecule that binds to a receptor.

Neuromodulators are substances that alter synaptic transmission indirectly. They cannot directly activate standard postreceptor transduction, but can modulate the ability of the primary transmitter to do this. A good example is that of the benzodiazepines, which enhance the actions of GABA (see below). Similarly, glycine acting at a site linked to the N-methyl-D-aspartate (NMDA) receptor indirectly gates calcium flux (see Fig. 3.6).

A feature of neuronal transmission that has become well established in the past decade is that of cotransmitters. It now seems likely that the majority of neurons release more than one substance at the same time. Frequently peptides are found in the same neurons as amino acid or monamine transmitters. It is presumed that both are released and that the peptide in some way modifies the actions of the primary transmitter. For instance cholecystokinin (CCK) and neurotensin have been shown to affect dopamine function differentially, and neuropeptide Y is thought to attenuate noradrenaline activity.

'Sensitisation' and 'kindling' refer to the same phenomenon, in which repeated application of certain drugs leads to an increase in activity rather than to the more usual tolerance, or desensitisation. One example is the progressive increase in dopamine release seen on repeated exposure to cocaine and amphetamine, which may contribute to the potential of these drugs to cause psychosis. Another is the increase in convulsant action of GABA antagonists that can produce a state mimicking spontaneous epilepsy. Physiological kindling has been suggested to explain the progressive worsening of alcohol withdrawal episodes, and may be due to changes in benzodiazepine and NMDA receptors.

Individual transmitters

In this section the neurochemistry, pharmacology and function of major brain transmitters are considered separately.

Excitatory amino acids

Synthesis and degradation

The predominant excitatory amino acid (EAA) transmitter is glutamic acid (glutamate). Studying glutaminergic transmission is difficult, as it is also an important intermediary in both energy and protein metabolism as well as being the precursor to GABA. Synthesis of glutamate that functions as a transmitter is by deamination of glutamine, whereas that subserving metabolic roles is derived predominantly from glucose via the tricarboxylic acid (Krebs') cycle. It is possible that other naturally occurring amino acids are also excitatory transmitters. Candidates include aspartate and some of the sulphur-containing amino acids such as homocysteine.

Receptors

There appear to be three main types of EAA receptors, called AMPA (amino methylisoxazole propionic acid; previously called the quisqualate receptor), kainate and NMDA, after the agonists which preferentially activate them. Glutamate acts at all three receptors, producing rapid trans-synaptic excitatory (depolarising) responses through AMPA and kainate receptors which gate sodium channels. Selective antagonists of AMPA receptors such as CNQX have been developed recently and these receptors are also blocked by a variety of anticonvulsants, anaesthetics, and barbiturates.

At NMDA receptors glutamate produces slower, longer-lasting depolarisations by opening a type of calcium channel. An important interaction has been discovered between AMPA and NMDA receptors in that the NMDA channel is usually blocked by magnesium ions (see Fig. 3.6). This block is released by AMPA receptor-induced depolarisation, thus allowing NMDA receptor activation and calcium influx. The changes in trans-synaptic enzyme function caused by increased levels of intracellular calcium facilitate the subsequent transmission, a process known as long-term potentiation (LTP).

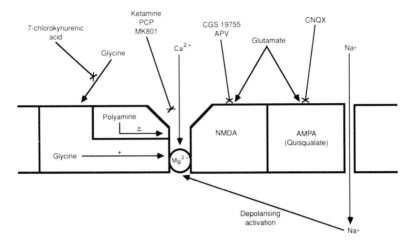

Fig. 3.6 The arrangement of the excitatory receptors for glutamate around two distinct but interacting ion channels. CNQX acts as a competitive antagonist at the AMPA receptor, whereas APV and CBS 19755 competitively block the NMDA site. MK801 (dizocilpine) and similar drugs as well as magnesium ions block the calcium channel directly. Glycine acting through the non-strychnine-sensitive receptor enhances NMDA receptor function – an action competitively blocked by 7-chlorokynurenic acid.

The NMDA receptor may be blocked by drugs which bind to it directly (competitive antagonists) such as CGS 19755 or by drugs which bind to the opening of the channel – non-competitive blockers such as dizocilpine (MK801), phencylidine (PCP), and ketamine. Moreover, alcohol, in concentrations in the intoxicating range, also antagonises EAA receptor function.

Additional modulation of NMDA receptor function is provided by two other allosteric sites, the polyamine and strychnine-insensitive glycine receptor. Glycine has a facilitatory role, and endogenous concentrations are saturating so that this is a tonic stimulation. Polyamines can increase or decrease NMDA receptor activity depending on their precise chemical structure, that is, some exhibit agonist and others inverse agonist activity (see under 'GABA', below). Others are pure antagonists that block the action of both of the other types.

Functions

Glutamate is the predominant sensory transmitter in the central nervous system, and so is responsible for rapid information transfer in the primary input pathways, and probably for much of the intracerebral and output projections as well. LTP has been well characterised in hippocampus and probably exists in most brain regions; it is thought to be the basis of learning and memory storage. LTP is blocked by both competitive and non-competitive antagonists, and these classes of drug have profound amnestic properties, so that focal injections of, for instance, dizocilpine into the hippocampus can prevent spatial (maze) learning in rats. Competitive antagonists have some anxiolytic potential, so it is possible that certain features of the anxiety disorders, such as the altered attentional set and the paroxysmal overactivity of panic, reflect local overactivity of EAAs. Current interest focuses on the glycine and polyamine sites, since drugs acting here may be less profoundly disturbing to normal sensory transmission. Glycine antagonists and partial agonists have been synthesised; both decrease NMDA function, and both have anxiolytic and anticonvulsant actions.

Dysfunctions

Overactivity of EAA input is a possible cause of epilepsy, and antagonists are potent anticonvulsants in animal models; unfortunately their ability to block memory and produce dissociative states will probably prevent their clinical use. There is growing evidence of glutamate being involved in schizophrenia with theories of both increased and decreased function; thus both agonists and antagonists have been suggested to have antipsychotic potential, although none have been tested yet, and the diverse function of glutamate may make this difficult.

The over-riding impetus to the frenetic development of EAA-acting compounds was the discovery that dizocilpine is both a non-competitive NMDA antagonist and a very powerful neuroprotective agent. In animals this drug prevents neuronal death produced by a variety of means, including head injury and arterial ligation. More impressively, it works even if given up to four hours after the lesion. Thus a potential treatment for stroke was envisaged. Most direct and indirect antagonists of NMDA receptors share this property to some extent and clinical trials are under way, as the side-effects of these drugs are minor in comparison with the severity of the illness.

Another aspect of this work was the revelation that EAAs themselves were neurotoxic. Kainic acid has been in experimental use as a local neurotoxin for many years, so it was not surprising that other EAAs could also cause cell death. Perhaps the excessive release of glutamate during childhood febrile seizures may be responsible for the mesial temporal sclerosis that later leads to temporal lobe epilepsy. The symptoms of alcohol withdrawal may in part be due to an increase in NMDA receptor function caused by an upregulation of receptor number and the loss of tonic blockade by magnesium. It is possible that this extra excitation contributes to the neuronal death underlying alcoholic dementia.

A further consideration is that endogenous or exogenous EAAs may cause other forms of brain degeneration such as Huntington's disease or the dementias. Some, such as quinolinic acid found in sago and kainic acid in seaweed, have been suggested as causes of local outbreaks of neuropathies and dementias such as are found in Guam and other Pacific rim islands where undercooked sago and seaweed are eaten regularly. The advent of selective antagonists may lead to treatments of these disorders.

Inhibitory amino acids

The important major inhibitory amino acids are GABA and glycine. GABA predominates in the brain where it has been estimated that about 40% of all synapses use it. Glycine appears to play a similar role in the spinal cord. Only GABA is considered below.

Synthesis and degradation

The synthesis and degradation of GABA are shown in Fig. 3.7, where the relationship between glutamate and GABA can be seen. This fascinating juxtaposition of the primary excitatory and inhibitory transmitters suggests that GABA evolved to moderate the excitatory actions of glutamate. The enzyme that allows this conversion, glutamic acid decarboxylase (GAD), is used as a marker of GABA-ergic neurons. Inhibitors of GAD cause seizures, showing that GABA is tonically active. Released GABA is inactivated by uptake into either neurons or glia. Then it is converted to a number of products, with the predominant route being to succinic semialdehyde, via GABA transaminase (GABA-T). Both the uptake sites and GABA-T have been targets for drug development, particularly anticonvulsants. A selective inhibitor of GABA-T is now on the market, gamma-vinyl GABA, which irreversibly blocks the enzyme. It has clinical efficacy in epilepsy and has been shown to raise CSF levels of GABA. It is also thought that part of the actions of sodium valproate is via GABA-T inhibition. Selective uptake blockers for both glial and neuronal uptake mechanisms have been synthesised (e.g. nipecotic acid derivatives such

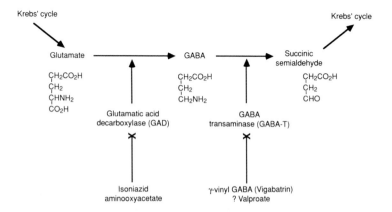

Fig. 3.7 The synthesis and degradation of GABA.

as CI-966). Unfortunately, testing in humans has revealed unexpected psychotomimetic and cataleptic actions. Direct-acting GABA agonists such as muscimol produce similar side-effects, which suggests that schizophrenia may be related to increased GABA activity.

Receptors

There are two quite distinct GABA receptors, A and B (see Table 3.1). $GABA_A$ receptors gate a chloride ion channel and are responsible for inhibitory activity, whereas $GABA_B$ receptors are positively coupled to G proteins and presynaptically modulate transmitter release.

The $GABA_A$ receptors have been well characterised over the past decade and their molecular structure is in the process of being elucidated. This is illustrated in Fig. 3.8 as a doughnut with the hole in the centre acting as the chloride ion channel. The receptor-ionophore complex is made up of five subunits that are under independent genetic control. At least 16 different

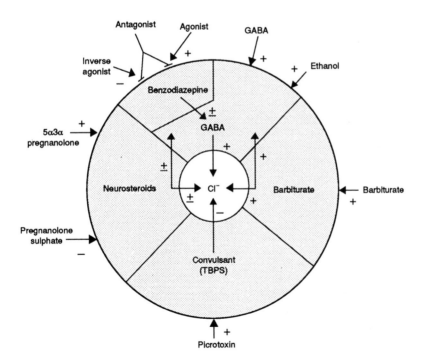

Fig. 3.8 Binding sites found on the $GABA_A$/benzodiazepine receptor complex. + refers to actions which mimic or potentiate those of GABA and result in net increases in chloride flux; − refers to the opposite sort of action, the reduction of GABA function.

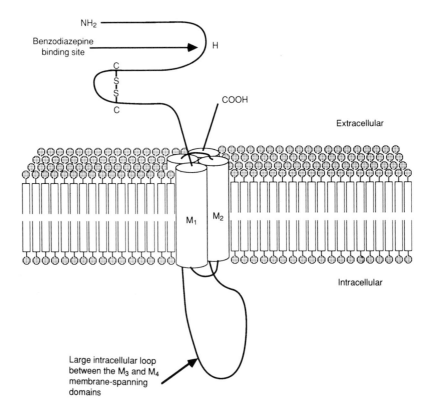

Fig. 3.9 The suggested orientation of $GABA_A$ receptor subunits across neuronal membranes illustrated with reference to an α subunit. The four M regions locate the subunit in the lipid bilayer. The binding site for the benzodiazepines is located in the extracellular domain. In this region is also found a dicysteine bridge which appears to be a feature of all ligand-gated ion channels.

subunits have been identified so far. These subunits are proteins that have four membrane-spanning regions (Fig. 3.9) and both intracellular and extracellular regions. On the basis of homology of amino-acid sequences, the subunits are divided into different families: alpha, beta, gamma and epsilon. Studies of specific subunits expressed from their RNA in cells that do not normally have benzodiazepine receptors (such as oocytes) have revealed important functional differences. For instance, although the benzodiazepine receptor is found on the alpha subunit, the ability of benzodiazepines to work is dependent on there being at least one gamma subunit in the complex. Certain newer benzodiazepines such as zopiclone and quazepam show high-affinity binding only to complexes with α_1 subunits, whereas for most benzodiazepines changing the nature of the alpha subunit has little effect.

The potential for receptor diversity presented by having such a large number of subunit pentamers is enormous, and it is not yet clear how many different types of complex are expressed in the brain. The finding that certain subunits are preferentially expressed in some brain regions offers scope for designing new drugs with highly selective sites of action, that may thus be free of the complications of the currently available benzodiazepines.

Many drugs modulate the actions of GABA (Table 3.2). Benzodiazepine agonists act indirectly to augment GABA; in the absence of GABA they have no action on chloride flux, whereas if GABA is present they make it more efficacious. The barbiturates also modulate GABA indirectly, in a similar fashion, but at higher concentrations they have *direct* channel-opening properties. This probably explains why barbiturates are so much more dangerous than benzodiazepines in overdose.

The modulatory actions of the benzodiazepine receptor allow drugs to inhibit GABA function. These compounds are called inverse agonists, and are convulsant and anxiogenic. It is possible to show that they act through the same receptor as the agonist benzodiazepines by blocking the actions of both classes of compound with the competitive antagonist flumazenil. By itself flumazenil has little in the way of either biochemical or pharmacological activity, which suggests that in the normal state there is no tonic activation of benzodiazepine receptors.

A more recent development is the discovery of partial agonists. These are compounds that enhance the actions of GABA but to lesser extent than the full

Table 3.2 GABA$_A$ receptor ligands and their actions

Site	Agonistic	Antagonistic	Inverse agonistic
GABA	GABA Muscimol isoguvacine	Bicuculline SR 95531 R 5135	N/A
Benzodiazepines	Conventional drugs (e.g. diazepam)	Flumazenil ZK 93426	FG 7142 Ro 15-4513 β-CCM
Barbiturates	Barbiturates (e.g. pentobarbital, meprobamate chlormethiazole)	?	?
Neurosteroids	$5_\alpha 3_\alpha$-pregnanolone THDOC Alphaxalone	?	Pregnanolone sulphate
Convulsant (TBPS)	?	?	Picrotoxin Leptazol TBPS Ro 5-3663

N/A, not applicable; ?, not yet described.

agonists (currently all clinically used benzodiazepines are full agonists). There is evidence that partial agonists (e.g. bretazenil and abecarnil) produce less sedation and ataxia than full agonists. As they also produce less tolerance in animals, there is hope they may lead to a new generation of safer anxiolytics and anticonvulsants.

It is important to realise that drugs which act at the benzodiazepine receptor have been synthesised from many different chemical series. For instance, the first inverse agonists were of β-carboline structure (β-CCE, FG 7142) although more recently agonists and antagonists have also been discovered in the same series. The functional interaction of a drug with the benzodiazepine receptor – and not its chemical structure or class – is the only relevant way to classify drugs acting on this receptor.

At least two other binding sites are found on the GABA receptor complex, one for convulsants and the other for the newly discovered neurosteroids. Convulsants such as picrotoxin and pentylenetetrazol close the channel, thus limiting inhibition and leading to seizures and anxiety. Such phenomena were commonly seen in the days ' before electroconvulsive therapy, when pentylenetetrazol was used to treat depression. The neurosteroids are derivatives of progesterone and cortisol that can modulate GABA in either direction. Some, such as $5_\alpha 3_\alpha$-pregnanolone, are potent sedative anticonvulsants, whereas others, such as pregnanolone sulphate, are convulsants. Their discovery offers an explanation for many of the altered neuropsychiatric changes accompanying pregnancy and the menstrual cycle. However, since both classes of compound derive from the same precursor it is unclear what the overall effect of increasing brain levels of precursor might be.

Some benzodiazepines (e.g. diazepam) also bind to another site that was first identified in tissues outside the central nervous system – the 'peripheral' benzodiazepine receptor. Selective ligands for this site have been discovered, the most potent ones being PK11195 and Ro5-4864. Recent data suggest there may be two sites, one a calcium channel on external membranes of cells and the other a transport site for cholesterol on mitochondrial membranes. The latter site has been implicated in neurosteroid production although this is still speculative. It seems unlikely that either site has an important role in the actions of benzodiazepines since many clinically active compounds do not bind to it.

Ethanol augments GABA-ergic tone, albeit only in some brain regions. The molecular basis of this has just been elucidated with the discovery that ethanol potentiation is critically dependent on the nature of the gamma subunit in the receptor. Two versions of the γ_2 subunit have been cloned which differ in the length of the intracellular loop (so-called alternatively spliced forms). Only cells expressing the long form of this subunit are sensitive to ethanol. An exciting implication of this work is that it allows investigation of the possibility that differential expression of this gene may underlie alcohol sensitivity and alcoholism.

The GABA$_B$ receptors are distinguished from GABA$_A$ ones on many grounds. They are not linked to benzodiazepines or barbiturates, they have different structure-activity requirements, and a distinct molecular biology that puts them in the G-protein class of receptors. The best-known synthetic ligand is baclofen, which acts as an agonist. Recently antagonists such as saclofen, phaclofen and CGP 15348 have been developed, and these should help the elucidation of the role of the $GABA_B$ receptor.

Functions

The need for an inhibitory transmitter has already been outlined, and GABA appears to fulfil that role. Thus it is thought to be important in all aspects of normal brain function, limiting and directing sensory inputs, motor outputs and the associative processes of learning and memory. The acquisition of memories may involve the appropriate loss of local GABA-ergic inhibition, permitting selected sensory inputs to be·laid down as memory traces via long-term potentiation. Conversely, increasing GABA function by benzodiazepines, barbiturates or GABA uptake blockers tends to produce amnesia.

The role of the other receptors on the complex is less clear, since it is not yet known if these sites are normally activated. They are critical for the actions of administered benzodiazepine agonists, as these actions can all be blocked by the antagonist flumazenil. Presumably such receptors did not evolve simply in anticipation of later pharmaceutical innovation, and one possibility is that naturally ocurring benzodiazepines exist (so-called endogenous ligands). It is now recognised that benzodiazepines are natural products found in a variety of plants, so perhaps these receptors evolved to enable animals to benefit from their ingestion. Alternatively, it has been proposed that the brain may make similar substances. Some peptides and other small molecules have been suggested as potential endogenous inverse agonists, which suggests that the natural function of the benzodiazepine receptor is to inhibit rather than to augment GABA function, to limit excessive cerebral depression.

The function of the $GABA_B$ receptor is less well defined. Again inhibition seems important, as agonists will limit the release of a variety of transmitters by acting at terminal receptors. Baclofen has a role in relieving spasticity, perhaps by reducing EAA release. It has been conjectured that $GABA_B$ antagonists might be antidepressant on the grounds that they should increase the release of monoamines, and clinical trials are under way.

Dysfunctions

Dysregulation of GABA receptors has been suggested as a cause of epilepsy, although there is somewhat limited evidence of receptor loss in surgically removed epileptic foci. More recently the use of positron emission tomography with ^{11}C-labelled flumazenil has shown reduced receptor occupation in similar foci. This could reflect a decrease in receptor number or alternatively the presence of an endogenous proconvulsant inverse agonist. This latter possibility is strengthened by reports that flumazenil has anticonvulsant actions.

The role of the benzodiazepine receptor in anxiety has been the subject of much research. On the evidence that flumazenil is anxiogenic in panic disorder, it has become possible to say that anxiety appears not to be due to an endogenous anxiogenic inverse agonist, but there may be tonic anxiolytic tone at the receptor in these patients. Alternatively, the receptor spectrum may be shifted in the inverse agonist direction, thus making flumazenil slightly inverse in action.

The concept of a 'setpoint' that may shift developed from studies on the mechanisms of benzodiazepine tolerance and withdrawal. In these conditions the actions of agonists are reduced, those of inverse agonists increased, and the antagonist flumazenil becomes somewhat inverse. Thus patients with panic anxiety may inherit a defect of benzodiazepine/GABA receptor function similar to that acquired by chronic benzodiazepine users. It seems likely that the syndromes of barbiturate and alcohol withdrawal share similar mechanisms, although alterations in other transmitters, especially the EAAs, probably also occur.

Acetylcholine

This transmitter, the first to be discovered, is well known as the primary excitatory transmitter at the neuromuscular junction and in preganglionic autonomic nerves, although a role in brain function has long been recognised.

Synthesis and degraauuon

Acetylcholine (Ach) is synthesised in cholinergic nerve terminals following the uptake of the precursor choline by a high-affinity transporter that is found only in these neurons. Choline comes from dietary sources and is transported to the brain by the blood. Giving it, or precursors such as lecithin, has been used in attempts to increase levels of ACh in the brain. Conversely, neuronal stores of ACh can be depleted by drugs such as hemicholinium, which block choline uptake. Within the neuron choline and acetylcoenzyme A combine to form ACh, a reaction catalysed by the enzyme choline acetyltransferase (ChAT). Since ChAT is only found in cholinergic neurons, it may be used as an index of the density of these cells. The finding that in Alzheimer's disease there is marked loss of this enzyme led to the cholinergic hypothesis of this disorder. The main cholinergic neurons are found in a series of nuclei running from the septum backwards to the nucleus basilis magnocellularis (nucleus of Meynert); these send projections to most of the forebrain. Local ACh neurons also exist in cortex and striatum, the latter seemingly involved in aspects of motor control.

The activity of intrasynaptic ACh is terminated by metabolism: the specific esterase, acetylcholinesterase, hydrolyses it to choline, which can then be taken back into the nerve terminal for a repetition of the cycle (Fig. 3.10). The actions of ACh can be markedly prolonged by drugs such as physostigmine and nerve gases which act as irreversible enzyme inhibitors.

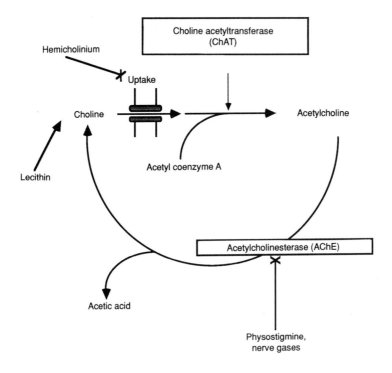

Fig. 3.10 The synthesis and degradation of acetylcholine.

Receptors

There are two distinct types of ACh receptors: the nicotinic, which gate
a sodium channel, and the muscarinic. Muscarinic receptors are linked
to G protein and PI (Tables 3.1 and 3.3) and have a number of secondary
actions, one of which is the inhibition of a particular type of potassium
conductance that then leads to increased cell excitability. Both classes
of receptors have now been cloned and shown to have a number of subtypes.
Selective agonists and antagonists are being developed, although there
are little clinical data available yet. The ligand QNB is of sufficiently high affinity
and selectivity to be used for *in-vivo* labelling of muscarinic receptors,
and an iodinated derivative has been developed for this purpose.

Many psychotropic drugs have high affinity at muscarinic cholinergic
receptors. In some cases this leads to difficulties, as with the urinary
retention, impaired accommodation, dry mouth and constipation seen with
amitriptyline and most of the original tricyclic antidepressants. However, it
may be beneficial, as in the case of the neuroleptics chlorpromazine
and thioridazine, where their potent anticholinergic actions minimise
extrapyramidal side-effects.

Table 3.3 Cholinergic drugs

	Agonists	Antagonists
Direct	Acetylcholine[1] ($M_1 = M_2$)	Atropine ($M_1 + M_2$)
		Scopolamine ($M_1 + M_2$)
		Benzhexol
		Procyclidine
	Carbachol[1] (M_2)	Pirenzepine[1] (M_1)
	+ arecoline (N + M)	
	Nicotine (N)	QNB ($M_1 + M_2$)
Indirect	Anticholinesterases	
	(e.g. physostigmine, neostigmine[1])	

1. Do not cross blood–brain barrier.
N, nicotinic; M_1 and M_2 are subtypes of muscarinic receptors.

Functions

The main function of ACh appears to be in modulating cerebral activity of ascending primary inputs. Since ACh has an excitatory action, and anticholinergic agents (such as scopolamine) are profoundly amnestic, it is thought to mediate memory consolidation by parallel activation of relevant sensory pathways. The popularity of nicotine in part reflects its ability to improve performance and yet reduce anxiety - a unique combination of actions. The addictive aspects of nicotine are thought to derive from its ability to release dopamine in those brain regions controlling reward.

In the basal ganglia ACh appears to act in unison with dopamine to regulate motor action, with ACh stimulating and dopamine inhibiting throughput. Thus an underfunctioning of dopamine, as seen in Parkinson's disease and following neuroleptic therapy, can be ameliorated by anticholinergics such as benzhexol and procyclidine, although these appear partly to block dopamine uptake, which also may contribute to their activity.

Dysfunctions

The main condition in which ACh deficiency has been implicated is Alzheimer-type dementia. However, a milder loss of ACh may also be implicated in the usual forgetfulness that comes with ageing. It now is thought that both nicotinic and muscarinic receptors in the brain are involved, and much effort is going into the search for ways to augment ACh function in these depleted brains. One approach centres on making more ACh available by blocking acetylcholinesterase with, for instance, tetrahydroaminoacridine (THA). Although results are still controversial, THA has been shown to be of clinical benefit in some studies. Another strategy is to make direct-acting cholinergic agonists. This is not difficult, but the binding of ACh to its receptor depends on the charged amine group, and such compounds, being highly polar, do not cross the blood–brain barrier very well. Moreover, they tend to have rather dramatic and unpleasant actions on the heart and intestinal tract (slowing and overstimulating respectively). The hope is that compounds selective for brain-specific subtypes can be developed.

A characteristic feature of severe biological depression is the occurrence of rapid eye movement (REM) sleep earlier in the night than normal. Antidepressant treatments reset this abnormality. Cholinergic processes are involved in REM sleep since it can be induced by giving cholinergic agonists and delayed by muscarinic receptor antagonists. Depressed people seem extra sensitive to the REM-promoting actions of cholinergic agonists such as arecoline, and one theory of depressive vulnerability suggests that this may reflect a primary dysfunction of cholinergic receptors in which they are supersensitive or overexpressed.

Dopamine

Dopamine is a catecholamine that is the immediate precursor of noradrenaline (Fig. 3.11). However, the more rostral localisation of the dopaminergic neurons

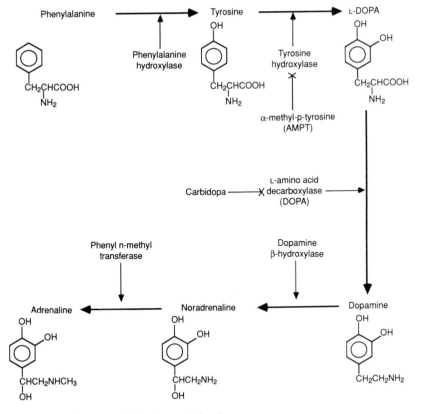

Fig. 3.11 The synthesis of catecholamines.

in the brain suggests that they were recruited into a transmitter role later in evolution than noradrenaline. The discovery that abnormalities of brain dopamine content were the cause of Parkinson's disease was one of the great insights made in neuropharmacology, and has perhaps been overly influential in encouraging the concept of a single transmitter underlying other neuropsychiatric illnesses.

Synthesis and degradation

Dopamine is produced from tyrosine, a dietary amino acid (Fig. 3.11). A small part of tyrosine derives from phenylalanine by a process of hydroxylation. The enzyme responsible for this is absent in phenylketonuria. The conversion of tyrosine to dopamine is completed in two steps, both of which can be inhibited selectively. Tyrosine hydroxylase is the rate-limiting step in the synthesis of the catecholamines, and this enzyme is carefully regulated by neuronal activity and autoreceptor activation. For these reasons increasing precursor (tyrosine) availability seems not to influence catecholamine levels, as it does in the case of 5-HT (see later). It is possible to increase the production of dopamine by administration of L-DOPA, with the simultaneous prevention of peripheral metabolism with a DOPA decarboxylase inhibitor that does not enter the brain (e.g. carbidopa). This strategy has been remarkably successful in the treatment of Parkinson's disease, for although there is a massive loss of cell bodies (over 80%), conversion of L-DOPA to dopamine can also be carried out in other neurons that possess aromatic amino-acid decarboxylase and also in the walls of blood vessels; so sufficient dopamine gets to the receptors to restore the impaired motor function. The fact that dopamine can act in the absence of close anatomical arrangements suggests a modulatory function, although at least in the basal ganglia some topographic organisation has been identified.

In the nerve terminal, dopamine is stored in vesicles similar to those for noradrenaline. Depolarisation causes the release of dopamine, which is then cleared by a high-affinity uptake system back into the nerve terminals, where it can be metabolised by monoamine oxidase A (MAO-A) or via a lower-affinity, higher-capacity uptake system into glial cells. The extra-neuronal metabolism of dopamine is by catechol-o-methyl transferase (COMT) (Fig. 3.12), or by MAO-B, the non-neuronal MAO for which dopamine is a preferred substrate. The products of each reaction then undergo conversion by the other enzyme to the common metabolite homovanillic acid (HVA). Brain, CSF and plasma levels of HVA have been used as an index of dopamine turnover; however, plasma HVA shows a very long lag in response to treatments which rapidly turn on brain synthesis (e.g. neuroleptics) and so probably is of little value in understanding brain dopamine function. The dopamine transporter responsible for the high-affinity uptake can be selectively blocked by drugs such as nomifensine and mazindol. Cocaine has affinity for this site also, and it is thought that part of its reinforcing action is related to this uptake blockade,

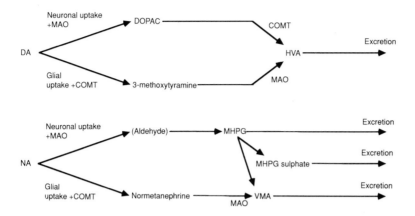

Fig. 3.12 The metabolic pathways by which dopamine (DA) and noradrenaline (NA) are cleared. DOPAC, dyhydroxyphenyl acetic acid; VMA, vanillylmandelic acid.

although it must also have other properties, perhaps directly releasing dopamine (as does amphetamine).

Brain dopamine derives from cell bodies in the mid-brain, the largest nucleus being the substantia nigra, which in man contains about 400 000 neurons. These form the nigrostriatal pathway projecting to the basal ganglia, which is the region with the highest dopamine concentration. Other brain regions well supplied with dopamine are the prefrontal and cingulate cortices and the nucleus accumbens. These supplies arise in the mesocortical/mesolimbic dopamine projection from much smaller nuclei in the ventral tegmental area. There is evidence from animal studies that control of the mesolimbic/mesocortical dopamine projections differs from that of the nigrostriatal. For instance, the mesolimbic system has a higher turnover rate of dopamine and shows more stress responsivity. These features may be due to a lack of autoreceptors. It has been suggested that overactivity of these projections might explain phenomena such as stress-induced exacerbations of schizophrenia. A separate local network of dopamine neurons exists in the hypothalamus, with the cell bodies in the arcuate nucleus projecting into the median eminence and inhibiting prolactin release. The galactorrhoea seen with neuroleptic treatment is due to blockade of dopamine receptors located on the lactotroph cells in the anterior pituitary which normally inhibit prolactin release.

Receptors

Despite the recent plethora of newly discovered receptors, there are really only two types of dopamine receptor – D_1 and D_2. The more recently reported D_3 and D_4 are variants of the D_2 receptor that have been discovered using molecular biology. They show essentially similar biochemical properties to the D_2 receptor, although there are some differences in relative affinity of antagonists such as neuroleptics. However, even small differences in relative binding properties may explain certain features of drugs such as clozapine. Moreover, the interesting regional variations in distribution exemplified by the association of the D_4 receptor with limbic structures offers scope for the synthesis of more discriminating antagonists that could revolutionise antipsychotic therapy.

Molecular variants of the D_1 receptor (such as the D_5) have also been recently described, again showing subtle differences in pharmacology and distribution. However, since the function of D_1 receptors is still uncertain, the therapeutic potential offered by these findings is somewhat obscure. An important observation is that of the interaction between D_1 and D_2 receptors. These may be stimulatory or inhibitory, so for instance the facial movements of tardive dyskinesia may be due to a relative overactivity of D_1 receptors in the presence of D_2 blockade by neuroleptics.

Selective ligands for the classic D_1 and D_2 receptor subtypes have been well documented (Table 3.4). One of the most influential insights in neuropharmacology was the discovery that the therapeutic action of neuroleptic drugs could be predicted by their ability to block the D_2 receptor. This strongly supported the dopamine theory of schizophrenia, which suggested that the positive symptoms of this disease were due to increased dopamine function in the central nervous system. In addition it explained the ability of neuroleptics to cause extrapyramidal side-effects by blocking nigrostriatal dopamine function. Subsequent searches for drugs free of the latter propensity led to more selective compounds such as sulpiride. Although neuroleptics are potent D_2 antagonists, many have activity at other receptors. For instance most of the first (chlorpromazine-like) and second (haloperidol-like) generation compounds also block α_1-adrenergic receptors and 5-HT$_2$ receptors. Chlorpromazine is also a potent antihistamine and anticholinergic. These extra actions probably do not contribute greatly to the antipsychotic actions, but can be useful; for example, the α_1 and histamine blockade promote sleep, and the anticholinergic actions alleviate the extrapyramidal side-effects. However, the preeminent role for D_2 blockade in the therapeutic response has been well documented in recent positron emission tomography studies which reveal that *in-vivo* receptor occupancy of over 75% is found with

Table 3.4 Dopaminergic drugs

Receptor type	Agonists	Antagonists
D_1	SKF 38393	SCH 23390
D_2	Apomorphine	Classic neuroleptics
	LY 141865	Sulpiride
	RU 24926	Domperidone
D_3	Pergolide	Classic neuroleptics
D_4		Clozapine

therapeutic doses; extrapyramidal side-effects emerge with greater than 80% receptor blockade.

The excitement generated by the resurrection of clozapine as a viable therapy, particularly for resistant cases of schizophrenia, has led to a reappraisal of the standard dopamine theory, since this drug has considerably higher affinity for other receptors (e.g. α_1 and α_2 adrenergic) than for the D_2 type. It is possible that the lack of specificity increases clozapine's efficacy. Alternatively an action at one of the other sites may explain the therapeutic gain. Attempts to address these issues by adding in selective antagonists of these other receptors to standard neuroleptics are now under way. The finding that clozapine has a higher ratio of $D_4:D_5$, $D_1:D_2$ and $5\text{-}HT_2:D_2$ blocking ability than conventional neuroleptics, despite being still significantly weaker in absolute terms, is also leading to the search for compounds with greater selectivity in these parameters, but clinical studies with these are a long way off.

A number of selective dopamine receptor agonists have been identified. Some, such as lysuride and bromocriptine, have been developed as potential therapies for Parkinson's disease, although as yet they appear to have a secondary role to L-DOPA. In overdose they can lead to psychotic states and motor disturbances, which further emphasises a role for dopamine in the latter conditions. Apomorphine has been used extensively as a probe of dopamine receptors, for it releases growth hormone. It has also been used in aversion therapy of conditions such as alcoholism as it is very emetic. Since dopamine is the major transmitter inhibiting prolactin secretion (prolactin inhibitory factor), synthetic agonists such as bromocriptine are used to suppress release in galactorrhoea and postpartum lactation.

Functions

Dopamine was first implicated in the control of movement, and it now appears that its action in the striatum is permissive, in that it allows the expression of cortically initiated voluntary movement.

The role of the mesolimbic/cortical projections is thought to be in promoting drive and reinforcement. Dopamine release in these regions is pleasurable, in that animals will work to receive electrical stimulation of these pathways or local dopamine administration in these regions. Conversely dopamine depletion leads to anergy and loss of drive. It is thought that this projection is involved in the experience of pleasure in humans, since euphoriant (opiates) and stimulant (amphetamine, cocaine, nicotine) drugs release dopamine in these regions. As mentioned earlier, abnormal cortical dopamine activity has been suggested to underlie some aspects of schizophrenia, with the current emphasis being on an imbalance of D_1 and D_2 receptor function.

Dopamine receptors in the area postrema seem to promote emesis, hence the use of antagonists such as domperidone or metoclopramide as antiemetics. Both can cause similar extrapyramidal side-effects to neuroleptics.

Dysfunctions

To some extent these have already been covered above. The loss of dopamine cell bodies as the cause of Parkinson's disease has been confirmed by recent mishaps with illicit 'designer drugs' that produced severe acute Parkinsonism in young drug users. Chemicopathological detective work revealed the unexpected production of the chemical methyl-phenyl-tetrahydropyridine (MPTP) which, when acted on by MAO-B, becomes toxic to dopamine neurons. This discovery heralded a new era of animal research in this field. It also raises the possibility that Parkinson's disease is caused by environmental toxins of similar type, particularly since the inheritance of the disease is low. The great epidemic of postencephalitic Parkinsonism may have been the result of a toxic viral product. Hopes of improved treatment were also generated because inhibitors of MAO-B (e.g. selegiline) minimise MPTP-induced damage and have been shown to slow the progression of idiopathic Parkinson's disease.

Many attempts have been made to demonstrate abnormally high dopamine function in schizophrenia, without very convincing results. The findings of an increase in the number of dopamine receptors in patients' brains either at autopsy or on positron emission tomography seem now to reflect receptor up-regulation caused by prior neuroleptic treatment. Although hemispheric asymmetry of dopamine levels and receptor number has been recorded, this is not a consistent finding. Growing evidence that this illness may be due to neurodevelopmental deficits suggests that dopamine dysregulation is probably a necessary but not sufficient component of schizophrenia.

It seems likely that dopamine is also involved in depression. Evidence includes the role of the mesolimbic system in pleasure, the clinical value of the dopamine uptake blocker nomifensine (now withdrawn for toxicological reasons) and the action that electroconvulsive therapy has on dopamine function. It is now thought that the ability of electroconvulsive therapy to increase food and fluid intake and decrease psychomotor retardation is due to an increase in dopamine function. Animal studies show that electroconvulsive shock increases synaptic availability of the transmitter.

Noradrenaline

Noradrenaline (called norepinephrine in the USA) is the other catecholamine that has a major transmitter function in the central nervous system. The noradrenaline neurons originate in the brainstem from a series of nuclei, the largest of which, the locus coeruleus, contains only about 30 000 cells that project to the whole of the forebrain. Thus a single neuron has axonal projections that spread throughout the central nervous system in a more extensive fashion than those found with an other transmitter system. Such diffuse projections allow the coordination of responses in the different regions and could underlie the involvement of noradrenaline in arousal, attention, learning, and emotional behaviour. The noradrenergic projections to the forebrain occur in two bundles, the dorsal to cortex and hippocampus, and the ventral to the hypothalamic areas. Selective lesions of one or the other have greatly clarified the role of noradrenaline in brain function.

Synthesis and degradation

The synthesis of noradrenaline follows the dopamine pathway, with the conversion of dopamine to noradrenaline being catalysed by dopamine-β-hydroxylase (Fig. 3.11). As this enzyme is located in the storage vesicles it is released with noradrenaline and can be used as a marker of noradrenergic neuronal activity. The concentration of noradrenaline in synaptic vesicles is high, and stability is maintained by it being complexed with ATP, which is also released and may have transmitter function in its own right. Drugs that prevent vesicular accumulation of noradrenaline (and the other amine transmitters) include reserpine and tetrabenzine. The observation that they predispose to depression was one of the foundations of the noradrenaline theory of this illness.

In some tissues, especially the adrenal medulla, and in some brainstem nuclei, noradrenaline is methylated to adrenaline. In the periphery, adrenaline appears to have a role in stress responses, but the function of brain adrenaline is less clear. It may act as the preferred agonist at α_2-adrenoceptors (see below) and inhibit neuronal activity.

Following release, noradrenaline is transported back into neurons by a high-affinity uptake system (uptake 1), although some diffuses away from the synapse and is cleared by a lower-affinity but higher-capacity system, uptake 2, into glial cells. The discovery that the tricyclic antidepressants are potent blockers of uptake 1 was one of the most important discoveries in psychopharmacology. Not only did it lead to a general hypothesis of drug action, but it also helped to found the noradrenaline theory of depression.

The noradrenaline transporter has been cloned and shown to have a unique structure. Subsequently molecular cloning was used to identify the GABA, dopamine and 5-HT uptake sites. Their similarities in structure suggest a common origin of all transmitter transporters.

The catabolic pathways for noradrenaline are shown in Fig. 3.12. In neurons, noradrenaline is metabolised by MAO-A to 3-methoxy4-hydroxyphenylglycol (MHPG). Non-neuronal metabolism occurs by COMT, which produces norme-tanephrine. Inhibitors of MAO such as phenelzine and tranylcypromine increase brain levels of noradrenaline. These drugs act by covalently bonding to the enzyme so recovery from their effects requires new enzyme to be synthesised. Newer, re-versible inhibitors (moclobemide, brofaramine) promise to have safety advantages over the older drugs, especially as they are relatively selective for MAO-A.

Neither noradrenaline nor, with the exception of MHPG, its metabolites cross the blood–brain barrier. Thus a significant proportion (about 40%) of plasma MHPG is derived from brain, which means it can be used as an index of central noradrenaline turnover. Although the rest arises from the peripheral sympathetic nerves, these are to some extent under descending noradrenergic control, so changes in total plasma MHPG may give an integrated view of central and peripheral noradrenergic activity. Alternative routes to assessing noradrenergic activity include the assessment of CSF levels of noradrenaline and metabolites, although this requires correction for the plasma component of MHPG, or the measurement of noradrenaline and all metabolites in urine. Such urinary measures give a value for whole-body turnover of noradrenaline and have been used to show that antidepressant drugs tend to reduce this. The reason why reuptake blockade leads to reduced output is probably due to the influence of autoreceptors (see below).

Receptors

Three distinct classes of noradrenaline receptors have been identified (Tables 3.1 and 3.5). The β- and α_2-adrenoceptors have opposite actions on G-proteins, whereas the α_1 subtype acts via the stimulation of PI. Subtypes of each class have been discovered, sometimes, as in the case of β-adrenoceptors, by the synthesis of compounds that discriminate in different functional tests. More recently the cloning of molecular subtypes has, for example, suggested at least three different protein structures of α_2-adrenoceptors. Of the three types of β-adrenoceptor, the main one found in brain is the β_1 subtype, which predominates in cortex, whereas β_2-adrenoceptors are particularly dense in cerebellum. The newly identified β_3-adrenoceptor is found in brown fat, where it has a metabolic role.

The role of brain β-adrenoceptors is unclear given the limited consequences of its total blockade throughout the central nervous system. One tissue in which their action has been utilised for psychopharmacological studies is the pineal, where they stimulate melatonin production. The isolated position of this

Table 3.5 Noradrenergic drugs

Receptor type	Agonist	Antagonist
β	Isoprenaline > Ad > NA	β_1-atenolol, practolol
	Terbutaline	β_2-ICI 118,551
	Clenbuterol	Both–propranolol
α_1	NA = Ad	Prazosin
	Phenylephrine	Many tricyclics and
	Methoxamine	neuroleptics
α_2	Ad > NA	Yohimbine
	Clonidine (p)	Idazoxan
	Lofexidine (p)	Fluparoxan
	Methylnoradrenaline	Piperoxane

Ad, adrenaline; NA, noradrenaline; (p), partial agonist.

noradrenergic synapse and the single hormone output makes it ideal for studying drug actions at noradrenergic synapses, especially as melatonin output gives an integrated measure of pre- and postsynaptic function.

The α_1-adrenoceptors seem to be located postsynaptically and to be involved in processes such as arousal. The sedative actions of many of the classic tricyclic and neuroleptic drugs is explained by their potent α_1-blocking properties, adding to their antihistaminergic actions. α_1-blockade also contributes to their tendency to cause postural hypotension. Directly testing α_1-adrenoceptor function in humans is difficult as selective agonists tend to have unacceptable actions on blood pressure and heart rate.

The α_2-adrenoceptors are located both pre- and postsynaptically. Postsynaptic receptors influence many functions, including release of growth hormone, arousal and blood pressure. Infusions of the agonist clonidine have been used to investigate α_2-adrenoceptor sensitivity in psychiatric disease. They have revealed a consistent blunting of growth hormone responses in depression and panic disorder that is consistent with α_2-adrenoceptor down-regulation. The sedating actions of clonidine may underlie its use in treating mania.

Presynaptic α_2-adrenoceptors are involved in the control of noradrenaline release, since transmitter in the synaptic cleft activates them and inhibits further release by increasing a potassium conductance that hyperpolarises the cell. This explains why the administration of tricyclic antidepressants leads to an inhibition of neuronal activity that offsets the action of the uptake blocker. Tolerance seems to develop to the autoinhibition of noradrenaline release by down-regulating the presynaptic α_2-adrenoceptor, so allowing the full benefit of uptake blockade to become manifest. The time it takes for this tolerance to occur has been suggested to be the explanation for the therapeutic time-lag with the tricyclic antidepressants. Recent studies have revealed that other antidepressant therapies such as electroconvulsive therapy also down-regulate these adrenoceptors.

Autoinhibition via the presynaptic α_2-adrenoceptors can be mimicked by clonidine and similar agonists, and blocked by selective antagonists such as idazoxan and yohimbine. The antagonists increase the availability of noradrenaline without inhibiting cell firing, and there is evidence they have antidepressant actions. One of the first indications of a role for such antagonists in depression was the finding that mianserin had significant α_2-adrenoceptor blocking properties. In animal studies a combination of such an antagonist with a tricyclic antidepressant leads to faster changes in noradrenergic adrenoceptors. Thus a similar combination could lead to better clinical response, although there might be an increased cardiovascular risk. Other receptors also reduce noradrenaline release; for example mu opioid receptors activate the same potassium conductance as the α_2-adrenoceptors. Tolerance to this action in opioid users leads to noradrenergic overactivity in withdrawal which explains why clonidine, by inhibiting noradrenergic activity, works in this condition.

Functions

The diffuse nature of noradrenergic innervation suggests a role in behaviour, including arousal and attention. At the cortical level, synchronisation of noradrenergic inputs with primary sensory ones and the release of vasoactive intestinal polypeptide (VIP) from interneurons is thought to produce a consolidation of synaptic inputs that underlies memory. Studies using implanted electrodes placed in the locus coeruleus of cats have shown that the firing of these cells is highly responsive to changes in environmental state, as it increases markedly with novel and threatening stimuli. These findings support a role in attention and suggest that noradrenergic processes may be important in anxiety. The ability of the noradrenergic system to activate many different brain regions simultaneously makes it a prime candidate for orchestrating the range of symptoms seen in fear and anxiety.

Dysfunctions

The hypothesis that depression is due to a deficiency of noradrenaline was derived from the insight that mood-elevating and mood-lowering drugs had opposite actions on noradrenergic systems. Attempts to show a deficiency of noradrenaline in brain, CSF or whole body in depression have proved disappointing. An inefficiency of noradrenergic synaptic transmission may underlie some forms of depression, especially bipolar. This may be due to a failure in the regulation of adrenoceptor function.

The idea that overactivity of noradrenergic systems may be important in anxiety has gained popularity. In particular it has been suggested that the paroxysmal anxiety of panic attacks may represent a sudden inappropriate activation of noradrenergic neurons. One explanation for such occurrences is the finding that α_2-adrenoceptor function is reduced in these patients, which would result in reduced inhibition. A similar attenuation of these inhibitory adrenoceptors is thought to contribute to many of the symptoms of alcohol and opiate withdrawal. The bouts of acute sedation that characterise narcolepsy are opposite in character to those of withdrawal states. Very recent studies suggest that they are caused by excessive activity of inhibitory α_2-adrenoceptors in the locus coeruleus.

A significant loss of noradrenergic neurons and adrenoceptors is found in both Alzheimer's and Korsakoff's dementias and in Parkinson's disease including progressive supranuclear palsy. Strategies to increase noradrenaline function in these conditions are being tried. They include the use of agonists such as clonidine and increasing noradrenaline release by blocking presynaptic α_2-adrenoceptors.

5-hydroxytryptamine (5-HT)

The alternative term for the indoleamine 5-HT is serotonin, which derives from its initial discovery in human serum. 5-HT is, like dopamine and noradrenaline, a monoamine transmitter whose neurons originate in several brainstem nuclei, most notably the dorsal and median raphe, and whose axons diffusely supply the forebrain. New data have revealed unexpected differences in the anatomy, physiology and pharmacology of the projections from these two nuclei which suggests important specialisation of function, although these have yet to be properly characterised.

Synthesis and degradation

Serotonin is synthesised in two steps from the dietary amino acid L-tryptophan (Fig 3.13). Neither of the two enzymes involved is saturated, therefore the supply of L-tryptophan is rate limiting. This explains why it is possible to increase the availability of 5-HT in brain by giving L-tryptophan, as is done in augmentation of antidepressant therapy. A similar effect can be produced by giving 5-hydroxytryptophan (5-HTP) although this tends to produce more side-effects, especially as it can enter other neurons and release other monoamine transmitters.

Depletion of 5-HT can be produced by the inhibitor of tryptophan hydroxylase – parachlorophenylalanine (pCPA) – by removing L-tryptophan from the diet, or by blocking its entry into the brain by loading with other neutral amino acids, such as alanine, that compete for the same transport process. Conversely, augmented L-tryptophan entry is seen when plasma concentrations of these amino acids are lowered. This happens after meals,

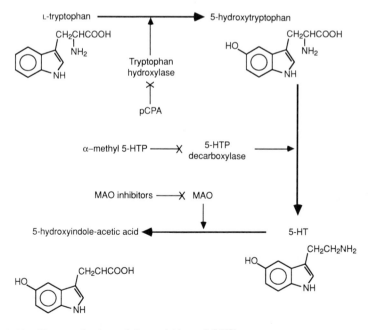

Fig. 3.13 The synthesis and degradation of 5-HT.

when the increase in insulin release promotes their metabolism in muscle; thus postprandial sedation may be due to increased L-tryptophan brain levels leading to overproduction of 5-HT. Deliberate reduction of L-tryptophan availability has been used to deplete brain 5-HT levels; in treated depressed patients, mood became dramatically worse.

The clearance of synaptic 5-HT follows the same pattern as the other monoamines. It is taken back into neurons and then degraded by MAO-A. As well as blocking noradrenaline uptake, the first-generation tricyclic antidepressants also show activity against 5-HT uptake. This finding led to the deliberate synthesis of analogues that were selective for 5-HT. The first, zimelidine, confirmed predictions that this class of compound would be antidepressant, and it became hugely successful until immunological adverse reactions necessitated its being abandoned. Since then four other 5-HT selective uptake blockers have been launched as antidepressants (fluvoxamine, fluoxetine, sertraline, and paroxetine). They are potent compounds that have clear differences in side-effects to the classic tricyclics. They are free of muscarinic, histaminergic and α_1-adrenoceptor antagonism, and they have the great advantage of not causing obesity. All tend to provoke nausea and impair sexual function. At the start of treatment they can be alerting and disrupt sleep, which explains their low alcohol potentiation and their tendency to exacerbate anxiety.

Almost all of the 5-HT in blood is stored in platelets; these have a very active 5-HT uptake system that seems to have the same pharmacology as that found in the brain. Thus in patients treated with uptake blockers, platelet 5-HT levels fall and plasma levels rise. It has been suggested that the platelet uptake site is abnormal in depression, with patients showing less effective 5-HT transport and fewer uptake sites. To what extent these abnormalities represent state or trait markers of the illness or are merely indications of prior drug treatment is still unclear.

Metabolism of 5-HT is to 5-hydroxyindole-acetic acid (5-HIAA), which is then transported out of the brain via the CSF or blood. Despite having a marked cervical–lumbar gradient, the concentration of 5-HIAA in human CSF has been shown to correlate with that in brain tissue, and so may be a useful index of central 5-HT turnover. Low levels of this metabolite have been shown to relate to or even predict violent and impulsive behaviour, for instance murder, arson and self-harm.

Receptors

The past decade has seen a revolution in the understanding of 5-HT receptors, with pharmacological and later molecular differentiation of at least six subtypes (Table 3.6). These can be grouped into three classes: the 5-HT$_1$-like; the 5-HT$_2$-like and 5-HT$_{1C}$-like; and the 5-HT$_3$-like. The 5-HT$_1$-like receptors are linked to G-proteins and differ in pharmacology according to their location. For instance, 5-HT$_{1A}$ receptors are found on the 5-HT cell bodies in the raphe

Table 3.6 Serotonergic drugs

Receptor type	Agonists	Antagonists	Localisation
5-HT$_{1A}$	5-CT 8-OH-DPAT Buspirone (p) Ipsapirone (p) Gepirone (p)	Pindolol Metergoline	Raphe cell bodies Hippocampus
5-HT$_{1B}$	RU 24969	β-blockers	Rat terminal autoreceptors
5-HT$_{1C}$	mCPP MK 212	Ritanserin Methysergide	Choroid plexus
5-HT$_{1D}$	5-CT	Metergoline	Man-terminal autoreceptors
5-HT$_{2A,B}$	LSD mCPP MK 212 DOI	Ritanserin Ketanserin Spiperone	Cortex
5-HT$_3$	2-methyl-5-HT	MDL 72222 ICS 205930 Ondansetron Zacopride	Vagus nerve
5-HT$_4$	5-methoxytryptamine Cisapride Zacopride	GR 113808 SD2 205557	Heart Brain

LSD, lysergic acid diethylamide; DOI, iododimethyloxyamphetamine; 5-CT, 5-carboxyamido-tryptamine; m-CPP, m-chlorophenylpiperidine; (p), partial agonist.

nuclei and postsynaptically in hippocampus. In both places they inhibit firing and the anxiolytic buspirone is believed to be a partial agonist that acts on the raphe to reduce 5-HT neuronal activity. Many follow-up compounds (e.g. gepirone, ipsapirone) are now under clinical trials as anxiolytics. A distinct receptor subtype is found on neuron terminals: 5-HT$_{1B}$ (in rat) or 5-HT$_{1D}$ (in man). This is a typical terminal autoreceptor at which agonists act to decrease 5-HT release. Much effort is now being directed towards synthesising selective antagonists at this site, as they should increase 5-HT availability and thus could be novel antidepressants. The most potent antagonists at present are the β-blockers, and it seems plausible that their tendency to cause nightmares may reflect blockade of 5-HT$_1$-like receptors in the brain.

The second class of 5-HT receptors are those linked to PI turnover – the 5-HT$_{1C}$ and 5-HT$_2$. These have similar molecular structure and it is a historical accident that gives them different numbers. 5-HT$_{1C}$ receptors are found in high density in choroid plexus and appear to have a role in feeding although their study is hampered by the lack of selective antagonists. The

5-HT$_2$ type are located in higher brain structures. Selective and potent antagonists such as ritanserin have been studied for some years and shown to increase slow-wave sleep as well as to have possible anxiolytic action. Three lines of evidence point to a role of 5-HT$_2$ receptors in depression: they are down-regulated following chronic treatment with antidepressants (although paradoxically electroconvulsive therapy up-regulates them); mianserin is a 5-HT$_2$ antagonist (as well as an α_2-adrenoceptor antagonist); and reduced density of these receptors has been found in postmortem studies of the brains of depressed suicide victims. Finally, a possible contribution to psychosis is suggested by the fact that LSD is a potent agonist at the 5-HT$_2$ receptor. Consistent with this possibility is the fact that most neuroleptics have 5-HT$_2$-blocking actions, and this is more marked in some atypical drugs such as clozapine.

The most recently defined 5-HT receptors are the 5-HT$_3$ and 5-HT$_4$ types. The 5-HT$_3$ receptor gates a sodium channel, and causes depolarisation. These receptors are found in large numbers on both central and peripheral ends of vagal afferent fibres. Potent and selective antagonists have been discovered which share the ability to prevent peripherally induced nausea and vomiting, especially that caused by cytotoxic drugs. Psychiatric interest in these antagonists was provoked by claims made on the basis of animal studies that they could be antipsychotic, anxiolytic, memory enhancing, and able to block various forms of drug withdrawal. As yet none of these potential indications has been convincingly demonstrated in clinical studies, and the paucity of 5-HT$_3$ receptors in brain cautions against the likelihood that all these claims will be substantiated.

The 5-HT$_4$ receptor is the only 5-HT receptor that is positively linked to G-proteins; stimulations by agonists such as 5-HT increases cAMP inside cells. In the heart this results in increased contractility – a positive ionotropic effect. The role of the 5-HT$_4$ receptor in the brain will undoubtedly be unravelled over the next few years, as selective antagonists have now been discovered.

Many attempts to study 5-HT receptor function in man have been made. Initially the probes used in receptor challenge studies were the precursors L-tryptophan and 5-HTP. More recently the releasing agent fenfluramine, the potent uptake blocker clomipramine, and direct agonists such as m-chlorophenylpiperidine (mCPP) and buspirone have gained popularity. Output measures used include endocrine stimulation (prolactin, growth hormone and cortisol release), changes in body temperature or sleep, and alterations in psychological ratings. No consistent demonstration of receptor abnormalities in psychiatric disorders has yet emerged from this work although some elegant clinical pharmacological insights have been made. For instance it has been shown that 5-HT uptake blockade potentiates the effects of tryptophan loading, that lithium augments 5-HT function and that benzodiazepines reduce it. Exacerbation of obsessional and anxious ideation by mCPP supports the contention that 5-HT dysfunction contributes to these disorders.

Functions

The diffuse nature of brain 5-HT innervation suggests this transmitter is involved in coordination of brain functions. Many roles have been mentioned already – sleep, impulse control and personality, mood and psychosis, among others. Depletion of 5-HT leads to insomnia and aggressive behaviour in animals, whereas increasing the concentration of this transmitter produces a range of bizarre stereotyped behaviours and locomotor activation (the 5-HT syndrome). This syndrome has been produced in man by the administration of uptake blockers with either L-tryptophan or MAO inhibitors. For this reason MAO inhibitors are prohibited with clomipramine or the newer selective 5-HT uptake blockers. Adequate time should be allowed for clearance of the uptake blocker before starting the MAO inhibitor; fluoxetine poses a particular threat on account of the very long half-life of its active metabolite. 5-HT also affects appetite; the releasing agent D-fenfluramine is currently marketed for the treatment of obesity, and the selective uptake blockers also tend to lead to weight loss.

Dysfunctions

The best established 5-HT-related disorders are those of increased impulsivity – violent suicide, murder and arson – conditions in which low CSF concentrations of 5-HIAA have been shown to predict violent acts against self and others. In a recent study of patients released from forensic psychiatric care the combination of CSF 5-HIAA concentration and response to the glucose tolerance test was shown to predict recidivism with about 90% accuracy. Some benefits have been claimed for regimes which increase 5-HT function in such populations. A link with alcoholism has also been suggested, and some selective 5-HT uptake blockers have been reported to reduce drinking.

A role in depression is strongly suspected on the grounds that 5-HT depletion has been shown to worsen symptoms and that drugs which increase 5-HT function are antidepressant. Moreover, some postmortem studies have shown reduced 5-HT content in raphe nuclei as well as altered 5-HT receptor number. In addition there is evidence that the postsynaptic 5-HT_1-like receptor mediating prolactin release is blunted in this condition. In contrast to the case with noradrenaline, chronic treatment with 5-HT uptake blockers appears to increase postsynaptic receptor sensitivity, as measured electrophysiologically.

Similar arguments have been put forward to suggest a role for 5-HT in anxiety and obsessional disorders, but the case is weaker. There are no postmortem data and the fact that uptake blockers and direct-acting agonists such as mCPP initially worsen symptoms complicates the issue. In anxiety, the selective 5-HT uptake blockers appear to be as efficacious as the tricyclics. Whether this is due to some change in 5-HT function or reflects adaptation in another transmitter system is still unclear. In obsessional disorder a more central role for 5-HT is suggested by the evidence that the 5-HT selective drugs are better than the non-selective type of uptake blocker.

Peptides

At least 100 different peptides have been claimed to be potential transmitters in brain. There is scope to mention only a few that appear to have immediate relevance to psychiatry. In general, peptides are formed by the cleavage of longer precursor peptides or proteins so that families of small peptides can be produced from a single large molecule. Thus the proopiomelanocortin (POMC) gene codes for adrenocorticotrophic hormone and melanocyte-stimulating hormone as well as for β- and other forms of endorphin. This enormous sophistication of potential actions offers a complexity of function that is very hard to unravel.

Endogenous opioids

These fall into three classes, based on the receptor subtype for which the individual peptides show the greatest affinity (Tables 3.1 and 3.7). The endogenous opioids appear not to exhibit much tonic activity but to be switched on in certain circumstances, especially by stress. A role in pain control was demonstrated by the ability of the antagonist naloxone to reduce the actions of natural and placebo-induced analgesia. The highly addictive nature of exogenous opiates such as morphine suggests that the endogenous opioids might be involved in reinforcement, perhaps by modulating dopamine release. The stress of starvation leads to increased CSF levels of endorphin in anorexia nervosa; this may explain the addiction to weight loss. In depression an absent euphoric response to opioids has been found, which may indicate that an abnormality of mu receptors underlies anhedonia in this condition.

A role for kappa receptors in depression and schizophrenia has been postulated because synthetic kappa agonists such as bremazocine produce dysphoria and are psychotomimetic. The fact that in some patients the non-selective antagonists naloxone and naltrexone have been claimed to ameliorate

Table 3.7 Opioid receptor drugs

Receptor type	Agonists		Antagonists
	Endogenous	Exogenous	
μ	β-endorphin, enkephalins	Morphine DAGO	Naloxone, naltrexone
δ	Enkephalins	DPDPE DSLET	Naltrindole ICI 174864
ϰ	Dynorphins	Spiradoline Pentazocine Bremazocine Tifluadom	Norbinaltorphimine

hallucinations and some self-destructive behaviour (e.g. in autism) supports the view that endogenous kappa agonists may contribute to mental illness.

A further use of these antagonists is in the treatment of opiate addiction. Administration of naltrexone produces a long-acting blockade of receptors which negates the 'rush' produced by morphine or heroin. An alternative approach is to use partial agonists such as buprenorphine. Such drugs reduce the actions of agonists by direct competition at the receptor. Moreover they produce a low level of reinforcement that leads to better compliance than with the pure antagonists.

Cholecystokinin (CCK)

This peptide was discovered in the gut, where it regulates the postprandial release of bile, but in common with most other gut peptides, is now known to be present in the central nervous system. The fact that in the brain one of the roles of CCK is to control appetite illustrates an important new concept in peptide hormone function: the coordination of peripheral physiological with central behavioural responses. Other examples are the role of the angiotensin/renin system in fluid balance and corticotrophin releasing hormone (CRH) in stress responses (see below). Two different CCK receptors have been identified by the production of selective ligands. The CCK_A receptors seem to be involved in appetite and feeding and possibly pain. In contrast, the CCK_B receptor may have a role in emotional behaviour, since antagonists are anxiolytic in animal models and infusions of CCK_4 have been shown to provoke profound anxiety in humans.

Corticotrophin releasing hormone (CRH)

This peptide (which is sometimes called CRF, F for factor) controls the release of adrenocorticotrophic hormone from the anterior pituitary. It also has a range of other actions in the central nervous system which have been conceived as integrating the body's response to stress. For instance, injections of CRH produce behavioural changes such as reduced appetite and sex drives, and when repeated can lead to a syndrome of weight loss and altered circadian behaviour that has many parallels with depression. Since one of the best-established findings in depression is overactivity of the pituitary–adrenal axis, it may be that excessive release of CRH has a pathogenic role in this disorder. Moreover, it could be the physiological link between stress and depression.

One intriguing new finding is that CRH neurons exist in a reciprocal arrangement with the noradrenaline neurons of the locus coeruleus. Thus noradrenaline causes CRH release and CRH stimulates locus firing by disrupting its normal inhibitory controls. The excessive noradrenergic activity seen in panic attacks and alcohol withdrawal could be provoked by CRH overactivity. Interestingly in both states there is evidence of overactivity of adrenocortical function, more severe in alcohol withdrawal than in panic disorder. As yet there are no peripherally active antagonists of CRH available; these are difficult to synthesise owing to the large size (41 amino acids) of CRH.

Thyrotrophin releasing hormone (TRH)

This is the smallest brain peptide, being only three amino acids long. It is a very primitive molecule that controls growth and differentiation in lower species and appears to have acquired its role in controlling the release of thyroid stimulating hormone later in evolution. As with the other peptides whose roles have been extended beyond simple hypothalamic hormonal function, TRH is found throughout the brain. The absence of an antagonist has made the study of its functions difficult, although TRH can be given intravenously as an endocrine challenge. Early experiments reported acute antidepressant activity, and although these were not substantiated they did lead to the discovery that a significant proportion of depressed patients have blunted response to thyroid stimulating hormone. The observation that CSF levels of TRH are elevated in depression suggests that the receptors may be desensitised.

The other condition in which TRH has been implicated is motor neuron disease, in which a stable analogue is being used with some success. TRH also has the ability to dramatically reverse sedation caused by a range of drugs including alcohol, barbiturates, benzodiazepines and scopolamine. This property, thought to be due to the release of dopamine and acetylcholine in the brain, suggests TRH may have a role in learning and memory, and perhaps some therapeutic potential in dementias.

Conclusion

Neuropharmacology and neurochemistry are the key disciplines for the understanding of both the pathophysiology and therapeutic basis of psychiatry. They are subjects in which, as this chapter illustrates, great advances in knowledge have been made in the past three decades. An understanding of the current status of this field will provide a solid basis for the appreciation of what is sure to be an equally exciting and revealing future.

Further reading

Ashton, H. (1992) *Brain Function and Psychotropic Drugs.* Oxford: Oxford University Press.

Cooper, J. R., Bloom, F. E. & Roth, R. H. (1991) *The Biochemical Basis of Neuropharmacology* (6th edn). Oxford: Oxford University Press.

Green, A. R. & Costain, D. W. (1981) *Pharmacology and Biochemistry of Psychiatric Disorders*. Chichester: Wiley.

Leonard, B. E. (1992) *Fundamentals of Psychopharmacology*. Chichester: Wiley.

Muller, W. E. (1987) The benzodiazepine receptor. *Trends in Neurosciences*, **10**, no. 7 (July), *Special Issue - Excitatory Amino Acids*.

Pratt, J. (ed.) (1991) *The Biological Basis of Drug Tolerance and Dependence*. London: Academic Press.

Webster, R. A. & Jordan, C. C. (eds) (1989) *Neurotransmitters Drugs and Diseases*. Oxford: Blackwell Scientific.

For reference

Meltzer, H. Y. (ed.) (1987) *Psychopharmacology: A Third Generation of Progress*. New York: Raven Press. (A magnificent source - ensure your library has a copy.)

4 Neurological examination and neurological syndromes

Ken Barrett

The assessment of CNS function • Examination • Investigation •
CNS symptoms, syndromes and disorders

Psychiatry evolved within the asylum movement of the early 19th century and was thus one of the first medical subspecialties. The asylum provided a refuge not only for the insane but also for many whose behaviour was impaired by brain damage or disease, and the earliest pathological and therapeutic studies of neurological disorders took place within this setting. The specialty of clinical neurology evolved later and focused particularly upon the functions of the lower nervous system – movement and sensation. The fact that much of the brain is concerned with the production and elaboration of behaviour ensured that psychiatry did not entirely lose interest in things neurological, and the Royal College of Psychiatrists has reasserted the importance to the psychiatrist of a knowledge of disorders of the central nervous system. This chapter provides an account of these disorders. Clinical history taking and examination in relation to them is discussed, including the assessment of higher and lower functions. Symptoms and syndromes of particular importance and relevance to the psychiatrist are described. Clinical material on vascular, infective, and neoplastic disorders of the central nervous system is presented in Chapter 6.

The assessment of CNS function

Clinical history

Taking a clinical history to exclude or identify disorders of the nervous system differs little from the general history taking familiar to any psychiatrist. The history provides the most important evidence of malfunction of the central nervous system (CNS), and so it is essential that it be taken thoroughly, with corroboration and additional information from relatives or other witnesses. The telephone can be as useful an investigative tool as the computerised tomography scanner. The history provides clues as to the form of CNS malfunction and the likely cause. Examination aids the localisation of a lesion.

Neurological history taking should address what could be called the life trajectory of the nervous system, extending from before conception to the

---

Box 4.1   Major hazards for the central nervous system

Genetic (inherited disorders, chromosomal additions, deletions, etc.)
Intrauterine (toxins, infections, malnutrition, metabolic or storage problems)
Perinatal (prematurity, foetal distress, birth trauma, infection)
Childhood developmental (infection, trauma, nutritional, social deprivation, specific and general learning disability, pervasive development problems)
Adult development (traumatic, infectious, vascular, neoplastic, metabolic, nutritional, toxic, autoimmune, degenerative)

---

present. The commoner hazards encountered along this trajectory are listed in Box 4.1

The history should cover the following topics.

Family history

The age and current state of health of parents and siblings and the presence or absence of any degenerative diseases, epilepsy, migraine or mental disorder in the family should be recorded.

Personal history

Information should be collected on the pre- and perinatal period and infancy, where this is readily available. Developmental delay and specific or general learning problems at school should be noted (delay or problems in literacy are the commonest and should be inquired about specifically). Childhood infections and head trauma should be asked about and participation in contact sports, particularly boxing, noted. Occupational history should include any potential or actual exposure to toxins (e.g. lead, solvents) or infective agents (e.g. time spent in the tropics). The recreational use of alcohol and other substances should be noted, along with quantity, duration and mode of administration (injection, inhalation, etc.). Sexual history and orientation should be covered where relevant.

Medical history

This should include specific inquiry about head trauma, black-outs, and infections.

Presenting problem

A detailed history of the presenting problem should be obtained from the patient, with corroboration or further information from an informant. The duration, mode of onset, exacerbating or relieving factors and associated symptoms should be recorded. Where the problem is episodic, as with headache or seizures, note should be taken of the variety of experiences. Their form or phenomenology and their relative frequency should be noted.

Examination

It is not unknown for the write-up of an otherwise thorough physical examination to include the words 'grossly normal' in the CNS section. The implication is that an individual's ability to stay alert and communicate during an interview without manifesting a gross disturbance of movement or consciousness may be sufficient indication that the CNS is intact. Alas, this is not the case. A further disincentive to examine, particularly in the setting of the psychiatric out-patient clinic, may be the array of specialist equipment apparently required for the task.

Much of the examination of the CNS, it should be remembered, can be completed without any equipment.

This section presents a simple and systematic approach to the examination of the CNS, including a brief screening examination for use with or without equipment. There are several excellent accounts of the examination of the central and peripheral nervous systems, from a neurologist's perspective, and the reader is referred to those cited in the bibliography for greater detail.

The areas listed in Box 4.2 should be examined. The aim throughout is to examine the function of various brain systems; that is, to search for localisable malfunction. This includes the lower CNS functions of movement and sensation, and higher functions.

Lower functions

Much of what follows employs only the hands and eyes of the examiner but also available should be: an opthalmoscope, patella hammer, stethoscope, and tuning fork. The stethoscope is important for the identification of cardiac murmurs, carotid and cranial bruit. During the examination look for specific abnormalities in turn rather than simply repeat a series of overlearned examination procedures.

Examine in a sequence that saves time and effort. Look at the gait when the patient walks into the room – is it ataxic (unsteady), shuffling, stiff-legged, broad-based (legs wide apart), dragging, limping, delayed in initiation? Test 'tandem gait' (walking toe-to-heel) and look for falling to one side or the other, or the appearance of 'overflow movements' of the arms (i.e. athetotic movements).

Look at the person sitting during the interview. Does the facial expression change? Is there any facial asymmetry (marked difference in the nasolabial folds); ptosis, titubation; involuntary movement of the head and neck or mouth/face/tongue; involuntary limb movement (tremor, chorea, hemiballismus

---

Box 4.2 Functions of the central nervous system to be examined

Lower CNS
Voluntary movements (gait disorder, reduced power)
Involuntary movements (tremor, chorea, athetosis, tics, hemiballismus
   and the absence of normal spontaneous movement)
Coordination (past-pointing, impaired rapid alternating movement)
Muscle tone (reduced, increased, cogwheel, asymmetric)
Tendon reflexes (increased, reduced and particularly asymmetric)
Primitive (release) reflexes (palmomental, grasp, and groping, pout,
   counter-pull)
Limb and trunk sensation (touch, vibration, proprioception)
Cranial nerves
   Visual system
      fundi, fields, pupillary responses, movements, nystagmus
   Hearing, smell and taste
   Movements of face, neck and jaw
   Movements of tongue, palate and vocal cords
   Facial skin and corneal sensation

Higher CNS
Orientation and attention
Memory (recall of recent and remote events, learning ability)
Dominant parietal
   Language ability
      fluency, paraphasic errors, naming, repetition, comprehension,
      reading, writing, ideomotor praxis
   Calculation
Non-dominant parietal
   Constructional (visuospatial/hand-eye) ability/praxis
Frontal
   Abstract reasoning
   Performance of alternating motor sequences

(a sudden shooting out of a limb), athetosis, or reduced spontaneous limb movement/unchanging facial expression? Look for wasting of the small muscles of the hands, or one hand markedly smaller than the other (suggesting maldevelopment, usually intrauterine).

Ask the patient to stand with arms outstretched horizontally in front with palms uppermost and eyes closed: note any flapping tremor, and drift into pronation or below the horizontal (an indication of mild weakness), any swaying or falling to one side (vestibular function).

Coordination

Ask the patient to touch your finger with eyes open and then his/her nose, while moving your finger from side to side: note any past-pointing or intention tremor. Then ask the patient to tap rapidly the front and back of his/her own hand or thigh: note any clumsiness (cerebellar sign).

Muscle tone

Take each of the patient's hands in turn as if shaking it. Support the elbow and rotate the forearm both ways at the wrist then extend and flex the elbow (a good way to test for cogwheeling, increased muscle tone, and counter-pull).

Power

Ask the patient to abduct the arms to 90°C, flexed at the elbow, with instruction to resist your attempt to push them downwards. Push both at once, pressing near the shoulder. You should not be able to move them; if you can this is an early sign of motor disturbance. Power at the elbow and wrist is easily assessed. Ask the patient to extend and abduct the fingers, again with the request to resist your attempt to adduct them, pressing near the metacarpo-phalangeal joint. You should only be able to move them a little. Ask the sitting patient to raise the knee and keep it raised while you push it downwards on the mid-thigh. You should be unable to move it. Similarly test the power at the knee and of dorsiflexion and plantar flexion of the foot at the ankle against resistance by pressing with the hand on the dorsum or sole of the foot with the heel kept on the floor. Do this on both sides. Any abnormality should lead to a fuller examination.

Reflexes

Using a patellar hammer, examine the biceps, triceps, supinator, patellar and Achilles' tendon jerks. Test the same tendon on each side before moving on to the next and look in particular for symmetry. Symmetrical hyper-reflexia is most commonly caused by anxiety. Brisk tendon jerks in the legs with reduced jerks in the arms suggests a cord lesion in the neck.

Gently but firmly press a key or thumb nail along the outer portion of the sole of each foot, moving medially over the metatarso-phalangeal joints, and note the movement of the big toe. Upward movement, without a withdrawal or dorsiflexion of the foot, indicates an upper motor neuron lesion.

Release signs

Gently but firmly draw a key across the thenar eminence of the hand while observing the mentalis area below the mouth. Contraction of the mentalis (the muscle between the lower lip and the chin) on the same side indicates frontal cerebral cortical damage or degeneration on the opposite side. A positive palmo-mental reflex is probably the most sensitive frontal release sign and so the best with which to screen.

Tapping the lips with a vertically held pen may evoke a pout reflex, another sign of frontal damage.

Other frontal release signs include the grasp and groping reflexes. Slip two fingers gently onto the patient's palm. A grasp reflex is generally a powerful gripping of the fingers which is maintained despite lifting your hand. If you do the same thing but instead of touching the palm slowly pull away from the hand, in the patient's vision, his/her hand may follow yours. This is a groping reflex. Both of these indicate severe frontal damage on the opposite side.

Counter-pull (or *Gegenhalten*) is present when the patient actively resists your attempts to passively flex or extend a limb joint. This is an indication of diffuse damage or degeneration, and is most often seen bilaterally.

Sensation

Test the sense of touch by lightly touching the outer border of the feet, and the back of the calves and thighs. Test both sides simultaneously and separately; inability to feel simultaneous touch, with single touch intact, suggests a mild or developing sensory neglect. most common on the left side. If there is any abnormality, test for discrimination between a sharp and blunt object. A partially straightened paper clip can be used, applying the sharp end gently and obliquely to the skin.

Test the patient's sense of joint position by moving the big toes up or down out of the patient's vision and asking the position. Test sense of vibration with a tuning fork applied to the ankles, patellae and wrists, but remember that vibration sense in the feet may commonly be reduced after the age of 60.

Cranial nerves

The sense of smell is perhaps the cranial nerve function least often tested, for the obvious reason that the customary bottles of aromatic substances are less readily available than the patella hammer, etc. A simple test can be carried out though using a substance that is ubiquitous in hospital and domestic settings: a bar of soap. Test one nostril at a time and ask the patient to describe the fragrance.

Test eye movements by moving a vertical finger to the left and right of the midline about 2 feet from the face (looking for nystagmus and failure of an eye to move) and then move towards the nose and look for convergence and constriction of the pupil. Move a horizontal finger up and down. Stand about 2 feet in front of the patient and ask him/her to look at your nose. Bring your extended index fingers upwards with your arms extended and your fingers half way between the two of you, until you can just see them. Ask if the patient can see your fingers; if so ask him/her to point to the one that moves – twitch the left, the right, and then both together. Do the same coming in from above the head. The ability to see each one move but not the two together indicates inattention, an early sign of a developing field defect or visual field neglect. Examine each eye separately by covering the other to look for any unilateral field defect.

You will need an opthalmoscope to examine the fundus. Using an opthalmoscope effectively can require considerable practice. If you are a similar height to the patient it is easier to look at the fundus with both standing. Do all you can to dim the light in the room. With your opthalmoscope, check that the pupils are equal in size and that both react to light. Ask the patient to look constantly at one spot in the room. If the patient wears glasses you could try leaving the glasses on, as that may save having to flick through the lenses of the opthalmoscope, but there is often too much glare. Look medially and downwards as you look for the optic disc. Look for a sharp disc margin (an ill-defined disc margin can indicate papilloedema, and that is what you are looking out for in particular; the vessels may also be curled over the swollen disc). Having looked at the optic disc, sweep around the margins and note any haemorrhage or exudate and whether the cross-over of a vein and an artery looks 'nipped'. If you cannot see the disc then ascertain whether or not the vessels are clearly visible. If not then try using the narrower beam on the ophthalmoscope. If still unsuccessful then try flicking slowly through the lenses, both ways. Portable ophthalmoscopes can help. They are lighter, smaller, and have fewer lenses. If you cannot see the fundus but are worried about the possibility of papilloedema then examine for a loss of colour vision in the centre of the visual field. This can be tested using the red top of a pen or similar small object by moving the pen horizontally across the field of vision and asking if the colour changes.

Asymmetric facial movement is not difficult to detect, and even in a deadpan face this can be associated with an asymmetric nasolabial fold. Remember that the forehead is supplied by both sides of the brain, which is interesting given its importance in expressing emotion.

Hearing may be tested by whispering a number some two feet from the ear. While testing one ear, occupy the other by rubbing a finger against the skin in front of it.

Asymmetric palate and tongue movements also present no difficulty. The ability to shrug the shoulders and turn the head from side to side against resistance and the absence of dysarthria in speech attest to the functioning of the accessory and vagus nerves.

The most important tests of cranial nerve function for the psychiatrist are examination of the fundus, visual fields and eye movements. This should include the identification of nystagmus.

An excellent detailed and authoritative account of the examination of the central and peripheral nervous systems is provided by Denny-Brown (1982).

Higher functions

There are two approaches to testing higher functions. The preferred one is analogous to the testing of lower functions: specific areas are tested with the aim of localising CNS dysfunction. The alternative is to use a series of tests that simultaneously test several functions, ending up with a general rating of higher function. The latter method is only applicable in seeking to identify global impairment, such as dementia.

Wherever possible tests should not be heavily dependent upon general intelligence and should test a single function. The following suggestions are drawn from the many available, and the reader is free to use alternatives while adhering to the general principles outlined.

Orientation and attention

Orientation, attention and concentration are traditionally tested first, and for good reason. If attention is impaired then performance in *all other* tests will be affected. Testing orientation is the best way of identifying a confusional state. Establish whether or not the patient knows where he/she is in time and place. The ability to sustain attention on a task may be tested by asking the patient to recite the months of the year in reverse, or the days of the week if that is too difficult. Digit span – the ability to repeat a series of numbers – is another useful test, but it is often administered incorrectly. It is important to say the numbers at about one-second intervals and without a change in voice intonation. Performed this way, a forward digit span of five or above is considered normal.

Memory

Asking about items in the recent news is a useful way of testing incidental learning, the automatic storage of information. The use of memory involves:

(1) registration
(2) storage
(3) retrieval
(4) consolidation.

The last is the process by which information is retained for more than the duration of the interview. The four areas constitute the ability to learn and recall new information. A useful test of learning is to ask the patient to identify four objects and then place them out of sight. Then ask the patient to recall the objects and where they had been placed, immediately and after an interval. The longer the interval the better, but ten minutes is a minimum. Failure to recall the objects immediately indicates an impairment of registration, which is dependent upon attention. Failure to recall the objects after a delay could indicate failure of storage or retrieval. It is worth distinguishing between the two and this can be done using a simple multiple-choice technique: the interviewer names one of the hidden objects and two new objects, and asks the patient to identify the correct one. This can then be repeated for each of the hidden objects. The more traditional test of ability to learn a name and address can also be administered in this way: offer a series of choices if any part of the name and address is not recalled. It is important to remember that the *retrieval* of information after a delay is commonly impaired by anxiety.

Functions of the parietal lobe and temporal lobe

Tests of language function should aim to identify the principal forms of dysphasia, which are caused by lesions of the dominant hemisphere. It is important to establish the handedness of the patient; in right-handed people the left hemisphere is usually dominant for language. Much information will already have been gleaned during the interview. In particular, is speech fluent, is there difficulty with word finding, and are there paraphasic errors (i.e. word substitutions)?

The single most important screening test of language function is probably confrontation naming, the presentation of objects to the patient with the request that they be named. About 10 – 12 objects should be used and the parts of a watch and the body are usually readily available. Other aspects of dysphasia include comprehension of complex commands (e.g. tap your knee three times then point to the window), the ability to repeat a phrase, reading and writing. Fluent speech which is paraphasic, or associated with anomia (an inability to name objects) or impaired comprehension, reading or writing indicates a dominant parietal lesion, usually on the left. A non-fluent aphasia with intact comprehension indicates a left lateral frontal lesion. Impaired repetition (the ability to repeat a phrase) implicates the region between these areas.

Ideomotor praxis, the ability to perform motor tasks on verbal command, can be tested by asking the patient to salute, shrug the shoulders, etc. Impairment again suggests a lesion in the parietal lobe of the dominant hemisphere. Impairment in the ability to perform simple calculations (dyscalculia) also points to a lesion in this area. This, together with failure to correctly identify fingers (finger agnosia), right/left disorientation and dysgraphia is called the Gerstmann syndrome.

Constructional praxis (visuospatial ability) can be tested by having the patient copy a design (e.g. three overlapping triangles or similar). Drawing a clock face can also be useful as this, along with the design, can provide an indication of spatial neglect (ignoring one side, usually the left, of the design or clock). Such impairment indicates a non-dominant, usually right parietal, lesion. It is not uncommon for a patient with this kind of disability to ignore one side of the body, most evident when dressing (dressing dyspraxia).

Functions of the frontal lobe

Abstract reasoning may be tested using the interpretation of proverbs. Abstract abilities are dependent upon general intelligence. A simple proverb such as "People in glass houses shouldn't throw stones" is generally adequate. With more intelligent patients, a less familiar proverb such as "The good is the enemy of the best" is indicated. Concrete interpretation of proverbs is also found in schizophrenia, an abnormality which may point to subtle frontal lobe dysfunction in that disorder. Abstraction can be impaired by frontal and more diffuse right hemisphere damage.

The dorsal convexity of the frontal lobes has a range of subtle cognitive and motor functions, including the ability to perform sequences of alternating movements, rapidly and repeatedly switching from one movement to another. This may be tested by presenting to the patient a pattern drawn on paper (Fig. 4.1) with the request that the sequence be continued along the page. Inability to perform this sequence of movement, with intact ability to copy a non-alternating design, indicates frontal dysfunction.

For further detail of cognitive testing the reader is referred to the excellent book by Strub & Black (1985).

Investigation

While chapters 8 and 9 detail the role of electroencephalographic and imaging investigations respectively, this section briefly considers the indications for such investigations. The indications for serological and cerebrospinal fluid examination, angiography and other specialised investigation is included where relevant.

Computerised tomography

Urgent computerised tomography (CT) of the brain is indicated where any of the following is strongly suspected:

(1) hydrocephalus
(2) sub- or extradural haematoma
(3) encephalitis
(4) cerebral abscess
(5) primary cerebral, pituitary or meningeal tumour
(6) aneurysm or arteriovenous malformation.

Non-urgent CT scanning is definitely indicated for the following clinical presentations:

(1) progressive cognitive/higher-function decline (focal or global)
     developing under the age of 65 years

Fig. 4.1 A test of frontal lobe function: the patient is asked to continue the sequence across the page.

(2) marked personality change where there is no history of functional psychosis or severe head injury

(3) treatment-resistant major affective or schizophrenic psychosis

(4) schizophrenia developing after the age of 40

(5) confusional state/delirium for which no metabolic or toxic cause is found

(6) marked and persistent, or variable, drowsiness

(7) mania without history of major depression developing after the age of 50

(8) confusion, gait disturbance and incontinence which has developed over weeks or months

(9) progressive deterioration in seizure control without alteration of medication.

There are some other possible indications. Some psychiatrists investigate all schizophrenic patients at first presentation. CT can be useful in the assessment of patients with brain damage, enabling more realistic planning of rehabilitation.

Electroencephalography

Electroencephalogram (EEG) reports have a reputation for being equivocal, but most EEG requests ask vague questions or no questions at all and so get vague answers. There are a limited number of questions that can be answered by EEG:

(1) Is there evidence of focal or generalised abnormality of brain rhythms?

(2) Is there evidence of focal or generalised epileptogenic activity (spike, spike and wave, and other paroxysmal activity)?

(3) Does the recording support a diagnosis of metabolic or toxic confusional state or encephalitis (herpes simplex or Creutzfeldt–Jakob disease)?

(4) Is there evidence of anticonvulsant or other drug toxicity?

Urgent EEG is indicated where the following are suspected:

(1) herpes simplex encephalitis

(2) some varieties of status epilepticus (complex partial, petit mal or epilepsy partialis continua)

(3) marked deterioration in seizure control without alteration in anticonvulsant medication.

Serial EEGs can sometimes be of value. For example, where evidence of organic, degenerative disease is sought, EEGs at 6-month or 12-month intervals may be useful. It is generally not useful to carry out an EEG within a month of a course of electroconvulsive therapy, except for the urgent indications noted above. Evoked brain potentials provide a measure of the response of the brainstem and cortical sensory areas to sensory stimuli. Visual evoked potentials are recorded as part of the investigation for possible demyelination; involvement of the optic pathways leads to a slowing of conduction time. They may be worth recording where (hysterical) blindness is suspected and where formless visual hallucinations are reported (as they may be caused by occipital pathology).

Magnetic resonance imaging

Magnetic resonance imaging (MRI) provides a detailed structural view of the brain, but facilities are less readily available in most centres than CT. They are valuable in a detailed search for structural pathology, such as an area of gliosis which may be giving rise to seizures. CT is however in general adequate for most problems relevant to the clinical psychiatrist.

Single-photon emission computerised tomography

Single-photon emission computerised tomography (SPECT) scanning of the brain provides an indication of cerebral blood flow and may be more sensitive in the detection of focal degeneration (in Alzheimer's disease for example) than CT. The precise clinical indications for this type of scanning are still being explored.

CNS symptoms, syndromes and disorders

Chapter 6 deals with the pathology underlying neurological and psychiatric states; below the clinical presentations and management are indicated.

Headache

Headache is perhaps the commonest symptom in the general population. Up to 40% of adults report experiencing headache at least once a month. Ten per cent of the population experience migrainous headaches. Against this background it is evident that headache is rarely caused by serious brain pathology. Some indications for further investigation of headache are listed in Table 4.1.

Migraine, headache with a vascular origin, is classically a throbbing unilateral or occipital pain preceded by or in other ways associated with a wide variety of other symptoms and signs. Nausea, vomiting, and photophobia are the commonest. Other symptoms are thought to arise from arterial constriction resulting in local cerebral malfunction. These constitute the migraine aura preceding the development of the headache proper. Visual disturbance is the commonest, usually teichopsia (wavy lines or 'fortification spectra'), followed by scotoma, or scotoma alone. Transient dyslexia can also occur, as can impairment in word-finding. Focal sensory and motor symptoms can occur

Table 4.1 Headache: when to investigate further

Clinical feature	Possible cause
Headache on waking, improving with change of posture	Space-occupying lesion, obstructive hydrocephalus
Temporal tenderness (especially over 60 years)	Temporal arteritis – usually associated with malaise
Gradually increasing in severity over several days, with vomiting, drowsiness, slowing of pulse	Increasing intracranial pressure
Migraine, associated with motor or sensory signs during or after, or with cranial bruit	Arteriovenous malformation
Headache, papilloedema, field defects, retinopathy, disorientation	Malignant hypertension/hypertensive encephalopathy

and, in hemiplegic migraine, motor deficits may last for several days. Migraine affecting the basilar arterial system is suggested by occipital headache. It is usually associated with marked lethargy/impairment in arousal, nausea and sometimes bulbar symptoms, including diplopia, blurring of vision, and vertigo or other dizziness.

The aetiology of migraine is unknown, but headaches may be triggered by many things including alcohol, hunger, tiredness, emotional stress, and a variety of foods.

Cluster headaches are severe head and face pains that, as the name suggests, occur in clusters extending over several days. They typically come on quickly, often at the same time in the day or night, last one to three hours, and are very disabling while present. Vivid descriptions, such as a red-hot poker sticking in the face, are used to describe these pains, which are often associated with unilateral lacrimation and local redness of the skin.

Severe unilateral headache arising after the age of 60 raises the possibility of cranial arteritis. Thickened and tender temporal vessels are typical. In such cases there is usually a marked malaise and the erythrocyte sedimentation rate is high. When headache is associated with the development of prominent superficial veins in the frontal and temporal areas, cavernous sinus thrombosis may be suspected.

Tension headache is typically bilateral temporal or circumferential ('like a band around the head'), or at the vertex, and is generally a pressure-like pain. Tension headaches and migraine often occur in the same person.

Post-concussive headache, following mild or moderate head trauma, is generally continuous and described as a dull ache with exacerbations. Throbbing, continuous or episodic headache can occur at the site of neurosurgical scars.

The treatment of different varieties of headache is summarised in Table 4.2.

Table 4.2 Treatment of headache

Type of headache	Treatment
Tension	Relaxation/stress-management/biofeedback Beta blockers Treat related psychiatric disorder
Migraine	*Prophylaxis* Beta-blockers (e.g. propranolol) Pizotifen Clonidine Usually 2 – 3 months in first instance *Acute episode* Minor analgesics Ergotamine and derivatives Methysergide only if very severe and unresponsive to above
Cluster	Anti-migraine preparations or non-steroidal anti-inflammatory drugs for acute episode Lithium carbonate for prophylaxis
Cranial arteritis	Steroids

If all else fails, if headaches are chronic or atypical, it is worth trying non-steroidal anti-inflammatory drugs (e.g. ibuprofen) or tricyclic antidepressants.

Epilepsy

About 1% of the population suffer from epilepsy, which can start at any age. It may be idiopathic or caused by many brain and systemic disorders. The classification of epilepsy presents similar problems to that of psychiatric disorder. The current international classification is essentially descriptive (Box 4.3). Seizures involving a loss of consciousness or amnesia for the seizure are 'generalised', other seizures 'partial' or 'complex partial'. Generalised attacks can be primary, or secondary: that is, develop from a partial seizure.

All classes of epilepsy have two features in common.

(1) There are recurrent, transient and generally stereotyped alterations in sensation, movement, behaviour or consciousness (i.e. seizures).
(2) There are characteristic electrophysiological changes which occur immediately before, during and after these seizures.

Seizures may involve any brain function, or combination of functions, and may or may not be associated with loss of consciousness or amnesia for the event.

Box 4.3 The classification of epileptic seizures

The system set out is that proposed by the Commission of Classification
and Terminology of the International League Against Epilepsy (1981)

I. Partial
A. Partial (focal/local) seizures with elementary symptoms
(Consciousness generally remains unimpaired)
  Motor (myoclonic, Jacksonian, versive, postural, aphasic/phonatory)
  Sensory (somatosensory, visual, auditory, olfactory, gustatory,
    vertiginous)
  Autonomic
  Compound forms (i.e. combinations of the above)

B. Partial seizures with complex symptoms
(Generally with impaired consciousness)
  Impaired consciousness alone
  Cognitive (amnesic, *déjà/jamais vu*, ideational disturbance)
  Affective
  Psychosensory (illusions, macropsia, metamorphopsia, hallucinations)
  Psychomotor (automatism)
  Compound forms

C. Partial seizures with secondary generalisation

II. Generalised
(Consciousness is impaired.)
  Absence (with or without tonic, clonic or atonic features, or automatism)
  Myoclonic
  Infantile spasms
  Clonic
  Tonic
  Tonic - clonic (the classic/grand mal/convulsion)
  Atonic

III. Unclassified

Seizures may be triggered by physical (light, sound) or psychological (anxiety,
imagery) events, or occur spontaneously. Psychologically triggered seizures
are, by definition, 'psychogenic'.

The term 'pseudoseizure' refers to an attack which fulfils criterion 1 above
(seizures often resembling epileptic attacks), but not criterion 2. There may
however be problems in completely ruling out a diagnosis of epilepsy on
electrophysiological grounds. Most centres have only routine scalp EEG
recording facilities available, but 24-hour monitoring may be required, and
even these are far from foolproof. The most bizarre seizures tend to be of

temporolimbic or frontal origin, and may be electrophysiologically undetectable unless sphenoidal, pharyngeal or depth electrode studies are carried out (see Waterman *et al*, 1985). Such investigations are far more invasive and are largely reserved for patients who are candidates for surgical treatment of epilepsy. The principal causes of epilepsy are listed in Box 4.4.

History

In establishing a diagnosis of epilepsy the history is all-important. The following aspects must be covered.

Are seizures stereotyped or variable in manifestation? What are their frequency and duration, variation over time, time of day? Are there any associations or triggers (tiredness, emotion, fever)? What are the prodrome/ warnings, aura, the patient's experience of the seizure and postictal state (amnesias, fear, postictal fatigue, headache). The patient should be asked directly about *déjà vu*, depersonalisation, paraesthesia and myoclonus. If hallucinations are reported, are they stereotyped, how long do they last, what are the associated features? Is there a family history of epilepsy, history of birth trauma, febrile fits or other childhood seizures, head injury, meningitis, time spent in the tropics, boxing? In order to get an accurate description of seizures and the postictal state it is important to consult a witness.

Primary generalised absence

Primary generalised absence seizures occur predominantly in the early years and over 90% cease by late adolescence. Most attacks last 30 – 45 seconds

---

Box 4.4 Causes of epilepsy

Idiopathic
Birth injury
Hypoxia
Hypoglycaemia
Congenital neural malformation
Trauma
Pyrexia
Encephalitis/meningitis
Arteriovenous malformation
Neoplasm
Alcohol withdrawal
Sedative/minor tranquilliser withdrawal
Cerebrovascular disease
Uraemia
Liver failure
Drug toxicity (e.g. lithium)
Electrolyte disturbance (e.g. hypokalaemia due to excessive vomiting)

and are associated with lip smacking, swallowing or blinking. The diagnosis may be confirmed by observation of the characteristic 3/s spike and wave discharge on EEG. Hyperventilation may be particularly valuable in triggering seizure activity during EEG recording.

The so-called 'petit mal variant' (the Lennox – Gastaut syndrome) is a form of absence occurring in association with severe mental handicap and with 2/s spike and wave discharge on EEG. Benign rolandic epilepsy is a generalised seizure disorder which is confined to childhood and associated with spikes and sharp waves in the rolandic area on EEG.

Complex partial seizures

Complex partial seizures arise in the temporal and frontal lobes and may involve a wide range of perceptual, cognitive, emotional and affective features.

Hallucinations may occur, and may involve any sensory modality, but these differ from those experienced during psychoses as they are almost invariably stereotyped, usually short lived, and there is no delusional elaboration. However, patients with a discharging temporal lobe focus, particularly on the dominant side, are at risk of developing a schizophreniform psychosis requiring neuroleptics for its resolution. In addition, seizures may occur in any sensory modality. Olfactory hallucinations are rare in functional psychosis but not uncommon in epilepsy with a medial temporal origin.

The classic temporal seizure commences with a sense of fear associated with epigastric churning sensations rising to the neck followed after seconds by a variety of perceptual and affective phenomena. Temporal lobe status epilepticus may present as a confusional state, or atypical psychotic state, but the diagnosis must be supported by a characteristic EEG.

A specific form of seizure arising from foci in the mesial frontal area has recently been described (Waterman *et al*, 1985). These are frequent, short-lived attacks consisting of shouting or screaming (sometimes obscenities), bilateral limb movements such as kicking or clapping, and a variety of affective displays.

Complex partial seizures may also include or be followed by automatism, semipurposeful actions of which the person has no recollection. These can be of variable length but generally last less than an hour.

Epilepsy and behaviour

There is wide agreement that violent acts occur only very rarely as part of an epileptic seizure. The relationship of interictal emotional or behavioural disturbance to 'subclinical' seizure-related electrical discharge is however far from clear. It is assumed, not unreasonably, that persistent limbic spiking and other abnormal electrophysiological activity can produce malfunction in the brain mechanisms controlling behaviour and determining subjective affective states. It could be argued therefore that such activity may lead to behavioural and affective abnormality even in the absence of clinical seizures. So goes the argument in favour of regarding episodic dyscontrol (episodic, uncharacteristic and uncontrolled episodes of rage triggered by a trivial irritation and followed by remorse) as a valid clinical syndrome with a discrete neurophysiological cause. Certainly, the frequency and severity of episodic rage and temper outbursts may sometimes be dramatically reduced by anticonvulsants, particularly carbamazepine. Hence whatever the precise aetiology of episodic, uncharacteristic and minimally triggered violence, a trial of treatment with carbamazepine is often worth while, although the complex psychosocial factors leading to loss of temper must also be addresssed.

Treatment

The treatment of epilepsy aims at obtaining a seizure-free state using the minimum amount of medication. The current approach is to avoid polypharmacy, pushing a single drug to tolerance before introducing a second. Satisfactory control is obtained along these lines in 80% of patients.

Carbamazepine is generally favoured for all forms of seizure, apart from primary generalised absence, where sodium valproate is effective. The latter drug is also effective in other forms of generalised epilepsy. The other first-line drug is phenytoin.

Anticonvulsant drugs produce side-effects in a significant minority which may or may not be dose related. Phenytoin requires careful monitoring of serum level as the therapeutic range and the level at which toxicity occurs is clear. Drug levels are less useful for the other drugs, except in monitoring compliance. Second-line drugs include vigabatrin, clobazam, clonazepam and acetazolamide. Barbiturates are now only rarely used. A promising new anticonvulsant is lamotrigine, which has a novel glutamate antagonist action.

Differential diagnosis

The differential diagnosis of brief loss of consciousness or awareness includes syncope, cardiac dysrhythmia, basilar migraine or ischaemia, narcolepsy, hyperventilation and other anxiety syndromes, dissociative (hysterical) and feigned seizures. A careful history with corroboration is usually all that is needed to arrive at a final diagnosis. Before syncope the individual may feel generally unwell or nauseous, or the event may have an environmental trigger (the sight of blood, heat, sudden emotion, etc.) It is often immediately preceded by nausea, sweating, pallor, unsteadiness, loss of peripheral vision, and generally followed by nausea, vomiting, malaise, but not usually confusion. Cardiac dysrhythmias such as the Romano – Ward syndrome may be more difficult to distinguish and, if suspected, EEG or electrocardiographic monitoring is required. Narcolepsy is discussed below. Basilar migraine is typically associated with occipital headache and lethargy, and bulbar symptoms may occur.

Involuntary movement disorders

Movement arises through a complex interaction of the motor cortices, cerebellum, basal ganglia, lateral thalamus and subthalamus. The basal ganglia and thalamus are particularly concerned with the initiation and maintenance of movement, and the involuntary modulation of muscle tone. Dopamine plays an important role in the reduction of muscle tone, an effect modulated and opposed by cholinergic neurons. Damage or degeneration of the basal ganglia or thalami, or their connecting neurons, can lead to alterations in resting muscle tone, and abnormalities in the initiation and maintenance of voluntary movement. The principal syndromes associated with such damage are Parkinsonism, chorea, athetosis, and hemiballismus.

Parkinsonism

Parkinsonism denotes a syndrome comprising bradykinesia, hypertonia and tremor, but several other features frequently occur in association with this syndrome. These include dystonias, oculogyric crises, reduced facial expression and sialorrhea. Tremor is typically most marked at rest and exacerbated by anxiety and fatigue. Parkinsonism is due to degeneration, damage or malfunction in the nigrostriatal pathway. There are many possible causes. The commonest form is drug-induced, caused particularly by antipsychotic drugs with dopamine-blocking action. Post-encephalitic Parkinsonism occurs following encephalitis lethargica. Parkinson's disease is discussed below (p. 146).

An uncommon cause of early-onset Parkinsonism is Wilson's disease (hepatolenticular degeneration). This is a disorder of copper metabolism which leads to cirrhosis of the liver and degenerative changes in the basal ganglia and other brain areas. The disorder is important in psychiatry as over a quarter of affected individuals present with behavioural and psychiatric abnormalities, including intractable depression. Hence the diagnosis should be considered by the psychiatrist in severe, treatment-resistant depression with onset in teenage and the early 20s. The diagnosis is made by identifying a low serum caeruloplasmin level.

Dystonia

Dystonia is a syndrome involving sustained involuntary muscle contraction that generally causes twisting of the limbs or neck, or postural abnormality. Most patients with dystonic syndromes do not have structural lesions of the CNS, but in a minority there are abnormalities in the basal ganglia or thalamus. Dystonia affecting a whole side of the body – hemidystonia – is more likely to be associated with brain lesions of the contralateral hemisphere. Dystonias associated with demonstrable CNS lesions are classified as secondary, the commoner idiopathic varieties as primary.

Most dystonias are focal, involving one muscle group. The commonest are blepharospasm, torticollis, and writer's cramp. All of these are typically exacerbated by anxiety, tension, and fatigue. They are irresistible, but cease during sleep. Drug-induced acute dystonia is discussed below.

Blepharospasm

Blepharospasm is an adult-onset focal dystonia involving spasm of the orbicularis oculi and associated muscles, leading to forced eye closure. Most cases are idiopathic, although the syndrome has developed in association with Parkinsonism, demyelinating disease, and brainstem infarction. It has also been induced by a variety of drugs, including neuroleptics (as a form of tardive dyskinesia), L-DOPA, and nasal decongestants. Onset is usually in the fifth or sixth decade, with a male:female ratio of 1:2. Most are bilateral, exacerbated by bright lights, and improved by relaxation, yawning, singing and talking. Up to 75% have other dystonias, usually facial. Spontaneous improvement or remission occurs in only about 10%, and the syndrome can be extremely disabling and disfiguring; over half of sufferers are functionally blind.

Treatment is difficult. Only about one in five gain benefit from drugs, usually anticholinergics, or dopamine agonists or antagonists. Surgical treatments involving muscle stripping have been used, but the current favoured treatment for disabling blepharospasm is local injection with botulinum toxin, giving reported benefit in up to 70%, although the effect lasts for several months only.

Spasmodic torticollis

Spasmodic torticollis is the commonest focal dystonia. The term describes sudden contraction of the neck muscles leading to abnormal deviation of the head, forward, backward or, more commonly, to one side. The annual incidence is about 1/100 000 but remission occurs in only 20%. Drug treatment is effective in less than half. Anticholinergics, dopamine agonists and antagonists, benzodiazepines and a variety of antispasmodics have been used, with very limited success. Surgical treatments have also been attempted, but botulinum toxin injection to the most affected muscle is now favoured.

Writer's cramp

Writer's cramp is characterised by difficulty in controlling a pen, and caused by gripping too tightly or by sudden jerking of the hand. Similar problems have also been described in typists, pianists and violinists (and presumably can occur in other musicians). Treatment is similar to that for other dystonias, though surgical intervention has less often been resorted to.

Neuroleptic-induced movement disorders

Most of the drugs used to treat schizophrenia have a dopamine antagonist or receptor-blocking action. This produces a range of early and late side-effects, including acute dystonias, Parkinsonism, akathisia, tardive dyskinesias and the so-called 'neuroleptic malignant syndrome'.

Acute dystonia

Acute dystonia occurs most commonly following treatment with the most potent dopamine blockers with the least anticholinergic action (e.g. haloperidol). Varieties include oculogyric crises, blepharospasm, grimacing, twisting of the tongue, trismus, torticollis and truncal and limb dystonias. These usually develop 12 – 36 hours after administration of the drug and subsequently remit. The incidence is difficult to estimate but can be as high as 10% for high-potency neuroleptics.

Parenteral anticholinergics such as procyclidine provide the most effective and rapid relief of what can be a painful side-effect.

Parkinsonism

Parkinsonism is the commonest side-effect, occurring in 50% or more of people on antipsychotic doses of neuroleptics. The first feature to develop is usually a reduction in spontaneous movement of the limbs and face, leading to 'wooden' appearance, with no arm-swing on walking.

There is often spontaneous remission after several weeks or months. Oral anticholinergics are effective to some extent in treating the syndrome.

Akathisia

Akathisia literally means 'not sitting'. The term was initially used to describe anxiety-related restlessness but has come to denote motor restlessness which could follow basal ganglia damage or dysfunction (without accompanying anxiety). Affected individuals move consciously to relieve discomfort that arises in their limbs when they keep still. Treatment is less straightforward than for the previously described syndromes. Anticholinergics are frequently ineffective but β-adrenergic antagonist drugs such as propranolol are often more useful. The α-adrenergic antagonist clonidine has also been used.

Tardive dyskinesia

Tardive dyskinesia is a neuroleptic-induced late-onset movement disorder characterised by choreiform or athetoid movements of the face and mouth, and less frequently by limbs and trunk. The syndrome may develop from three months to several years after continuous treatment with neuroleptics, or on sudden withdrawal of the drugs. The disorder is commoner in women, the elderly, patients receiving concurrent anticholinergic therapy, and those with brain damage. The overall prevalence for people receiving long-term neuroleptic therapy is about 25%. In 80% of those affected, the dyskinesia is confined to the face and mouth usually tongue protrusion, lip-smacking/ pursing or grimacing.

Increasing the dose of neuroleptic, or the prescription of a more potent dopamine-blocking drug, produces a short-term improvement, and this has led to the suggestion that the syndrome, or syndromes, are caused by the development of supersensitive dopamine receptors. Several other neurochemicals have also been implicated however, and the precise mechanism is not yet known.

Numerous drugs have been used to treat the syndrome including benzodiazepines, α- and β-adrenergic blockers and presynaptic bioamine depletors (such as tetrabenazine). None has provided marked long-term relief, although modest improvements have been reported. When tardive dyskinesia is detected, the withdrawal of neuroleptics should be considered, but the possible benefits must be weighed against the risk of psychotic relapse. Reduction of dosage or withdrawal of neuroleptics causes an increase in severity in the short term, but in about half of cases improvement or complete resolution eventually follows.

Neuroleptic malignant syndrome

A syndrome of hyperpyrexia, muscle rigidity and confusion, sometimes leading to death, has been described as a rare side-effect of treatment with neuroleptics. The development of these features should lead to early treatment as lethal complications, including rhabdomyolysis and respiratory arrest, can rapidly develop. Dopamine agonists, such as bromocriptine, should be administered. Assisted ventilation and dialysis may also be required. Neuroleptics are subsequently contraindicated or should be used with great caution.

Dementia

Dementia may be defined as a global cognitive impairment which is generally slowly progressive and not, at least in the early stages, associated with clouding of consciousness. The latter is characteristic of delirium (see below).

Dementia most commonly presents as a progressive impairment of memory and ability to perform tasks of day-to-day living. These include the ability to learn and retrieve information, the exercise of language, and perceptuomotor and social skills. More complex human abilities related to the planning and regulation of behaviour are also compromised and may be the first signs of a progressive decline.

Skills can be viewed as cortical functions with recognised localisation. Hence progressive disorders that present as loss of various skills (the commonest being Alzheimer's disease) have been referred to as 'cortical dementias'. The effective exercise of everyday and more complex skills may, however, also be compromised by an impairment in the speed with which those skills are exercised. The ability, for example, to tie a shoelace is of little value if the operation takes several hours to perform. Similarly, the ability to store new information is of limited value if its retrieval takes minutes rather than seconds. This speed of processing is dependent upon intact subcortical structures, particularly the diencephalon and basal ganglia. Dementia of this type (e.g. in association with Huntington's disease or progressive supranuclear palsy) is referred to as 'subcortical' (Cummings, 1986). In practice, many disease processes affect both cortical and subcortical structures and so a mixed picture is not uncommon. The cortical/subcortical concept has been helpful in moving us away from simplistic notions of 'brain failure' and is valid, at least in the early and middle stages of these degenerative disorders.

In addition to cognitive impairments, dementing disorders may have other clinical features, including alterations in drive and motivation (agitation, abulia, stupor), affect (fatuousness, depression, irritability, fear, anger), sleep – wake cycle (insomnia or hypersomnia), appetite, and sexual behaviour. These can often be far more disturbing for carers than cognitive impairment. Patients with frontal lobe dementia present with personality change, particularly fatuousness and impaired judgement, and later progress to apathy and abulia. Forgetfulness and disinterest also develop as the disease progresses.

Pseudodementia is a disorder of higher function that is caused by a major depressive disorder, particularly where marked retardation is a feature. It is most likely to occur in the elderly, has a subcortical or mixed picture, and should be suspected where there is a history of major depression. Treatment is as for other forms of major depression. Further detail of particular dementing disorders is provided under 'Degenerative disorders' (p. 145).

Causes of dementia are given in Box 4.5.

Delirium/confusional states

Global mental impairment of acute onset, with or without clouding of consciousness, can occur either where brain metabolism and energy production are impaired (due to reduced oxygen or glucose supply, or enzymal dysfunction caused by toxins or vitamin deficiency), or by impairing attention and arousal. Arousal is a function of the brainstem and may be impaired by lesions or vascular dysfunction in that area, or by sedative drugs. Attention is in part dependent upon level of arousal but is otherwise difficult to localise. It has been observed, though, that right-hemisphere stroke is more commonly followed by a confusional state than left-hemisphere stroke, and this has led to the suggestion that the right hemisphere may be particularly important for attentional processes.

While impaired attention and disorientation are the common features of all confusional states, a number of other features may be present, particularly where the cause is toxic or related to alcohol withdrawal. These include fear, altered arousal (increased or decreased), agitation, illusions and hallucinations (particularly visual and often associated with a characteristic groping at the air or plucking of bed sheets). The principal causes of delirium are given in Box 4.6.

Amnesic states

Amnesic states are disorders in which cognitive impairment is restricted to the ability to learn and recall new information. Consciousness must be clear

Box 4.5 Causes of dementia

Cortical
  Alzheimer's disease
  Multi-infarct states
  Lewy body
  Mixed state (e.g. multi-infarct and Alzheimer's)
Subcortical
  Huntington's disease
  Progressive supranuclear palsy
  Parkinson's disease
  AIDS
Mixed (cortical and subcortical)
  Multi-infarct and other vascular
  Alcoholic and other toxic agents (e.g. heavy metals)
  Nutritional (e.g. B vitamin deficiencies)
  Endocrine (e.g. hypothyroidism)
  Infective (AIDS-related, syphilis, Creutzfeldt–Jakob disease)
  Storage and transport diseases (e.g. Kufs', Wilson's)
  Severe brain injury (trauma, anoxia, hypoglycaemia)
  Hydrocephalus
  Other causes of multiple cerebral lesions (e.g. demyelinating
    disease, metastatic neoplasm, systemic lupus erythematosus)
Frontal lobe
  Pick's disease
  Idiopathic (gliosis of unknown cause)
  Neoplastic (e.g. glioma, meningioma)

Box 4.6 Causes of delirium

Alcohol and minor tranquilliser withdrawal
Intoxication (e.g. drugs, solvents)
Systemic infection
Hypoglycaemia
Trauma
Epilepsy (complex partial or generalised absence status, or postictal)
Encephalitis
Meningitis
Hypoxia
Stroke (particularly involving the right hemisphere)
Poisoning (e.g. heavy metals)
Uraemia
Liver failure

and attention relatively unimpaired before a firm diagnosis can be made, as inattention and drowsiness impair all abilities, including memory.

Amnesic states arise where the hippocampus, fornix, mamillary bodies or medial thalamus are damaged or their function disrupted. Progressive memory disorder occurs most commonly in the context of dementia, and is often the first sign of Alzheimer's disease. Non-progressive causes of memory disorder include alcohol abuse, thiamine deficiency (the Wernicke – Korsakoff syndrome), trauma, herpes simplex encephalitis, anoxia and hypoglycaemia, and space-occupying lesions or other focal pathology such as thrombosis. Wernicke's encephalopathy, which is caused by acute and severe thiamine deficiency, is described on p. 207. The disorder often results in an enduring memory deficit, first described by Korsakoff. In Korsakoff's syndrome the immediate recall of learned information is intact but recall after a delay of three minutes or more is severely impaired. Another striking feature of the syndrome is confabulation, in which answers to questions are fabricated. Persistent and troublesome delusional beliefs may also develop.

Episodic or variable memory disorders, in the absence of confusion/delirium, raise the possibility of medial temporal lobe dysfunction, particularly epileptic.

Sleep disorders

The sleep – wake cycle is controlled through an interplay of systems in the brainstem and basal forebrain. Pathology in these structures, and the diencephalon, can produce a range of sleep disorders including insomnia, hypersomnia, brief sleep episodes, and inversion of the cycle.

Insomnia is usually functional – related to pain, worry, apprehension, depression or psychosis. In addition, up to half of insomniacs attending specialist sleep-disorder clinics with overnight monitoring facilities have been found to have normal sleep, but retain no sense of having slept. Insomnia may occur as a result of a variety of brain disorders but is perhaps particularly common in degenerative diseases, particularly Alzheimer's and other dementias.

Hypersomnia

The commonest form of hypersomnia is psychogenic, related to stress or adjustment difficulties.

Hypersomnia is a feature of the Kleine – Levin syndrome, with hyperphagia. This is an uncommon disorder affecting predominantly males under the age of 25. The patient sleeps for 20 hours or more each day, waking every few hours in a drowsy but intensely hungry state and consumes large quantities of food and sometimes non-food items. During these waking periods the individual may be confused or even appear psychotic. The episodes last for several days and then remit, to recur after an interval of several days or months. The disorder usually follows a viral illness or head injury and in most cases is self-limiting. The cause is unknown. Similar disorders have however been reported secondary to midbrain and diencephalic pathology.

Hypersomnia may occur as a result of sleep apnoea. This is usually obstructive in origin and occurs in obese people ('the Pickwickian syndrome') but may also occur in obstructive airways disease. Hypoxia develops shortly after the onset of sleep, leading to the recurrent waking. Hence the person feels perpetually tired and will attempt to sleep whenever possible, only to be awoken in seconds or minutes as hypoxia develops.

Less severe hypersomnia may occur during or following infection, after head injury or stroke, and through basal neoplasm. It is also associated with uraemia, liver failure, diabetes and major depression.

Narcolepsy and cataplexy

Narcolepsy is characterised by brief episodes of irresistible sleep (lasting 15 - 60 minutes), generally coming on when the person is relaxed. In its classic form the patient slips directly into rapid eye movement (REM) sleep. Onset is usually under the age of 30. Most cases are idiopathic, although one in three are familial, in which the DR2 type of human lymphocyte antigen appears to be characteristic.

Cataplexy is a sudden loss of muscle tone, often causing a fall to the ground, and generally triggered by a sudden emotion such as laughter. Narcolepsy and cataplexy may occur together, and with sleep paralysis or hypnogogic hallucinations (the tetrad is Gélineau's syndrome). The syndrome responds to amphetamine. Where cataplexy occurs alone clomipramine may be used. Initial investigation must exclude metabolic causes, structural brain lesion and epileptic disturbance.

Fatigue

Fatigue is one of the commonest complaints encountered in medical practice. The wide range of possible causes are presented in Box 4.7. There may be a distinction between physical and mental fatigue or fatiguability, but in practice it is often difficult to draw such a distinction as the two have similar effects upon activity. The neural systems that subserve physical and mental vitality have not been clearly identified, but it is presumed that the symptom arises through disruption of these systems by physical pathology or other stressors. Serious physical pathology is, however, identified in a minority of patients with fatigue. For the rest the symptom is generally regarded as a feature of functional disorders. The aetiological status of chronic fatigue which follows relatively minor physical illness is much disputed.

The chronic fatigue syndrome is essentially another name for neurasthenia, a descriptive term denoting persistent fatigue in association with a variety of other symptoms, including headache, poor concentration, irritability, anhedonia, myalgia and others. Chronic fatigue may follow or accompany an

---

Box 4.7 Causes of chronic fatigue

Infection (tuberculosis, brucellosis, infectious mononucleosis, hepatitis, etc.)
Vascular disease (heart failure, following myocardial infarction, stroke)
Respiratory (chronic obstructive airways disease, or any cause leading to hypoxia/hypercapnia)
Endocrine (hypothyroidism, Addison's disease, Cushing's disease, hypogonadism)
Haematological (anaemia)
Trauma (following head injury of any severity)
Muscle disease (myasthenia gravis)
Nutritional (B group and other vitamin deficiencies, general malnutrition)
Neoplastic (metastatic disease, or cerebral neoplasm)
Metabolic (diabetes mellitus, uraemia, liver failure)
Toxic (alcohol dependence, heavy metals, industrial solvents/hydrocarbons)
Degenerative/demyelinating disease (multiple sclerosis, Parkinson's disease)
Collagen disease (rheumatoid arthritis)
Affective disorder (major depression)
Idiopathic (neurasthenia, exhaustion)

---

infection or exhaustion, or arise from continued emotional stress. The fact that the condition (or conditions) may be initiated by physical and psychological factors is worthy of note.

The contribution of viral infection in the causation of chronic fatigue has been a focus of much recent investigation. The prominence of myalgia in some cases of postviral fatigue has led to the coining of a new term for this condition, 'myalgic encephalomyelitis' (ME). To date no virus or group of viruses has been found to be responsible for chronic fatigue/ME, other than in a small proportion of patients. The recent public debate on ME has however underlined the disheartening fact that 'organic' causation continues to be seen as respectable while 'psychological' causation is stigmatising, no matter that the final common neurophysiological pathways may be identical.

The single most important treatable cause or sometimes consequence of chronic fatigue is major depressive disorder. In the absence of depression the treatment of disabling idiopathic fatigue is difficult, and all that can be said at this point is that an approach which gradually but firmly encourages activity is better than one which emphasises rest (David *et al*, 1991).

Dizziness/giddiness

Balance and the maintenance of an upright posture is dependent upon the function of the semicircular canal, VIII cranial nerve, vestibular nucleus and cerebellum. The higher perception of postural stability is not so clearly localisable and may be impaired by anxiety.

Giddiness and dizziness are common complaints in psychiatric practice but organic causes can usually be identified in the history. Examination is more valuable in localising the site of causal pathology. The following are guidelines rather than absolute criteria which may help in distinguishing organic from functional giddiness/dizziness:

(1) neurological
    (a) including the experience of rotation
    (b) induced by postural change
    (c) induced by movement
    (d) associated with nystagmus

(2) functional
    (a) constant or situational
    (b) vague sense of disequilibrium
    (c) sensation of the floor coming up to meet you
    (d) associated with depersonalisation
    (e) associated with somatic anxiety.

Examination should seek to identify signs of cerebellar and vestibular dysfunction. Hyperventilation and benzodiazepine withdrawal may lead to or exacerbate functional variants.

Developmental disorders of the CNS

Optimum function across the range of human skills and emotions is dependent upon an intact and correctly developed nervous system. The development of the CNS of the embryo and foetus can be disrupted by many agents and influences:

(1) chromosomal defect
(2) radiation
(3) placental insufficiency
(4) microcephaly
(5) drugs
(6) alcohol
(7) storage and transport diseases (e.g. phenylketonuria)
(8) infections (e.g. rubella, cytomegalovirus)
(9) others.

The most vulnerable period is the first 12 weeks after conception, the period in which the neural tube differentiates and neuronal proliferation and migration occur. Maldevelopment due to genetic or environmental causes (Table 4.3) can have a profound effect on the individual and the family that extends throughout life. Such maldevelopment is remarkably common, being present in about 1% of babies. In addition, 2 – 3% of children show significant learning disability. The commonest CNS disorders at birth are Down's syndrome and spina bifida.

Maldevelopment or early damage can lead to failure to acquire cortically based skills, which can give rise to a generalised learning disability or specific learning problems (language or numerical difficulties, etc.). Developmental dyslexia is a specific learning disorder of the ability to read, write and spell.

Chromosomal abnormalities

The principal chromosomal abnormalities that affect the nervous system are listed in Table 4.4. Down's and fragile X syndromes are the commonest causes of general learning disability (mental handicap). Fragile X occurs in 1 in 1000 men and 1 in 2500 women. Dominant transmission of the affected gene occurs and female carriers have been found to suffer more schizophrenia-like disorders than the general population. By contrast, almost half of affected males exhibit features of infantile autism or other pervasive developmental disorder. Infantile autism is a pervasive developmental disorder characterised by a failure to develop language and social interactional skills, with impaired emotional response and the development of repetitive ritualistic behaviour.

Table 4.3   Congenital disorders of the central nervous system

Classification	Examples
Disorders	
Neural tube defects	Spina bifida, encephalocele, meningocele, Chiari malformation, spinal dysraphism
Cerebral hemisphere disorganisation	Corpus callosum defects, holoprosencephaly
Cerebral cortex dysplasia	Heterotopia of grey matter, lissencephaly, schizencephaly
Destructive lesions	Porencephaly, hydranencephaly, acquired processes such as birth infarcts
Phakomatoses	Tuberous sclerosis, Sturge – Weber disease, the various forms of neurofibromatosis
Vascular lesions	Arteriovenous malformations, aneurysms
Genetic disorders	Down's syndrome, fragile X syndrome

Table 4.4 Chromosomal abnormalities associated
with maldevelopment of the CNS

Abnormalities	Manifestation
Trisomies (extra limb)	
21	Down's syndrome
22	Varies. IQ may be normal. Features that may occur include anal atresia, congenital heart disease, cleft palate
9p	Learning disability, short stature, microcephaly, hyperteliorism, prominent nasal bridge, small fingers
8 mosaic	Hypertelorism, high arched palate, absent patellae, congenital heart disease, agenesis of the corpus callosum
Deletions	
5p	'Cri du chat' syndrome. Profound learning disability with occasional milder forms, mewing cry, short stature, microcephaly, wide nasal bridge, congenital heart defects
18p/q	Profound learning disability, range of facial and genital malformations
Prader - Willi syndrome (possibly 15 deletion)	Infantile hypotonia, learning disability, short stature, small hands and feet, obesity, hypoplastic genitalia, hyperphagia and obesity
Fragile X	Learning disability, and pervasive developmental disorder, high forehead, prominent ears, large mandible and testes, sometimes broad-based gait
Sex chromosomes	
X	Turner's syndrome. Failure of sexual development at puberty
XXY	Klinefelter's syndrome. Apathy, fatigue, specific learning problems

Congenital disorders and malformations

There are a number of idiopathic disorders and malformations of the central
nervous system. The principal abnormalities are listed in Table 4.5.

Table 4.5   The principal congenital malformations of the CNS

Malformations	Abnormality
Cerebellar malformations	
Arnold – Chiari	Downward elongation of brainstem and cerebellum. Hydrocephalus and ataxia
Dandy – Walker	Atresia of foramina of Luschka and Magendie. Hydrocephalus
Complex malformations	
Aicardi	Agenesis of corpus callosum, epilepsy, severe mental handicap, retinal pigmentation
De Lange	Severe mental handicap, self-mutilating behaviour
Other malformations/abnormalities	
Agenesis of the corpus callosum	
Tuberous sclerosis (Bourneville's disease)	Tuber-like astrocytic lesions in the CNS leading to epilepsy and variable mental handicap
Encephalofacial angiomatosis (Sturge – Weber syndrome)	Facial naevi, epilepsy, intracranial angioma, mental handicap
von Hippel – Lindau disease	Retinal and cerebellar angioma leading to raised intracranial pressure
Generalised neurofibromatosis (von Recklinghausen's syndrome)	Multiple neurofibromas. Lead nerve root, cord or cerebellar compression and epilepsy

Foetal alcohol syndrome

Alcohol abuse in pregnancy leads to low birth weight and a range of congenital malformations involving the CNS, heart, skull, and other structures. The current recommendation is to keep alcohol intake to a minimum during pregnancy. The CNS abnormalities include porencephaly and agenesis of the corpus callosum. Spinal dysraphism can also occur.

Cerebral palsy

Cerebral palsy refers to a non-progressive and predominantly motor disorder that arises through damage or maldevelopment of the brain before or at birth. The motor disorder may be unilateral or bilateral spasticity, dyskinetic (usually athetotic), ataxic or a combination. About 2 per 1000 babies who survive infancy have cerebral palsy. Foetal cerebral lesions can have many causes. The most vulnerable are infants born prematurely, particularly when there has been foetal distress. Aetiological factors relevant to full-term births include anoxic or mechanical damage, the latter leading to haemorrhage from meningeal or cerebral vessels. Other causes include perinatal meningitis and kernicterus. Cerebral infection or trauma in infancy are later causes.

In addition to these well recognised causes there remain a significant number in whom the cause is unknown. The commonest clinical picture is spastic hemiplegia and about half have learning disabilities in addition. Epilepsy is also common. Athetotic cerebral palsy is most commonly related to kernicterus and cerebral hypoxia. Dysarthric speech is common and may mask normal or near-normal intellect.

Spina bifida

Spina bifida and anencephaly are defects in the intrauterine development of the neural tube. Minor neural tube abnormalities are thought to be present in up to 5% of the population without neurological deficit, but in more severe cases meningeal protrusions occur through a malformed vertebral column, with varying degrees of exposure and tethering of nerve roots. In the most severe form, anencephaly, the cerebral hemispheres fail to develop and the diencephalon is left exposed. Differentiation and closure of the neural tube occurs 18 – 26 days after conception. The cause of maldevelopment in most cases of spina bifida is unknown. Monozygotic twins may be discordant, but recurrence in a second baby is 1 in 20. The incidence varies considerably around the world, and even in different areas in the UK the rate is between 3 and 8 per 1000 births. Foetal ultrasound and amniotic fluid alphafetoprotein assay can identify 90% of serious neural tube defects *in utero*.

Trauma

Head injury

Head injury is common, and survival after severe head injury more common than ever before. Most head injuries are 'closed', that is, the skull and meninges are not breached, but powerful deceleration leads to contusion to the surface of the brain, and stretching and snapping of axons and blood vessels. When severe this leads to extensive capillary leakage, leading to cerebral oedema, increasing intracranial pressure, reduced cerebral perfusion, anoxia, and eventual respiratory arrest. Intracranial haemorrhage can lead to similar effects but sometimes over a longer period. Damage to the thoracic cage, shock, and fat embolism can compound the process. Meningitis can occur following open injury, or if the sinuses are breached.

These often fatal processes can now be modified to varying degrees using a number of techniques to reduce cerebral oedema and haemorrhage. The result is an increasing number of survivors, each having a unique patchwork of mechanical haemorrhagic, embolic, inflammatory and anoxic damage. The areas most vulnerable to contusion are the frontal and temporal poles, the base of the brain, and brainstem. The most common and enduring sequelae of head trauma are therefore behavioural and psychiatric.

Over 1% of the population of the UK attend hospital accident departments each year as a result of head injury. Most of these are considered minor; trauma did not lead to, or produced only a brief period of, unconsciousness. Over 90% are oriented on initial assessment and have suffered no skull fracture. Few are admitted to hospital, and most of these are not followed up after discharge. Patients who are not admitted are traditionally given written instructions to return if certain symptoms arise (those that suggest that intracranial haemorrhage is occurring) though the risk of intracranial haemorrhage in the absence of skull fracture is slight. Where a skull fracture has occurred and the patient is disoriented the risk is much greater, hence the need for in-patient observation.

Having had a previous head injury, being male, aged between 16 and 25, drinking alcohol in excess, and being a poor educational achiever increase the individual risk of injury. The more severe the injury (as judged by the duration of coma and post-traumatic amnesia) the greater the risk of residual disability. It has been estimated, on the basis of population surveys, that the prevalence of such disability in the general population is over 50/100 000. The prevalence is increasing, as more people are surviving the severest injuries and in these life expectancy is not dramatically reduced. The effects of repeated minor head injury are cumulative, as evidenced by studies of professional boxers, who may suffer damage to subcortical structures even if they have never been knocked out.

In patients who suffer a prolonged period of unconsciousness the depth and duration of coma, and the duration of post-traumatic amnesia (PTA) (the time from injury to the point at which the individual is aware continuously of where he/she is, what has happened, and can store sequential memories – i.e. is 'making sense of things'), give an indication of the likely severity of the resulting disability. Coma may be assessed using the Glasgow Coma Scale (Teasdale & Jennett, 1974) which records the best verbal, motor and pupillary response throughout the period of unconsciousness. Post-traumatic amnesia of less than 24 hours will generally result in mild sequelae; of one to seven days moderate sequelae; of 7 – 21 days severe sequelae (significant persisting disability); and of over 21 days very severe sequelae. There are though exceptions to this. Relatively mild trauma can lead to disabling and persistent postconcussive symptoms, and some patients who experience very long coma can make remarkable recoveries.

Late deterioration may occur from several weeks to several years after injury, and this is characterised by decline in cognitive function and motivation. The commonest causes of such deterioration are:

(1) subdural haematoma
(2) hydrocephalus

(3) epilepsy
(4) affective disorder
(5) schizophreniform psychosis
(6) progressive encephalopathy.

Postconcussion syndrome

Head injury which leads to unconsciousness and confusion lasting less than one hour rarely leads to marked, persistent cognitive deficits. Some symptoms after such injury are however almost invariable. Such 'postconcussive' symptoms usually resolve within six months, but in a significant minority some symptoms will persist for a year, and occasionally for very long periods, with considerable disablement. Headache, fatigue, dizziness, irritability, impaired concentration and anxiety are the commonest symptoms. While premorbid personality has some influence on the development of chronicity, up to 40% of such individuals have been found to have slowed brainstem evoked potentials, and it is known that relatively minor trauma can produce axonal damage (Montgomery *et al*, 1991). Hence the aetiology is likely to be multifactorial. Treatment is predominantly symptomatic and antidepressants may be required in some cases.

Degenerative disorders

Alzheimer's disease

Alzheimer's disease is a degenerative disorder of the CNS characterised by a progressive amnesic syndrome and loss of parietal and frontally based skills.

The characteristic pathology includes cerebral atrophy, neurofibrillary tangles, β-amyloid-containing plaques, and gliosis. The cortex, hippocampus and amygdala are the most affected. Degeneration of cholinergic neurons is pronounced.

The disease is commonest in the seventh and eighth decades, but can develop from the fourth decade onwards, with the highest prevalence in people aged over 85 years. It is unknown whether the neuropathology represents the end of a single or several different disease processes. Some cases are familial, the deficit arising from chromosome 21. There is a much higher incidence of the disorder in Down's syndrome (trisomy 21). Early-onset cases are generally more rapidly progressive. Other than familial cases, the aetiology is unknown. Recent interest has focused upon the role of environmental aluminium: amyloid plaques contain relatively high levels of aluminium and the metal is known to be neurotoxic, though the characteristic neuropathology which follows high-dose exposure is not identical to that seen in Alzheimer's disease. While epidemiological evidence, based on local levels of aluminium in drinking water, have suggested a relationship, a causal role is yet to be proven (*Lancet*, 1989). Head injury has also been implicated in the aetiology of Alzheimer's disease, and may at least lower the age of onset (van Duijn *et al*, 1992).

The clinical features of Alzheimer's disease are those of a cortical dementia. In addition to a progressive memory disorder and loss of skills which depend upon intact parietal lobe function, social skills also deteriorate, and there is a decline in drive, initiative and intellect. Emotional changes and responses range from profound depression, anxiety or aggression in the early stages to emotional lability, blunting or unconcern as the disease progresses. Severe agitation and impairment in the sleep – wake cycle are common in the later stages.

There is as yet no treatment of the degenerative process as such, but relief of particular symptoms is often possible. Agitation and sleep disturbance may be managed with major tranquillisers. In the early stages selegiline may improve alertness and concentration, and antidepressants may be indicated, particularly where insight is retained. Various cholinergic strategies have been tried, most with disappointing results. Some limited benefit has been found with the acetyl cholinesterase inhibitor tacrine, although liver toxicity has been reported to occur in up to 40%, and this has delayed the drug's licence for general use.

Caring for a loved one with such a devastating disorder is emotionally and physically draining, and day care, respite care, and other home support is important. Life expectancy must depend upon the age at onset. Although early-onset cases appear to progress more rapidly, the resulting infant-like dependency can continue for many years if general health is sound.

Pick's disease and other frontal lobe dementias

In these conditions dementia is characterised by a marked reduction in drive, motivation and judgement, with marked personality change in the absence of the more characteristic parietal features. It arises through the selective degeneration of the frontal and anterior temporal lobes, and has recently been named frontal lobe dementia (FLD). Pick described such a disorder at the beginning of the century, in which the characteristic pathology was marked frontal and anterior temporal cortical atrophy with associated 'balloon cells'. One in ten cases are familial and onset is usually in the fifth decade. Women are affected twice as often as men. FLD associated with the characteristic pathology of Pick's disease is uncommon. FLD is more commonly associated with non-specific but local gliosis. The cause is unknown (Orrell & Sahakian, 1991).

Parkinson's disease

Parkinson's disease is a familial disorder with an autosomal dominant transmission, the syndrome developing in about a quarter of carriers. The mean age of onset is 55, but the course of the disorder varies considerably between affected individuals and this has led to speculation that environmental factors may be contributory. Severe disability or death occurs in about 25%

after five years. The disorder arises through the degeneration of the substantia nigra, the course of dopaminergic input to the basal ganglia. An increased sensitivity to free radicals may be important aetiologically, and free-radical scavengers are currently being studied as potential therapeutic agents (Olanow & Lieberman, 1991).

Parkinsonism developing after the age of 60 is generally considered to be atherosclerotic in origin, presumed to be caused by infarction within the basal ganglia. Psychiatric features are common in people with the disease, particularly depressive disorders. Cognitive impairment also occurs, progressing to dementia in some, the prevalence increasing with age. This appears to be associated with the concentration of 'lewy bodies' in the brain. Also, all anti-Parkinsonian drugs have been associated with the development of a variety of psychiatric side-effects, particularly psychotic and hallucinatory disorders.

Findings on physical examination include cogwheel-like muscle tone, unilateral or bilateral tremor, typically at a frequency of 5 Hz. Movements and responses are delayed in initiation and performance and the gait is characterised by short, rapid, unsteady steps. An unchanging and blank facial expression is also characteristic.

Treatment is with anticholinergics such as benzhexol, L-DOPA and dopamine agonists such as bromocriptine and lysuride. Selegiline has also been used to enhance the effects of dopamine agonists. The surgical implantation of foetal brain cells in the basal ganglia is currently being explored.

Huntington's disease

This is a familial disorder with autosomal dominant transmission and complete penetrance. The prevalence is approximately 5 - 8 per 100 000. Onset is usually in the third or fourth decades, although earlier-onset and later-onset cases occur. The initial presentation is often psychiatric, usually personality change, affective or schizophreniform disorders. Choreiform movements are initially slight but become more pronounced as the disease progresses, affecting the limbs, head and neck, and trunk. Dysarthria is common, as is dysphagia in the later stages. Facial expression is typically blank. Continual movement leads to profound weight loss. Blunting of drive and a global impairment of cognition, a 'subcortical' dementia, occurs.

Diagnosis is based upon the typical clinical and family history. Atrophy of the head of the caudate nucleus is a characteristic, but not invariable, finding on CT scan.

Chromosome 4 has been identified as the site of the gene, and the area responsible has recently been discovered (Harper, 1993).

Symptomatic treatment of Huntington's disease is possible with tetrabenazine and dopamine blockers such as haloperidol. Psychiatric features may be treated with appropriate psychotropics. Calorie supplements are almost always required to compensate for weight loss. The fact that the clinical onset of the disease usually does not occur until the patient is 30 years of age or more means that many sufferers have children, and the family's distress at the implications of the diagnosis is often considerable and ongoing. Where several affected family members are available, predictive testing is possible, using recombinant DNA techniques.

Motor neuron disease

Motor neuron disease, or amyotrophic lateral sclerosis, is a degenerative disorder which almost exclusively affects motor neurons in the spinal cord, brainstem and motor cortex. The annual incidence is approximately 1/100 000 and prevalence 4/100 000. The peak age of incidence is in the sixth decade and the condition is rare under the age of 50. Men are affected slightly more than women, and 1 in 20 cases are familial, with dominant transmission. The course is almost invariably progressive, with only 20% survival at five years.

The commonest presenting features are weakness and wasting of the hands associated with fasciculation. Muscle wasting, with heightened tendon reflexes, is characteristic. Bulbar forms present with dysarthria, but dysphagia develops later. Affective lability is also common, as are wasting and fasciculation of the tongue. Frontal release signs develop late in the course of the illness. There is also evidence that cognitive decline may occur late in the disease in a minority of patients.

Management is generally directed at helping adaptation to progressive disability. The differential diagnosis includes spinal cord compression and inflammation, and Creutzfeldt – Jakob disease, which can present with muscle wasting and cognitive decline and should be considered where onset and subsequent deterioration is very rapid.

Demyelinating disease

The annual incidence of multiple sclerosis (MS) in Europe and North America is approximately 10 per 100 000 per year in the 20 – 50-year age group, with half or less that incidence in Japan and Australasia. This topographical variation is thought to indicate that there is an important environmental contribution to the aetiology of the disorder, a slow virus being one possibility. Women are affected approximately twice as often as men and the condition develops very rarely in childhood or after the age of 50. The disorder is to some extent familial; near-relatives of MS patients are said to be up to ten times more likely to develop the disorder than the general population.

The commonest presenting features include unilateral visual loss (due to retrobulbar neuritis), transient diplopia, paraesthesia or paresis, and urgency of micturition. Beyond this the range of possible clinical features is large and diverse. These can be motor, sensory, bulbar, cognitive or behavioural. Optic neuritis, which occurs at some stage in the illness in almost half of patients, presents as total or partial loss of vision, generally in one eye, often associated with pain on eye movement. Trigeminal neuralgia can occur and MS must be considered where this develops in younger patients. Severe pains, like electric shocks, down the spine are a characteristic later feature. Other common features include persistent fatigue and depression, although euphoria may occur in the later stages, usually in association with marked cognitive and intellectual decline. Confusional states may develop late in the disease but usually arise from complicating skin or urinary-tract infection. Epileptic seizures of any type may occur.

The course is usually one of repeated attacks of varying frequency and duration manifest by varying symptoms and signs. In a quarter of cases the course is slowly progressive. Very rapidly progressive cases, with death in weeks or months, are rare; 80% of sufferers are alive at 10 years after diagnosis, 30% with little or no disability.

Diagnosis is based on the characteristic natural history and investigation. Examination of CSF reveals raised oligoclonal immunoglobulin G, and visual evoked potentials show prolonged latencies in up to 80% of cases. The differential diagnosis includes occlusive and other diseases of the eye, spinal cord and other focal brain lesions.

Treatment of the acute attack is with adrenocorticotrophic hormone, with benzodiazepines and baclofen for spasticity. The prevention of pressure sores and urinary tract infections is a therapeutic challenge in the later stages of the disease.

Acknowledgements

The author acknowledges the valuable comments of the editors and two colleagues who read the manuscript, Drs William Barker and Michael Jorsh.

References

Commission of Classification and Terminology of International League Against Epilepsy (1981) Proposal for revised clinical and electroencephalographic classification of epileptic seizures. *Epilepsia*, **22**, 489 – 501.

Cummings, J. L. (1986) Subcortical dementia. *British Journal of Psychiatry*, **149**, 682 – 697.

David, A. S., Wessely, S. & Pelosi, A. J. (1991) Chronic fatigue syndrome: signs of a new approach. *British Journal of Hospital Medicine*, **45**, 158 – 163.

Denny-Brown, D. (1982) *Handbook of Neurological Examination and Case Recording*. Cambridge: Harvard University Press.

Lancet (1989) Aluminium in Alzheimer's disease. *Lancet*, *i*, 82 – 83.

Fontaine, R., Breton, G., Dery, R., *et al* (1990) Temporal lobe abnormalities in panic disorder: an MRI study. *Biological Psychiatry*, **27**, 304 – 310.

Harper, P. S. (1993) Clinical consequences of isolating the gene for Huntington's disease. *British Medical Journal*, **307**, 397–398.

Harrison, P. G. & Roberts, G. W. (1992) "Life, Jim, but not as we know it"? Transmissible dementia and the prion protein. *British Journal of Psychiatry*, **158**, 457 – 470.

Montgomery, A., Fenton, G. W., McClelland, R. J., *et al* (1991) The psychobiology of minor head injury. *Psychological Medicine*, **21**, 375–384.

Neary, D., Snowden, J. S., Northern, B., *et al* (1988) Dementia of frontal lobe type. *Journal of Neurology, Neurosurgery and Psychiatry*, **51**, 353 - 361.

Olanow, C. & Lieberman, A. (eds) (1991) The scientific basis for the treatment of Parkinson's disease. Carnforth: Parthenon.

Orrell, M. W. & Sahakian, B. J. (1991) Dementia of the frontal lobe type. *Psychological Medicine*, **21**, 553-556.

Strub, R. L. & Black, F. W. (1985) *The Mental Status Examination in Neurology* (2nd edn). Philadelphia: F.A. Dixon.

Teasdale, G. & Jennett, B. (1974) Assessment of coma and impaired consciousness: a practical scale. *Lancet*, *ii*, 81 - 84.

van Duijn, C. M., Tanja, T. A., *et al* (1992) Head trauma and the risk of Alzheimer's disease. *American Journal of Epidemiology*, **135**, 775-782.

Waterman, K., Purves, S. J., Kosaka, B., *et al* (1985) An epileptic syndrome caused by mesial frontal lobe seizure foci. *Neurology*, **37**, 577 - 581.

Further reading

The following texts are recommended for further reading on topics covered in this chapter.

Albert, M. L., Goodglass, H., Helms, N. A. *et al* (1981) *Clinical Aspects of the Dysphasias*. New York, Springer-Verlag.

Anderson, W. W. (ed.) (1991) *Neuroepidemiology*. Boston: CLC Press.

Brooks, N. (ed.) (1984) *Closed Head Injury. Psychological, Social and Family Consequences*. Oxford: Oxford University Press.

Denny-Brown, D. (1982) *Handbook of Neurological Examination and Case Recording*. Cambridge: Harvard University Press.

Gardner-Medwin, D. (1987) Developmental abnormalities of the central nervous system. In *Oxford Textbook of Medicine* (2nd edn). (eds D. J. Weatherall, T. G. G. Ledingham & D. A. Warrell). Oxford: Oxford University Press

Harding, A. E. (1988) Molecular genetics and neurological disease. In *Recent Advances in Clinical Neurology, No. 4* (ed. C. Kennard). London: Churchill Livingstone.

Kandel, E. R. & Schwartz, J. H. (eds) (1986) *Pinciples of Neural Science* (2nd edn). Philadelphia: Elsevier/North Holland.

Laidlaw, J. A., Richens, A. & Oxley, J. (1988) *A Textbook of Epilepsy* (3rd edn). Edinburgh: Churchill Livingstone.

Lishman W. A. (1987) *Organic Psychiatry* (2nd edn). Oxford: Blackwell Scientific.

Mesulam, M. M. (ed.) (1985) *Principles of Behavioural Neurology*. Philadelphia: F. A. Davis.

Parkes, J. D. (1985) *Sleep and Its Disorders*. London: Saunders.

Quinn N. P. & Jenner, P. G., (eds) (1989) *Disorders of Movement*. London: Academic Press.

Strub, R. L. & Black, F. W. (1985) *The Mental Status Examination in Neurology* (2nd edn). Philadelphia: F. A. Dixon.

5 Neuropsychology
Stephen Hallett

Neuropsychology and psychiatry ● History of neuropsychology ●
The process of neuropsychological assessment ● Neuropsychological
testing in clinical practice ● Testing of patients with psychiatric disorders ●
Testing of patients with neurological and neurosurgical conditions ●
Neuropsychological rehabilitation ● Conclusions

Neuropsychology can be defined as the study of the relationship between brain structure and behaviour. As an experimental science, it bridges the disciplines of neurology and experimental psychology and seeks to understand how behaviour, emotion, cognition and perception may be related to, and underpinned by, the chemical, electrophysiological, anatomical and integrative functions of the central nervous system (CNS). Neuropsychology itself may be subdivided into subdisciplines.

Experimental neuropsychology is concerned with the purely academic aim of analysing the intricate relationships between normal brain structure and action, and is, perhaps, interested in the clinical effects of brain damage to the extent that studies of individuals with definable organic impairment may throw light on normal brain processes.

Cognitive neuropsychology seeks to understand the neuroanatomical and neurofunctional correlates of discrete cognitive processes and to analyse the microprocesses involved in everyday cognitive functions. It differs from experimental neuropsychology in its overt aim of dividing large-scale cognitive functions into ever smaller levels of processing, and it draws heavily on in-depth analyses of case studies of individuals with well defined CNS lesions.

Clinical neuropsychology has, as its broad aim, the assessment and rehabilitation of people with disturbed function consequent upon brain injury, illness or trauma.

While distinctions between these broad subdisciplines are not absolutely clear-cut, the focus of this chapter is on the methods of clinical neuropsychology.

Neuropsychology and psychiatry

Neuropsychology and psychiatry are both fundamentally concerned with the effects of alteration in cognition and emotion. In practice, neuropsychology is generally thought to be only concerned with services to brain-damaged people, while in principle it is applicable to all phenomena which result in alterations in mental function.

At both a theoretical and a clinical level, neuropsychology complements psychiatry by virtue of the clear observation that psychopathology, almost by definition, results in disturbance of cognition, emotion and behaviour.

Methodologically, neuropsychology offers a robust system for the measurement and quantification of cognitive function, emotional state and behavioural repertoire through standardised testing, questionnaire and observation, and it can therefore be used as a complementary system of analysis to psychiatry in the documentation and understanding of psychopathology. While it is not an alternative to psychiatric examination, neuropsychological assessment may prove useful as an aid to psychiatric diagnosis, appropriate placement, and in therapy and rehabilitation.

Furthermore, neuropsychology and psychiatry may be seen as complementary in the field of neuropsychiatry, which is broadly concerned with the understanding and treatment of psychological disturbance as a direct consequence of CNS trauma, injury or disease.

The methods of neuropsychology and psychiatry are clearly quite different, and the initial emphasis of this chapter is to understand the nature of neuropsychological methods. To understand this in context, however, it is necessary first to review briefly the historic antecedents of modern neuropsychology.

History of neuropsychology

Neuropsychology has its origin as far back as the early to mid-19th century and is exemplified by studies such as those of Broca, Wernicke and Dax, who observed a clear relationship between specific disturbances of language and loss of tissue at discrete sites in the CNS. We still think of language disturbances (that is, the aphasias) as distinct entities associated with localisable brain damage, for example Broca's aphasia associated with lesions of the third frontal convolution of the dominant (usually left) hemisphere. The approach and studies of such individuals led to the fashionable view that most, if not all, cognitive functions could be clearly localised to discrete cortical tissue.

This 'localisationist' view of brain function still influences current theoretical views and clinical practice in its endeavour to assess brain damage. This paradigm is evident in the structure and interpretational guidelines of most clinical test batteries in common use to detect the presence and nature of brain damage (the Halstead–Reitan Battery (HRNB), the Wechsler Scales of Intelligence and Memory, Raven's matrices, etc.) (Incagnoli *et al*, 1986).

Batteries such as the Halstead–Reitan have their genesis at theoretical level (that is determining the key cortical sites responsible for intelligence) and practical level (namely assessing the impact of penetrating missile wounds on the individual). This battery stands as a representative of the psychometric tradition in neuropsychology, an approach which may be seen to have a number of specific elements.

(1) Tests or test items are administered in an inflexible and rigid fashion to standardise administration across subjects and examiners. Thus the format of the test and the instructions and questions are expected to be rigidly adhered to.

(2) The results of each test or item (be this verbal, written, or drawn) are scored according to specific criteria.

(3) The overall results of a test are interpreted in two specific ways:

    (a) by recourse to overall population statistics which provide cut-off points or ranges of ability (i.e. normative data derived from a range of clinical populations such as normal versus brain damaged; right versus left frontal damage)

    (b) by, in some instances, comparing intra-individual variability across test procedures or subtests to determine whether the variability is normal or abnormal.

This approach additionally permeates research into the differences in cognitive, sensory, motor and perceptual function between the right and left cerebral hemispheres.

This is not to imply that the localisation of brain function or dysfunction is misguided, since there are statistically and clinically determined relationships between specific cognitive disturbances and damage to discrete cortical and subcortical areas. Where, perhaps, such an approach has its limitations is in its attempt to 'locate' complex cognitions, such as reasoning and abstraction, to single sites of action while ignoring the possibility that such complexity is likely to reflect integrated function across separate processing sites. This integrational approach to brain–behaviour relationships is best exemplified by the approach of the pre-eminent Soviet neuropsychologist, A. R. Luria (1966).

Luria's model is essentially three-dimensional in that, more explicitly than other approaches, it acknowledges the interaction between cortical and subcortical systems. It additionally relies on the concept of functional systems. Thus Luria envisaged that complex processes arise from the concerted and integrated action of separate and autonomous cortical and subcortical processing sites. Thus, for example, language comprehension may be viewed as a complex interaction of more discrete cognitive faculties such as phoneme and grapheme discrimination, visuoperceptual and auditory-perceptual function, syntactic manipulation, semantic processing and recognition and recall abilities. Each cognitive process may reflect the operation of autonomous and encapsulated processing units. When, however, their action is integrated in a related and concerted fashion, the functional result is that of language comprehension. This integrated action of independent units constitutes the functional system.

Accordingly, the understanding of cognitive processes and their dysfunction relies on analysis of individual processing units, the networked actions of such units, and the nature of communication between such units.

Clinically, these two approaches give rise to very different methods for determining the integrity of brain function. On the one hand, therefore, clinical neuropsychology uses highly standardised or psychometric procedures (such as the revised Wechsler Adult Intelligence Scale (WAIS - R) and Wechsler Memory Scale (WMS-R)) whereby the administration and scoring of tests is a structured, inflexible process. The interpretation of such tests is, almost without exception, based upon normative statistical data and hence a statistical process of analysing a person's ability against population norms. On the other hand, the approach expounded by Luria results in an idiosyncratic and flexible administration of procedures designed to assess specific cognitive processes. Test items may be modified or manipulated by the examiner to determine the individual's strengths and weaknesses, and there is a greater emphasis on *how* people approach the task and *why* they fail, rather than just whether or not they fail. Test results are not necessarily interpreted on the basis of quantifiable scores but more qualitatively, and the interpretation ultimately reflects the skill of the examiner and his/her approach to, or model of, brain function. This latter point emphasises that neuropsychological tests do *not*, of themselves, measure brain function or damage. Rather they measure aspects of cognitive function which are *interpreted* in relation to models of brain function and damage.

Clinical assessment is ultimately not an 'either-or' process in terms of these methods, and they should not be seen as mutually exclusive. To exemplify this, the original clinical procedures of Luria have been modified and revised by Charles Golden and colleagues at the University of Nebraska. This has resulted in the development of a standardised administration, scoring and interpretational process while still retaining the elements of flexibility espoused by Luria. The resultant test - the Standardised Luria–Nebraska Battery - may in a real sense be seen as a merger of widely differing practices and principles.

The process of neuropsychological assessment

Neuropsychological assessment may be used clinically:

(1) to determine the presence or absence of organic pathology
(2) to determine, within the individual, the interaction between organic and non-organic processes which lead to pathology
(3) to determine change of function over time, for example as a consequence of treatment or spontaneous recovery, or alternatively to monitor deterioration
(4) to plan cognitive rehabilitation.

Assessment comprises initially a comprehensive interview covering medical, psychological, social, educational and vocational history in relation to the emergence and course of disturbed cognition, emotion and behaviour.

In addition it is clearly desirable to obtain a detailed account of the manifestation of cognitive disturbance within the person's natural environment. More often than not this constitutes an extended interview with the client and relatives.

On the basis of such interviews, an assessment is instigated, the precise nature of which undoubtedly varies across practitioners. One approach is the application of a comprehensive, standardised battery such as the Halstead–Reitan or Luria–Nebraska battery (see Appendices 2 and 3 to this chapter). These have the advantage of being psychometrically robust, highly reliable discriminators, with clear normative data. Their disadvantages are the lengthy administration time and the need for lengthy training and experience to avoid misinterpretation. Their accuracy, in the diagnostic sense, does however make them desirable tools, their sensitivity to the presence of brain damage being of the order of 95%.

An alternative (but again not mutually exclusive) approach would be a stepwise process such as follows:

(1) assessment of fundamental problem areas (using specific procedures such as an aphasia battery, memory test or tests of perceptual disturbance); the aim here is to obtain a precise understanding of the degree of disturbance of a specific function

(2) use of general organic screening procedures (e.g. tests such as the Stroop, Category Test and Trail Making Test are highly sensitive to the presence of brain damage but tell us little, when used in isolation, in respect of possible localisation); the use of organic screens helps to determine whether the primary problems reflect organic impairment (brain damage) or functional (psychogenic) disturbance

(3) flexible assessment to determine precise cognitive strengths and weaknesses, thereby gaining a more complete understanding of the specificity of disturbance as well as documenting intact functions or retained abilities

(4) further testing, determined by hypothesis testing (namely a hypothesis of localisation); such an approach may be termed 'hypothesis driven'.

In addition to specific cognitive testing, use may be made of self-reporting questionnaires of emotional state such as anxiety, depression, hypomania, anger or hostility, and so on.

The interpretation of a neuropsychological profile, particularly for differential diagnosis, must be made on the basis of a convergent analysis of the test results and the consistency between test results and symptoms. Thus:

(1) The presence or absence of brain damage ought in most cases to be made upon confirmation from a number of organic screens rather than a single item.

(2) It is necessary to determine the precise reasons why an individual fails on a particular test. Thus the Trail Making Test is an example of an

organic screening procedure which assesses visual scanning, number and letter sequencing, rote memory, visuomotor coordination, psychomotor speed, and ability to alternate between conceptual categories. Practically, this test comprises two components. On the first, the examinee is required to draw a continuous trail sequentially between the numbers 1 to 25 (presented in a random spatial arrangement). In the second part the examinee connects the numbers 1 to 13 and letters A to L in an ascending but alternating fashion (1-A-2-B-3-C, etc.). While failure on this test may indicate acquired brain damage, it may not be clear *why* the individual failed or which specific cognitive process is impaired. Thus failure could arise from numeracy difficulties, problems in scanning, ordering or sequencing, poor planning, psychomotor disturbance or inability to shift mentally between categories. In practice, the precise determinants of failure can be ascertained by further administration of more discrete and subtler tests of each process.

(3) Similarly the determination of reduced concentration as, for example, by simple digit span procedures, may tell us little about the *facets* of attentional disturbance, and more exacting procedures ought to be used. It should also be noted, and is often forgotten, that digit span assesses auditory/verbal concentration and is, therefore, an incomplete and perhaps simplistic examination of concentration abilities.

(4) If interpretation involves localisation of brain damage, then clearly that interpretation ought to account for all observed areas of retained and disturbed function.

(5) Disturbance of function as detected by assessment ought, in the final analysis, to complement and explain the described symptoms.

As for most investigative processes, neuropsychological interpretation is not 100% accurate in its sensitivity to brain damage, and cannot be used as a 'stand alone' system. In practice neuropsychological assessment is part of a multidisciplinary process in which neurological, neurophysiological, neuro-radiological and neuropsychological data are examined and analysed for consistency by the skilled practitioner in the formulation of diagnosis. However, assessment batteries such as the Halstead-Reitan boast a dis-criminative accuracy in the region of 85-95% (Incagnoli *et al*, 1986) – such tests will accurately classify an individual as normal or brain damaged on 85-95% of occasions. This compares extremely favourably with electro-encephalography (Chapter 8), computerised tomography, or magnetic resonance imaging (Chapter 9).

There are, therefore, major strengths with neuropsychological test procedures. Their reliability and accuracy make them powerful tools for diagnosis, descriptive interpretation and rehabilitation. Their major weaknesses fall within the area of cost-effectiveness – they are time consuming and hence relatively expensive.

Table 5.1 Global cognitive disturbance as a function of site of damage, and tests of use in its localisation

Site of damage; cognitive disturbance	Test
Frontal lobe	
Expressive language disorders	Benton Verbal Fluency Test
Disorders of planning, programming, execution, monitoring and regulation of behaviour	Trail Making Test
Disturbance of reasoning, abstraction and logical analysis	Wisconsin Card Sorting Test and Halstead Category Test
Rigidity of cognitive processing	
Disorganisation of complex motor actions	
Disturbance of focused attention	
Memory disturbance	
Dysregulation of mood	
Personality disturbance	
Temporal lobes	
Auditory-perceptual defects	Speech Sound Perception Test and Seashore Rhythms Test
Visual field disturbances	
Disorders of visual organisation	
Short-term memory deficits	Benton Visual Retention Test, Complex Figure of Rey, and Revised Wechsler Memory Scale
Amnesic syndrome	
Receptive lanaguage disorders	
Parietal lobes	
Sensory and perceptual disturbance	
Disorders of intersensory association	
Spatial disorientation	Left–Right Disorientation Test
Impaired location and topographical memory	
Constructional apraxia	Complex Figure of Rey, Block Design and Object Assembly of the WAIS-R and Tactual Performance Test
Spatial dyslexia and dyscalculia	Arithmetic Subtest of the WAIS-R and Arithmetic Scale of the Luria-Nebraska Battery
Unilateral spatial neglect	
Spatial agnosias	
Receptive language disorders	
Occipital lobe	
Cortical blindness	
Visual agnosias	
Pure word blindness (agnosic alexia)	

Ultimately there are a number of approaches to neuropsychological testing and innumerable tests which can be used to assess cognitive function. To document the nature, characteristics and functions of each of the major tests is beyond the scope of this chapter. However, Appendix 1 of this chapter describes and details commonly used and widely known procedures in terms of their aims, uses and key characteristics, while Table 5.1 summarises tests which may be of particular value in localising brain damage. For a detailed review of neuropsychological procedures, the reader is referred to Lezak (1983).

Additionally, to facilitate awareness of commonly used neuropsychological test batteries, Appendix 2 and Appendix 3 detail respectively the Halstead-Reitan and Luria-Nebraska tests. It is worth stating again that the provision of such batteries should not convey the impression that they are either easy to administer or unproblematic to analyse – they should not be considered 'assembly kit' approaches to neuropsychological diagnosis.

In summary, neuropsychological assessment may be seen as an approach to the quantification of cognitive function. In the interpretation of neuro-psychological data, inferences as to the integrity of brain function and the localisation of brain damage are made on the basis of the pattern of cognitive strengths and weaknesses within the individual. It must be borne in mind, however, that neuropsychological interpretation rests only partly on numerical scores obtained from performance tasks.

As important, and in some instances more so, is a more qualitative understanding of the nature of and changes in cognitive, emotional and behavioural status reported by the individual.

Since neuropsychological interpretation in the determination of brain damage is an inferential process, it is not strictly equivalent to or an alternative to neurological diagnostic procedures such as radiological scanning, and it is extremely rare that interpretation of disease process can be made from neuropsychological assessment in isolation. This brings to the fore the need to view neuropsychological assessment as an investigative adjunct to other clinical examinations. It is only, perhaps, in the realm of cognitive rehabilitation that neuropsychological assessment may be viewed as operating largely independently from neurological examination.

Neuropsychological testing in clinical practice

Cognitive, behavioural and emotional function may be disturbed in a variety of conditions in an apparently similar fashion. Certain psychiatric disturbances such as reactive and endogenous depression, intractable anxiety and psychosis may be associated with disturbance in specific cognitive abilities such as concentration, short-term memory, learning ability, and intellect. The process then of discriminating between cognitive disturbance as a consequence of organic or psychiatric processes is extremely difficult as is, for example, discriminating discrete cognitive change as a consequence of specific types of organic syndrome.

The following sections summarise the neuropsychological data relevant to a number of organic and psychiatric conditions. The aim is not to provide an exhaustive review, but to summarise the key neuropsychological findings associated with particular disorders, in order to aid the clinician's diagnosis.

Testing of patients with psychiatric disorders

Schizophrenia

Our view of schizophrenia has gone through marked swings, from predominantly sociopsychological theories through to a firm determination that the basis of schizophrenia is biological in nature. Current thinking is probably consistent with an interactionist-type model, in which it may be argued that the vulnerability towards schizophrenia is genetically determined and may constitute some disturbance in brain function. The manifestation of schizophrenia as a complex disturbance of thought, emotion and behaviour may best be thought of as a consequence of an on-going interaction between constitutional vulnerability and environmental stressors (see Birchwood *et al*, 1988). Biological research also strongly supports the conclusion that schizophrenia is a heterogeneous disorder – that is, that there may be several distinct types of schizophrenic subsyndrome, each of which may have different aetiologies.

One such dichotomy which has been purported to reflect aetiological differences is that of type 1 versus type 2 schizophrenia. Type 1 refers to schizophrenic symptoms which may be considered positive additions to behaviour (e.g. the first-rank symptoms of Schneider). Type 2 schizophrenia, or negative schizophrenia, is characterised by losses of behaviour and emotion, such as withdrawal or flattening of affect. The separation of type 1 and 2 schizophrenia implies clearly distinguishable subtypes, each of which is argued to reflect distinct anomalies. The distinction also clearly implies that, clinically, individuals may only manifest type 1 or type 2 symptoms, when in reality they present with a mix of positive and negative symptoms. It is also evident that many of both the positive and negative symptoms once thought to be pathognomonic of schizophrenia are in fact found in other forms of psychosis, such as mania and manic–depression.

The search for distinctive CNS substrates of schizophrenia is unlikely to be clear cut; however, elucidating distinct mechanisms which may be associated with specific types of psychotic symptoms is both theoretically and clinically important. One can perhaps support this view by drawing parallels with neuropsychological research into traumatic head injury. Thus, an understanding of the cognitive correlates of, for example, diffuse axonal injury, concussion, shear damage, orbitofrontal damage and localised ischaemic changes is of clear clinical importance in being able to understand the precise needs of the head-injured patient. This clinical and research database is of additional value in neuropsychiatry, medicolegal assessment and in determining within the individual the relative influence of organic and non-organic factors. It is partly because of this database that the neuropsychologist is able to formulate inferences as to the presence and type of brain damage from patterns of cognitive impairment.

The important point in the present discussion is that such inferences are possible despite the fact that head-injured patients rarely present with focal damage or single symptoms. Rather, patients will present with mixed symptoms underpinned and produced by the operation of multiple organic mechanisms, with the acknowledgement that particular symptoms arise by virtue of specific mechanisms.

In the same manner it is theoretically possible to examine the neuro-psychological and neuroanatomical correlates of specific schizophrenic symptoms in the hope of determining neurobiological determinants of schizophrenia, despite the fact that schizophrenic patients present with mixed symptoms. With this in mind it remains instructive to review evidence suggesting distinct neurobiological correlates of negative and positive symptoms.

Negative symptoms

The evidence from biological studies indicates that the negative symptoms of psychosis may reflect a more generalised form of brain damage. Studies on schizophrenic populations presenting with predominantly negative symptoms (usually chronic patients) indicate that, relative to normal subjects, there is evidence of a significantly higher ratio of the size of the ventricles to the size of the brain; schizophrenic patients presenting with a predominance of positive symptoms do not have a higher ratio. While the specific significance of this increased ventricle:brain ratio are not known, there is evidence that it reflects cortical atrophy, including neuronal loss, rather than raised intracranial pressure.

Neuropsychological studies indicate that negative schizophrenia is characterised by overall deterioration in IQ, disturbances in short-term memory, and generalised neuropsychological performance deficits (such as sensory and motor disturbance, perceptual difficulties, and deficits in higher order reasoning). These deficits are similar to those associated with certain global types of brain damage such as dementia or damage by virtue of long-term alcohol abuse.

Positive symptoms

The symptoms classified as positive are in themselves unusual and include specific types of auditory hallucination, feelings of passivity (as if someone else is controlling one's behaviour) and specific types of delusions of significance. These types of symptoms were originally thought to be unique to schizophrenia, although it is now clear that they are evident in other forms of psychosis as well as in specific organic states such as temporal lobe epilepsy and in tumours and necrosis of the corpus callosum.

The evidence for an anatomical correlate of positive symptoms does not suggest global changes in neuronal density. Thus in the normal brain there is evidence to indicate that the left planum temporale is significantly wider than the right planum temporale, this asymmetry apparently correlating with the fact that the left hemisphere is usually the one dominant for language comprehension. Additionally, in normal brains, the right frontal plane is significantly wider than the left frontal plane (although the significance of this is not clearly understood). In contrast, schizophrenic patients with predominantly positive symptoms tend to show the reverse pattern of asymmetry. It has been argued that this reversal forms the basis of abnormalities in cognitive processing which may result in such symptoms as auditory hallucinations and feelings of passivity (see Birchwood *et al*, 1988).

The unilateralist model

The best way to summarise the neuropsychological findings is in relation to current theoretical modelling. At present it may be argued that there are a few core hypotheses as to the nature of the brain deficit associated with positive symptoms. The first of these may be considered as a unilateralist model, in which it is argued that the primary disturbance of function in schizophrenia arises as a consequence of subtle damage or impairment to the dominant frontotemporal circuitry (e.g. Flor Henry, 1969), a hypothesis derived from the observation of similarities between the symptoms of schizophrenia and of temporal lobe epilepsy where the epileptic focus is on the left and not the right side.

At a neuropsychological level, there is also consistent evidence of a left temporofrontal disturbance. Thus schizophrenics tend to perform poorly on neuropsychological tests that may be considered to assess frontal function and temporal function (such as the Category and Wisconsin Card Sorting tests, and the Speech Sounds Perception test respectively). Thus, by way of example, schizophrenic people tend to show poor performance on Trails B and not Trails A of the Halstead–Reitan battery (Trails B specifically assesses the ability to shift flexibly between cognitive sets, inflexibility being most clearly associated with frontal lobe dysfunction). In addition they show a weakening of dominance on the right hand in comparison with the left, as manifested by reduced finger tapping speed. On tests such as the Category Test and Wisconsin Card Sorting Test (which assess higher-order reasoning), schizophrenic people again do far more poorly than either controls or other psychiatric controls.

In addition there is evidence to indicate specific disturbances of short-term memory, in particular verbal short-term memory (Kapur, 1988). The precise characteristics of this memory disturbance are again not clearly understood, but it is thought that they may reflect both specific features of concentration as well as encoding and storage of information.

If we view specific test procedures as assessing functions which are in principle localisable to specific areas of the nervous system, then there does seem to be an abundance of evidence to indicate that those tests which assess temporal or frontal lobe function are more poorly carried out by schizophrenic populations than by others. It must be borne in mind, however, that the differences between groups on such tests are statistically derived and it is not necessarily the case that the magnitude of deficit on a particular test is of clinical significance. We must therefore be very careful when interpreting purely statistical differences between groups as being of diagnostic utility as opposed to clinically meaningful disturbances of function.

In the final analysis, the value of neuropsychological discriminations relies on the fact that there is a definable entity that can be termed 'schizophrenia'. As schizophrenia is not a unitary disorder, we have to ask what type of schizophrenia we are trying to discriminate from 'traditional' organic syndromes.

Having pointed out these difficulties, it is the case that standard batteries such as the Halstead-Reitan and Luria–Nebraska batteries contain guidelines for the clinician for discriminating schizophrenia from organic states, which suggests that there may be some use in using cognitive assessment as an adjunct to psychiatric interview and neurophysiological assessment to assist in the diagnostic process.

The integrationist model

The second model which has been put forward may be envisaged as an integrationist approach, and argues that the primary deficit in schizophrenia lies not within a single hemisphere but arises as a consequence of faulty communication between the two cerebral systems (termed 'interhemispheric transfer deficit'). The hypothesis is derived from investigations of the split brain condition and much of the method used to assess this process is drawn from experimental neuropsychology (see Hallett (1987) for a detailed review).

The model has been put forward to explain the fact that certain positive symptoms of schizophrenia and the neuropsychological correlates of faulty interhemispheric communication are not found in research populations presenting with predominantly negative symptoms. While this model is somewhat in its infancy and requires more thorough investigation, Green (1986) and Hallett (1987) have shown its value in clinical diagnosis.

Clinical implications

Many of the commonly used general neuropsychological tests, such as the Halstead-Reitan Battery, Wisconsin Card Sorting Test and most memory scales, contain population norms for discriminating schizophrenia from other psychiatric disorders and from neurological disease. However, it is clearly not the case that schizophrenia can be solely diagnosed on the basis of neuropsychological testing, nor is it being suggested that this should be the eventual aim. Rather, neuropsychological assessment may be of value to the psychiatric profession theoretically as well as clinically.

At a theoretical level, neuropsychological studies support the contention that there may be distinct CNS substrates to certain types of symptoms. In conjunction with other methods, such studies contribute to a greater understanding of the disorder and ultimately to better treatment and management.

Clinically, neuropsychological assessment may assist the psychiatric practitioner:

(1) by providing detailed information on a cognitive state, which may help in placement and in rehabilitation
(2) by contributing to an understanding of the interaction between organic and non-organic factors in an individual's presentation or by ruling out the presence of contributory but independent factors
(3) by assisting in the diagnosis and understanding of complex cases, in which an individual's primary problems may be adversely influenced by, for example, long-standing learning difficulty or intellectual deficit.

Anxiety states and depression

It is widely acknowledged that anxiety may adversely influence performance on neuropsychological tests, and one of the preliminary roles of the clinician is to attempt to ensure that this test-related anxiety is minimised. Similarly, it is widely accepted that adverse effects on cognitive function may arise as a consequence of depressed affect.

Both anxiety and depression affect cognitive testing by virtue of their initial influence on concentration. Thus anxiety may often result in a state of distractibility by virtue of over-worrying thoughts and heightened autonomic arousal, which have the net effect of reducing concentration span. Depression may result in a similar end state by virtue of introspective and negative thinking and difficulty in orientation to the outside world. Principally, then, they may be seen to lessen cognitive effort and active attention. Seen in this way, both states may result in an overall flattening of scores on, for example, tests of short-term memory and new learning ability (e.g. the revised Wechsler Memory Scale) as well as reduced performance on tests of concentration (e.g. Digit Span).

In principle it could be argued that depression and anxiety may interfere with performance on any task which requires concentration or cognitive speed or which has a significant loading on short-term memory. Thus in cases of severe emotional disturbance, a general flattening of cognitive performance may be seen on IQ tests such as the Wechsler Adult Intelligence Scale. Anxious and depressed subjects may under-perform on certain subtests such as Digit Span and Digit Symbol, and may generally do relatively poorly on the Performance scales, since these are timed.

Finally, both states may result in disturbance of motor function, as a consequence of muscular tremor and rigidity in anxiety and psychomotor retardation in depression.

Since such general reductions in cognitive function might also be associated with certain generalised forms of neurological impairment, it raises the question of their diagnostic value. The resolution to this lies in a number of areas. Firstly, cognitive test results are not interpreted in isolation from medical and psychological history, which often provide the important clues to aetiology.

Secondly, depression and anxiety can in principle be isolated by the degree of impaired performance across a range of cognitive procedures (where generally it may be assumed that such psychological disturbance will result in milder forms of disturbance than that attributable to neurological impairment).

Thirdly, differential diagnosis can be assisted by comparison of an individual's performance between those tests considered highly sensitive to the effects of mood state and tests which are more resistant to mood state.

Finally, it should be emphasised that assessment is a convergent process across a range of general procedures. Thus, in an attempt to discern whether short-term memory disturbance is of psychological or organic origin, the clinician will have recourse to organic screening tests of good clinical discrimination. In addition, the use of standardised anxiety and depression scales provides an important adjunct to cognitive methods.

To complicate matters, there is growing evidence to indicate that depression, for example, is associated with a more pervasive disruption of cognitive processes deemed to be subserved by the non-dominant (usually right) cerebral hemisphere, and that certain forms of depression may be linked to specific cognitive processes such as the inability to recognise affective components in, for example, faces, and more generally may be linked to deficits in spatial processing. Research supporting this approach carries the same sorts of practical difficulties as that associated with schizophrenia and we are, in truth, a long way off from being confident enough in this database to use it routinely in clinical practice.

Testing of patients with neurological and neurosurgical conditions

Head injury

The use of neuropsychological procedures in cases of head injury is perhaps somewhat removed from standard diagnosis. Its foremost value is in terms of documenting the degree of cognitive disturbance, and this may have several facets:

(1) to document the individual's strengths and weaknesses in the planning of rehabilitation programmes
(2) to determine the degree and likelihood of continuing change over the initial months following head injury
(3) to determine the degree to which the cognitive and emotional changes consequent upon head injury may be inferred to reflect primary damage to the CNS, or may reflect psychological factors associated with the trauma of head injury (in particular post-traumatic stress disorder) or with the psychological difficulties individuals may experience in coming to terms with their disabilities.

Many people with a history of head injury may at some stage find themselves referred to a psychiatrist, and neuropsychological testing provides a further valuable role in determining the degree to which current disturbance of function may be related to historic organic insult.

Ultimately, the commonest type of head injury is likely to be closed head injury through road traffic accidents or industrial or sporting injury, and brain damage may arise from concussion, haemorrhage, the destruction of grey and white matter tissue, secondary damage by virtue of meningeal intrusion or infection, as well as oedema and ischaemia. This is discussed further in Chapter 6 (p. 218–219).

The cognitive, emotional and behavioural sequelae of head injury may be deemed multifarious and clearly dependent upon the site or sites of injury, as well as the actual mechanism of injury. It would be unproductive even to begin to review the precise neuropsychological attributes of this population, and the reader may wish to peruse Richardson (1990) for a detailed exposition. For a brief resumé of the commonly observed cognitive deficits associated with damage to specific brain regions, see Table 5.1 (p. 157).

It may rather be more instructive to address certain discrete issues which serve to illustrate the importance of neuropsychology in decision making and the management of head injury.

Amnesia

Amnesic difficulties commonly follow head injury, that is post-traumatic amnesia (PTA) and retrograde amnesia (RA).

Retrograde amnesia refers to a specific impairment of memory for events immediately before the injury. It is considered to arise directly from shear forces within the brain and rotational movement of the brain within the skull which, respectively, give rise to diffuse lesions and more specific lacerations and contusions of the frontal and temporal regions.

The length of RA broadly varies as a function of severity of head injury as judged by duration of unconsciousness, but the number of complications surrounding this rule cast doubt on its reliability. These complications include the following:

(1) Extended periods of retrograde amnesia can occur in head-injury victims who do not lose consciousness or suffer impairment of consciousness. Furthermore, extended periods of RA may be observed in instances where other objective measures (e.g. brain scan) deem the severity of head injury to be mild.

(2) The duration of RA normally shrinks as the individual recovers, raising difficulties in determining its precise length, or in deciding at which point in time during recovery the assessed period of amnesia is important for prognosis.

(3) RA is rarely a blanket period of complete memory loss but is often characterised by islands of memory which can be difficult to assess accurately in time and which, in themselves, increase with recovery.

(4) The duration of RA in some instances can be determined as such by emotional trauma arising out of the event leading to head injury. Inasmuch as emotional trauma is difficult to quantify, the interaction makes for a complex equation in terms of relating RA to severity of head injury.

Retrograde amnesia constitutes a disturbance of memory for personal events and experiences. Prior general information and knowledge may be only partially impaired and skilled behaviour unaffected. Assessing RA is therefore, in many instances, an imprecise process of determining the most recent event or experience an individual can remember before head injury from the patient's own reconstruction of events.

The assessment of RA is useful in understanding the nature of the memory deficits responsible for memory loss and may clinically offer insights into the effects of the psychological trauma experienced, but it must be generally considered that RA is an unreliable index of injury severity and prognosis.

By contrast, PTA is usually considered to vary directly with length of coma and is widely used as a clinical guide to severity of head injury and prognosis. Additionally, length of PTA may also be used as a practical estimate of the severity of cognitive disturbance following head injury.

In principle, PTA refers to the period subsequent to head injury for which the individual has no memory and is taken to end at the time which the patient can give a clear and consecutive account of what is happening to him/her. The end of PTA, determined as a return of continuous memories, highlights the fact that PTA constitutes two separable disturbances – the first being anterograde amnesia (namely the inability to remember the continuous flow of new experiences) and disorientation (inability to locate oneself in time and place). Thus only when both factors have normalised can it be said that PTA is ended. Estimating the duration of PTA can thus be problematic and can lead to inappropriate clinical statements if both elements are not monitored. Furthermore it is important to determine continuity of memory over a reasonable period since islands of recall can occur within an on-going dense PTA.

In addition, PTA may be intuitively seen to begin once the individual has regained consciousness. Contemporary practice, however, measures PTA from the actual time of the head injury. As such the total duration of PTA includes not only the period of anterograde amnesia and disorientation but also the duration of coma.

The above factors raise the risk of underestimating the total time of PTA and hence underestimating the severity of injury and may possibly lead to an inaccurate prognosis.

It is also possible to overestimate the length of PTA, since in most cases of moderate to severe head injury there will also be quantifiable but more focal disturbances in memory function which continue beyond the end of actual PTA.

Thus, while PTA may be seen to be an accurate predictor of severity and prognosis, care must be taken to assess its duration accurately. In this respect several factors need to be borne in mind:

(1) The relation between severity, coma length and PTA is less reliable in older clients, where extremely short duration of coma may be followed by a disproportionately long period of PTA.

(2) PTA of many hours can occur in patients who do not lose consciousness and in some such instances PTA may not begin at the time of the actual injury but some time later – the individual apparently exhibiting normal orientation and consciousness before lapsing into PTA. This point is raised since, clinically, PTA, while used as an index of severity, is often only seen as of significance for patients who present initially unconscious or comatose. This raises the possibility that in instances of PTA in the absence of coma there may be a tendency to misdiagnose.

(3) The prognostic value of PTA is most clearly seen in closed or blunt head injury, and its value is weaker in crushing or penetrating injuries in which individuals may experience shortened coma and PTA.

Notwithstanding the above, the general rule as applied to PTA stands, and PTA duration is well recognised to predict recovery, and long-term neurological, psychological and occupational outcome.

The duration of PTA comprises the time between the actual head injury and full return to continuous memory. Care must be taken therefore in evaluating whether an individual is exhibiting a full return or an island of memory. Care must also be taken when assessing PTA retrospectively, because a patient's reports may often contain information about earlier stages of their recovery which have been given to them by carers and relatives.

Periods of less than one hour of PTA will be difficult to measure and it is perhaps arguable whether smaller subdivisions are clinically useful, since most classifications include a cut-off point at the one-hour period.

It is arguable that assessing PTA purely by interview is difficult given the above and as such quantifiable measures have been developed to assist in estimating duration. The Wechsler Memory Scale and its revised version have been used to assess PTA since they include measures of disorientation as well as more general measures of short-term memory. In truth, however, the orientation subtest (containing questions such as 'What day is it?', 'What month is it?') may well be the most reliable measure since other aspects of these scales are also sensitive to more focal deficits of memory which persist beyond PTA.

A specific test of PTA (see Richardson, 1990) is the Galveston Orientation and Amnesia Test (GOAT), which contains 12 questions assessing simple biographical memory, knowledge of circumstances of the injury, and temporal and spatial orientation. This test yields a global index with a maximum score of 100, with separate estimates of RA and PTA. Administered at least once per day, PTA is defined as a score of less than 75, and hence PTA may be considered to have ended if a score of more than 75 is reached on several consecutive administrations. Such scales as the GOAT have also been found to be good predictors of neuropsychological outcome for patients with prolonged PTA after no or limited coma.

The ultimate key in the neuropsychological assessment of PTA is not absolutely in terms of the complexity of tests used, but in terms of repetition of assessment to determine accurate as opposed to apparent termination of PTA.

Cognitive effects

There is an accumulation of research and clinical evidence to indicate that it is the cognitive and psychosocial deficits consequent upon head injury, rather than physical disabilities, which are the primary contributors to long-term disablement and interfere most with independence. As such, the determination of the extent and precise nature of these difficulties lies firmly within the neuropsychological sphere.

Broad assessment of disablement using, for example, intellectual and memory screens (such as the Wechsler scales) carries us only part way to documenting the needs of the individual in terms of rehabilitation, although they may be of value in documenting definable change of function over time. In addition, it is often easy to misinterpret the key disturbances if one solely uses broad screening devices.

Thus the revised Wechsler Adult Intelligence Scale may indicate disturbance of intellectual function, but may under-rate the contribution of slowed information processing and deficits in arousal and attention which are common sequelae of closed head injury. Procedures such as the Luria–Nebraska

Neurological Battery arguably provide a more detailed and comprehensive examination, in that the emphasis of the test is in the determination of individual strengths and weaknesses and in identifying discrete but significant disturbances in cognitive chains.

It is useful here to consider the findings concerning an individual with closed head injury whose performance on intellectual assessment indicated a significant disparity between verbal IQ (in the average range) and non-verbal IQ (within the mentally defective range). Closer investigation revealed a specific disturbance of information processing in the rotation of information in mental space, the effect of which manifested itself across a range of apparently disparate cognitive abilities including concentration span, arithmetical calculation, and constructional ability. While clearly this adversely influenced certain features of the client's intellectual function, it could not be justifiably inferred that the client suffered from an absolute deficit in intellect. As importantly, the differential interpretation between a global IQ deficit and a specific focal disturbance (which in itself adversely influences a range of independent abilities) would have entirely different implications for treatment.

A further issue relates to the correlation between anatomical and neuropsychological assessments of the degree of brain injury following head injury. In clinical practice, it may often be inferred that a normal computerised tomography (CT) scan carries with it the implication that any disturbance of cognitive function must relate to psychological sequelae. This may be especially important many years after initial head injury, when the causal link between historic head injury and current symptoms may be difficult to ascertain, particularly if medical evidence is tenuous. Wilson (1990) points out, however, that CT is most generally sensitive to accumulation of blood after head injury, but that in many patients there may be other indices of severe brain injury in the absence of an abnormal CT scan. Thus Snoek *et al* (1979) observed that of 60 head-injury patients without haematoma undergoing CT, some 38% had normal CT scans despite the fact that they had experienced coma lasting over six hours.

Other studies have shown that CT has a sensitivity of only 18% for non-haemorrhagic lesions, compared with a sensitivity of 93% for magnetic resonance imaging. Neuropsychological assessment is, by contrast, in the region of 90–95% sensitive to the presence of organic damage in the same type of cases, although perhaps less so to its location.

This raises the important issue that the use of neuropsychological assessment in common clinical practice is arguably of greater value than CT in determining the degree and nature of impairment following injury and, in particular, may be of greater value in evaluating cases of mild brain damage and concussion.

Concussion is of particular importance when assessing an individual some months after initial injury. Persisting symptoms at that stage may be interpreted as reflecting a 'post-concussional syndrome' (PCS). Many clinicians adopt the view that PCS largely reflects the operation of psychological factors, particularly if symptoms persist beyond 12 months. This view is bolstered by the fact that in many such cases CT is likely to be normal. By contrast, in many cases of PCS, the neuropsychological profile is abnormal and consistent with disturbances in concentration and short-term memory which reflect residual and focal brain damage.

A final point is the value of neuropsychology in medicolegal assessment, in which it is arguable that cognitive assessment can provide a more detailed and sensitive assessment of the effects of traumatic head injury than is the case from the interpretation of routine CT scans. The convergent nature of neuropsychological interpretation associated with the ability to discriminate between neurological and psychological factors makes it a highly desirable tool for litigation purposes.

Cerebrovascular accidents

A cerebrovascular accident (CVA) may be taken to mean any disruption of brain function which arises as a consequence of pathology involving the blood supply, and hence this broad heading covers a range of disturbances arising from haemorrhage, infarction, clotting, or venous malformation.

As with head injury, cognitive and psychosocial factors appear to be decisive in determining outcome over the longer term, and yet there are few studies relating neuropsychological indices to the outcome of stroke.

The value of neuropsychological assessment again mainly lies in the area of rehabilitation (see later). In addition, however, cognitive assessment may be used to assist diagnosis of people who may have experienced a transient ischaemic attack (or 'mini-stroke') or in whom the use of more invasive exploratory techniques such as cerebral angiography are contraindicated.

Site of lesion

When considering the effects of CVA there are several factors which need to be taken into account, which include the site, size and depth of the lesion. In addition the type of disease or injury which led to the CVA needs to be considered, since this may imply dysfunction by virtue of injury or systemic illness. Despite this, the organisation of the cerebrovascular system is such that specific patterns of deficit may be characteristically associated with the occlusion of the major cerebral arteries. Thus disorders affecting the anterior cerebral arteries may be associated with disturbance of higher cognitive functions such as amnesia, aphasia and adynamia (see Walsh, 1985).

Adynamia refers to an unusual state characterised by apparent alertness while being behaviourally inert and verbally unresponsive and corresponds to the psychiatric label of stupor. This may be associated with disturbance of function of the deeper aspects of the frontal lobes, but additionally may arise as a function of damage to the anterior of the corpus callosum, which is thought to play a significant role in both the regulation and initiation of speech. This may well be associated with language difficulties such as reduced verbal fluency and, in extreme cases, by akinetic mutism. These difficulties may reflect the disruption of the regulation of speech arising from more general disturbance in motor control.

The amnesia resulting from CVA has been likened to that associated with Korsakoff's psychosis, and is characterised by confusion, temporospatial disorientation, and confabulation as well as anterograde amnesia (that is, inability to recall events or 'lay down memories' after injury) in the face of relatively intact attentional capacity.

Specific attention has been given to disturbances of memory following cerebrovascular disturbance of the anterior communicating artery. Disturbance ranging from global amnesia and severe confabulation to more discrete dysfunction in temporal ordering and recall have been reported. In discrete aneurysms of the anterior communicating artery two specific features of memory disturbance have been noted – susceptibility to interference and impaired temporal discrimination resulting, respectively, in disturbance in the contents of recalled information, and confusion in the ordering of facts or events. It is, however, unclear as to whether these cognitive disturbances reflect a compromising of frontal lobe function or ultimately reflect damage to underlying limbic structures.

In addition to the above, cerebrovascular disturbance of the anterior cerebral and anterior communicating artery may disrupt executive functions such as reasoning and abstraction skills, planning and monitoring of problem solving and flexibility of cognitive processing. Such disturbances reflect themselves in deficient performance across a wide range of procedures, such as the revised Wechsler Intelligence and Memory Scales, and tests sensitive to frontal lobe function such as the Wisconsin Card Sorting Test, Halstead Category Test and Trail Making Tests.

It may be noted here that certain of the observed disturbances associated with anterior artery CVA, such as aphasic and amnesic difficulties, pose certain theoretical problems in that the neural centres involved are not ones considered to be vital for expressive speech or memory function. Recently, however, it has been argued that disruption of such skills may not reflect focal disturbance of key processing sites responsible for such skills, but rather that these difficulties may arise as a consequence of disruption to over-riding executive or 'supervisory' systems which monitor and regulate these specific processes.

Disturbance of the middle cerebral arteries may produce a more diffuse and widespread pattern of cognitive disturbance by virtue of their widespread distribution to the lateral aspects of the frontal, occipital, parietal and temporal lobes, as well as to important subcortical sites such as the thalamus and internal capsule. Dysphasia appears to be a common sequela, as do sensory disturbance and motor weakness. The precise nature of language disturbance reflects the site of the lesion. Thus disruption of the frontal branches may result in Broca's or non-fluent aphasia, while receptive or fluent aphasia arises from disturbance of the temporal and parietotemporal branches. Disturbances in spatial orientation and recognition may additionally arise, and constructional apraxia is a common effect. There has been surprisingly little work on memory disturbance following impaired flow in this artery, although confusional states and disturbance in selective attention have been observed.

Finally, disruption of the posterior arterial system may affect temporal and occipital lobe function in addition to having diverse effects within the midbrain.

The subcortical effects arising from such lesions include sensory disturbance, homonymous hemianopia and certain extrapyramidal disturbances.

Cortically, temporally centralised lesions may result in receptive dysphasia and disturbances in short-term memory. Extreme conditions such as cortical blindness may result from bilateral disturbance of the occipital lobes and smaller lesions arising from posterior disruption result in specific conditions such as alexia (i.e. word blindness).

Although by no means exhaustive, the above review points to the possible specificity of neuropsychological impairment as a function of disturbance of particular arterial flow. This raises the possibility that such assessment, in certain cases, may be profitably used as a valid adjunct to diagnosis.

Dementia

'Dementia' is a term applied to many brain disorders with variable clinical manifestations and aetiology. The term can often be abused to describe any condition in which there is progressive and at some stage pervasive loss of higher cognitive function which is deemed irreversible.

In reality the dementias may be subdivided into those which are primary and due to direct degenerative changes within the cerebrum, and those which are secondary and associated with either systemic or other neurological conditions. Thus we must discriminate between alcoholic dementia, multi-infarct dementia, normal-pressure hydrocephalus, Alzheimer's disease, post-traumatic dementias, and those produced as a consequence of drug toxicity.

The ensuing review largely concentrates on those forms of dementia in which neuropsychological assessment is most commonly used.

Alzheimer's disease

The most frequent discriminative issues surround Alzheimer's disease, which, neuropsychologically, is characterised by a progressive deterioration in certain features of intellectual ability, particularly reasoning, inferential skills and conceptual and abstract thinking (assessed, for example, by the Similarities, Comprehension, Picture Arrangement, Block Design, Object Assembly and Arithmetic Scales of the revised Wechsler Adult Intelligence Scale and by the Raven's Progressive Matrices).

In addition the disease is characterised by a disturbance of short-term memory predominantly associated with poor retention of semantic information as demonstrated by rapid forgetting on verbal recall tasks (see Kapur, 1988). Such patients perform particularly poorly on the delayed recall components of such tests and they exhibit significant difficulties in new learning ability while retaining long-term memory and well learned skills. Fragmentation of personality, which is reflected in poor self-care and flattening of affective style, may also be noticed.

Clearly, the progressive nature of the disorder suggests that the neuro-psychological discrimination of Alzheimer's disease should be determined by repeated assessment, a few months apart, rather than by the interpretation of a single administration. Since well learned abilities and skills are relatively intact until the later stages, discrimination relies on subtle and careful administration of appropriate memory tests rather than on gross assessment. Simplistic batteries such as the Kendrick tests of dementia which rely on the administration of a simple psychomotor test and an immediate visual memory task are likely to be clinically misleading.

Pseudodementia

Neuropsychologists are often required to discriminate between dementia and depression or depressive pseudodementia. There is a close similarity of symptoms between depressive pseudodementia (behavioural and cognitive disturbances resembling those of degenerative dementia but attributable to functional disturbance) and the dementias of neurological origin, such that differential diagnosis is extremely difficult in the early stages of their clinical course. Clearly, however, such a distinction is of particular importance if it is the case that disorders such as depression, for which there are effective interventions, go untreated because of misdiagnosis. This is especially important since estimates of treatable, functional 'pseudodementias' may be 10–40% of elderly patients referred for diagnosis. From the neuropsychological viewpoint, it is tempting to use simple procedures to instigate this process. It should be borne in mind, however, that depressed subjects may under-perform on both components of the Kendrick battery by virtue of psychomotor retardation and disturbance of spatial short-term memory.

More comprehensive tests do suggest that it may be possible to discriminate between these two processes. Thus it has been suggested that dementia and pseudodementia may be discriminated on tests of attentional span, semantic recall and, in particular, the rate of forgetting of learned information. The difficulty with such studies is that they are retrospective, that is, tests have been used on patients who have been confidently diagnosed by clinical means. There have been few studies which are either prospective or longitudinal, or which have assessed the sensitivity of neuropsychological tests to early cognitive changes in dementia.

One such study, by Jones *et al* (1992), does report neuropsychological data on patients referred for evaluation of suspected dementia and in which assessment took place over two periods separated by six months. Predictably, at the second test, neuropsychological data significantly discriminated between dementia and pseudodementia. However, this ability was at a stage when clinical examination was confidently able to diagnose. Furthermore, at the first tests, 73% of subjects diagnosed as dementing on clinical grounds retained this diagnosis after six months. The significant predictors of dementia were poor performance on a Temporal Orientation Questionnaire (assessing knowledge of the day, date, month, year and time), poor Block Design performance on the revised Wechsler Adult Intelligence Scale (poor visuoconstructive ability) and poor performance on a spatial short-term memory test (reduced ability to reproduce designs from memory). Those subjects receiving an eventual diagnosis of dementia gave an impaired performance, while those confirmed as having pseudodementia performed within normal limits. This latter finding substantiates the view made earlier in this chapter, that while depressed subjects may under-perform on specific tests of cognitive function, their performance is not within organic limits.

While studies such as this provide evidence that neuropsychological test data may be sensitive to early cognitive disturbance in dementia and hence useful in early diagnosis, it remains to be seen whether neuropsychological results are any more sensitive than clinical examination. Clearly, however, there is the possibility that diagnosis achieved by conjoint assessment may be more sensitive than either used in isolation.

Alzheimer's disease is most characterised by early changes in memory function, with more global deficits emerging later. Discriminating between this and, for example, multi-infarct dementia and normal-pressure hydrocephalus cannot necessarily be achieved by neuropsychological assessment alone, and this emphasises again that cognitive testing cannot be seen to be a 'stand-alone' system.

Multi-infarct dementia and normal-pressure hydrocephalus

Thus some of the characteristics of multi-infarct dementia are an abrupt disturbance of gait associated with motor slowness and dysarthria (Walsh, 1985), and clearly the determination of the presence of multiple sites of infarction more exclusively lies within the realm of anatomical and blood flow investigations.

Similar disturbances may be associated with normal-pressure hydrocephalus and in many instances the distinguishing factors are their neurological presentation, speed, and age at onset.

Localisation

In principle, it may be possible to determine the difference between global deficits resulting from generalised damage to the CNS and multiple sites of focal disturbance. Thus if we accept the premise of localisation of cognitive function within the caveats set out at the beginning of this chapter it should be possible 'geographically' to map the brain in terms of its function.

Inferentially it should then be possible, given the precise pattern of test results, to determine whether there is a global deficit in adjacent areas of neuronal tissue or whether functional disturbance is multifocal.

In practice, however, parsimony dictates that the utility of neuropsychological testing in isolation must be rather limited, and diagnosis must ultimately be a multidisciplinary process.

Toxic and deficiency syndromes

Most attention has been given to the neuropsychological consequences of Korsakoff's psychosis (see Chapter 6, pp. 207, 209). While attributable to a number of causes, frequent attention has been given to its genesis via the combined effects of chronic alcohol misuse and vitamin deficiency. Particular attention has been given to the effects this syndrome has in terms of memory function, and the evidence is consistent with a specific pattern of retained and disrupted abilities. Thus, in Korsakoff's psychosis, memory impairment is usually prominent on tests which exceed the individual's immediate memory span (i.e. tests in which the number of definable memory units is greater than the amount of information which can be held within working memory) or if the individual is required to retain information while engaged in distractor tasks. Overall, the deficits in memory may be summarised as a profound difficulty in acquiring new information (anterograde amnesia) in the face of normal or preserved immediate concentration and attentional processes. Many aspects of learned or skilled behaviour are preserved, but recent recall of events is often characterised by confabulation (i.e. the filling in of subjective memory gaps with extraneous information).

On tests such as the revised Wechsler Memory Scale, a sufferer's performance is typically characterised by good performance on tests of immediate concentration but with uniform deficits in immediate and delayed recall for both verbal and spatial information and by retarded learning and rapid forgetting of new information.

By contrast, for example, chronic alcohol abuse resulting in encephalopathy is associated with a general lowering of all aspects of short-term memory, but with particular deficits in visual memory as opposed to verbal recall (Parsons & Farr, 1981).

Neuropsychological rehabilitation

Most professionals associate the term 'neuropsychological rehabilitation' with traumatic CNS injuries such as may be incurred from a road traffic accident. There is however a role for 'neurotherapy' across a variety of CNS disturbances such as might arise from CVA, cerebral infection and degenerating conditions, and it may be argued that it also has a role for those experiencing cognitive difficulties as a consequence of functional illness.

Furthermore, neuropsychological rehabilitation is often seen as being synonymous with cognitive rehabilitation, when the latter is best seen as one element of the former. Thus neuropsychological rehabilitation may be seen to comprise the following:

(1) Informational care – the provision of information to enable the client and carers and relatives to understand and gain insight into their cognitive, behavioural and emotional difficulties. A key component of this aspect of care is that it should seek to facilitate understanding while also allaying anxieties and dispelling misconceptions.

(2) Psychotherapeutic support – to monitor and alleviate emotional suffering with good practice aimed at preventing further emotional difficulties. In many instances, psychotherapy is aimed at helping the individual work through and come to terms with the traumatic events which form the onset of the individual's current difficulties.

(3) Cognitive rehabilitation – specific procedural approaches aimed at the remediation of cognitive dysfunction, such as memory retraining.

(4) Social and vocational skills training – aimed at reintegration into the social milieu and worthwhile employment.

It would be fair to say that cognitive rehabilitation most intimately reflects the specialist skills of the neuropsychologist and relies heavily upon psychometric, qualitative and ecological assessment.

Less than ten years ago it was generally considered that following traumatic CNS injury any residual brain damage evident beyond the period of spontaneous recovery was permanent. It is now more readily acknowledged that cognitive rehabilitation may play a vital role in the restoration or remediation of cognitive disturbance following brain damage, both in respect of facilitating the potential for restoration during the period of spontaneous recovery and in facilitating reorganisation of brain function beyond this phase.

Current cognitive rehabilitation comprises three approaches, which may be described as: the use of compensation to enable the client to minimise or work round deficits; substitution, whereby alternative methods are used to solve cognitively mediated problems; and retraining methods to stimulate specific impaired functions. In many respects, comprehensive rehabilitation programmes may draw from all three approaches. The terms 'compensation' and 'substitution' may be taken to imply procedural or environmental manipulations and prostheses that may ameliorate the magnitude of cognitive deficit, and at one level this is certainly the case. There is however a higher-order meaning to these approaches which derives from theoretical neuropsychology, in which it is argued that an individual's deficits may be ameliorated by functional reorganisation. This concept is based upon the premise of localisation of function – that specific abilities are carried out by (or are manifestations of) the action of task-specific cortical and subcortical sites. When these 'sites' are damaged, the programmes of cognitive function (like cerebral software) may be effectively transferred to adjacent areas of brain tissue. This view accounts for the observation in head-injury sufferers with definable brain damage of a gradual (though not necessarily total) restoration of function over time despite the fact that the key processing sites have been destroyed.

While this is an attractive hypothesis, there is little direct evidence to support it, and an equally plausible hypothesis is one which rests on a networked view of cognitive function whereby restoration of function arises from the fact that complex and higher-order abilities are not carried out by single processing sites.

Despite the theoretical dispute over the mechanisms of reorganisation, there is ample evidence that restoration can be facilitated by the use of specific procedures and learning techniques, in which the individual is taught to use alternative functional skills and processes to carry out cognitive operations which are dysfunctional. A general example of this would be to teach an individual who experiences verbal short-term memory deficits to analyse, translate and encode information on the basis of its visuospatial properties, and hence to facilitate the use of cognitive strength to 'bypass' a cognitive weakness.

To achieve such an aim ultimately requires detailed and highly specific neuropsychological assessment, whereby the aim of testing is to gain as full an understanding as is possible of the individual's cognitive strengths and weaknesses, and as discrete as possible an understanding of the elements of processing which are dysfunctional. This 'process-specific' approach to rehabilitation relies on a hierarchical modelling of cognitive function (such as that expounded by Luria (1966)), in which it may be assumed that large-scale abilities such as reasoning, short-term memory, and so on can be divided into smaller processing modules. The focus of rehabilitation then becomes these identified dysfunctional modules (in a sense weak microlinks in a cognitive chain) rather than more global functions, and it is both arguable and demonstrable that this type of modelling and approach to rehabilitation is more successful and powerful than more general approaches.

Such a 'process-specific' approach to both assessment and treatment is considered by some to be one which is largely independent of other types of investigation, such as CT and magnetic resonance imaging, although clearly one should never seek for total independence, since in neuropsychological rehabilitation the assessment of dysfunction still needs to be carried out with an understanding of the biological mechanisms leading to it, and these can only be ascertained by other means.

Conclusions

This chapter has highlighted some of the clinical uses of assessment, rather than attempting to condense a vast area into such a small space. Inevitably important topics have not been covered or have been sacrificed in order to provide a relatively clear description of the broad range of the specialty. Those requiring convincing evidence of the power and application of neuropsychological assessment across a variety of clinical settings can refer to Incagnoli *et al* (1986). The aim in this chapter has not been to suggest that neuropsychological assessment is an infallible tool.

Neuropsychological assessment is a time-consuming process which requires on the part of the practitioner an all-round knowledge of clinical psychology, psychological test theory and practice, a working knowledge of neuropsychology, and familiarity with neurosciences such as neurology, neuroanatomy, neuropathology and, in some settings, neurosurgery. Indeed, the findings of neuropsychological assessment can only be interpreted reliably in the light of evidence from all of these.

Clearly, neuropsychology is open to abuse: there may be a temptation to derive seductive inferences from minimal test data, and the interpretation of neuropsychological profiles is one which is open to frank misinterpretation. But in skilled hands, cognitive assessment is a powerful process which can be applied across a range of clinical settings. In some instances the neuropsychologist's role is one of contributing a database for diagnosis, and this may be seen in the same light as requests for CT scans or electroencephalography.

Neuropsychological assessment has particular importance because of its ability to describe the functional strengths and weaknesses of the individual. This allows crucial rehabilitation strategies to be devised and coordinated, with the aim of ameliorating the effects of brain injury and impaired cognitive processing.

In all of its applications, the strength of neuropsychological assessment is its quantification of the cognitive correlates of structural alterations to the CNS, but one must always view such assessment as part of an integrated approach to diagnosis and treatment, incorporating all of the relevant neurological disciplines.

Appendix 1. Neuropsychological tests in common practice

Intellectual function

Wechsler Adult Intelligence Scale - Revised

Areas assessed Establishes current IQ by the assessment of general information, verbal and non-verbal reasoning, vocabulary, comprehension, auditory concentration, arithmetic, constructional ability and visual-verbal integration.

Methods Comprises 11 subtests predominantly in the form of question and answer for the verbal items. For non-verbal items instructions are given verbally, the answers comprising either the construction of three- and two-dimensional objects, rearrangement of visually presented story pictograms, or drawing.

Memory function

Wechsler Memory Scale - Revised

Areas assessed   Establishes broad memory function by assessment of rote memory, orientation, recognition, concentration, verbal and non-verbal short-term memory, verbal and non-verbal learning ability.

Methods   Consists of a simple orientation questionnaire, drawing of designs from memory, verbal recall of stories, learning of new word pairs and of pairs of patterns.

Adult Memory and Information Processing Battery

Areas assessed   Assesses immediate and delayed verbal and non-verbal memory, verbal and non-verbal learning, cognitive processing speed, motor speed.

Methods   Similar materials to the above scale. The test comprises recall of designs and stories, learning of word lists and of a complex design, cancellation tasks, and a simple motor speed task.

Warrington Recognition Memory Test

Areas assessed   Forced-choice recognition of verbal (words) and spatial (faces) material.

Methods   Subjects view 50 words and 50 faces. For both sets of stimuli the subject is then shown 50 word pairs or face pairs - the aim being to pick out the original words and faces.

Rey Auditory Verbal Learning Test

Areas assessed   Assesses rate of learning and degree of forgetting, susceptibility to interference, primacy and recency.

Methods   Subjects learn a list of words over a number of trials. They then have to learn a new list and then finally recall the original test.

Rey-Osteirreith Figure

Areas assessed   Test of immediate and delayed recall of complex spatial material. Also assesses planning and constructional ability.

Methods   Subjects first copy a complex design, then attempt to draw it from memory.

Language function

Boston Diagnostic Aphasia Examination

Areas assessed   Wide-ranging assessment of receptive and expressive language. Encapsulates interpretational profiles associated with the major aphasic syndromes.

Methods   Multiple assessment method involving drawing, writing, spelling and verbal responses to a range of stimuli.

Revised Token Test

Areas assessed   Pure assessment of receptive language skills. The use of a motor response makes this a useful tool with individuals with expressive language difficulties.

Methods   Subjects carry out motor actions to verbal commands. 'Tokens' of different size, shape and colour are moved in response to commands of increasing difficulty.

Benton Verbal Fluency Test

Areas assessed   A simple procedure assessing fluency and word-finding ability.

Methods   Subjects are required to say as many words as they can beginning with specific letters of the alphabet in one minute.

Information processing tasks

These are often used to screen for organic impairment.

Stroop Colour-Word Interference Test

Areas assessed   Speed of processing for simple verbal and non-verbal information. Also assesses cognitive flexibility.

Methods   Comprises three components: (1) reading out rapidly an array of 100 words made up of a random presentation of the words RED, GREEN, BLUE; (2) reading out the colour hues RED, GREEN and BLUE; (3) the words RED, GREEN and BLUE are written in coloured ink such that colour hue does not match the colour word. Subjects read out the colour hue only.

Trail Making Test

Areas assessed   See Appendix 2, p. 183.

Methods   See Appendix 2, p. 183.

Visual Search Test

Areas assessed   Assesses pattern recognition, visual scanning, speed of visuospatial processing.

Methods   Subjects pick out a pattern from an array which correctly matches a central pattern.

Paced Auditory Serial Addition Test

Areas assessed   Assesses attentional processes, monitoring, tracking and sequencing, speed of computational processing.

Methods   Subjects listen to a series of numbers presented at defined time intervals and have to add up successive pairs.

Tests of laterality

Annett's Handedness Questionnaire

Areas assessed   Assesses handedness by the miming of actions.

Methods   Involves miming the actions (e.g. writing, striking a match).

Harris Test of Lateral Dominance

Areas assessed   Assesses handedness, eyedness and footedness.

Methods   Involves miming a variety of actions.

Dichotic Listening Tests

Areas assessed Experimental procedures which assess auditory perceptual asymmetries for verbal and non-verbal material from which inferences of cerebral dominance can be made.

Methods   Subjects are auditorily presented with groups of word pairs which are simultaneous and presented one word to each ear. After each group, subjects recall as many words as they heard.

Neurological tests

Finger Oscillation

Areas assessed   Dominant and non-dominant hand motor speed.

Methods   Involves the rapid depression of a manual counter with the right or left index finger, to determine the number of taps within 10 seconds. Scores are rated for each hand over several trials.

Finger Tip Number Writing

Areas assessed   Finger pad graphaesthesia.

Methods   The examiner inscribes single digits on each finger pad while the examinee tries to identify the number written.

Finger Agnosia

Areas assessed Somatosensory recognition and naming.

Methods Subjects name which finger the examiner has touched.

Right–Left Orientation

Areas assessed Inter- and extra-personal spatial disorientation.

Methods Involves the execution of pointing or touching actions on command (e.g. 'touch your right shoulder'; 'point to my left hand with your right hand').

Double Simultaneous Stimulation

Areas assessed Auditory, visual and manual suppressions.

Methods Unilateral or bilateral presentation of simple auditory, tactile or visual stimulus.

Appendix 2. The Halstead–Reitan Battery

This takes five to eight hours or more to administer. The asterisked items are useful independently for screening for organic impairment.

Wechsler Adult Intelligence Scale (revised)

Measures Intellectual function.

Method See Appendix 1.

*Category Test

Measures Hypothesis formation, rule learning, planning.

Method Subjects view a series of stimulus cards each with four definable patterns. For each card the aim is to find the odd man out by determining rules about similar and dissimilar features across the four patterns.

Speech Sounds Perception Test

Measures Phoneme discrimination, attention.

Method Subjects listen to 60 nonsense words. For each word they pick out what they think they have heard from a visual array of four options.

Seashore Rhythms Test

Measures   Rhythm and pitch discrimination, attention.

Method   Subjects listen to 30 pairs of tone sequences. For each pair they determine if the sequences are identical or different.

*Trail Making Test

Measures   Visual scanning, visuomotor coordination, psychomotor ability, sequencing, category alternation.

Method   Trail A involves drawing a single line sequentially connecting the numbers 1 to 25 (presented in random visual order). Trail B involves connecting numbers and letters in ascending but alternating fashion (1-A-2-B-3 etc.).

Finger Oscillation Test

Measures   Dominant and non-dominant hand motor speed.

Method   See Appendix 1.

Tactual Performance Task

Measures   Astereognosis, spatial memory, spatial learning, orientation, uni- and bimanual function.

Method   Subjects, while blindfold, place three-dimensional objects into their matching cut-outs. Trial 1 uses the right hand only; Trial 2 uses the left hand only; and Trial 3 is a bimanual trial. Following this, subjects have to draw from memory the shapes and their location.

Sensory Perceptual Examination

Measures   Finger agnosia, finger tip number writing, visual, auditory and manual suppression, astereognosis.

Method   See Appendix 1.

Aphasia Screen

Measures   Broad but brief assessment of language comprehension and production.

Method   Short standard aphasia screen including drawing of designs, writing to dictation, word repetition, spelling, etc.

Minnesota Multiphasic Personality Inventory

Measures   Personality.

Method   A lengthy questionnaire in which subjects respond 'true' or 'false' to each question.

Appendix 3. The Standardised Luria–Nebraska Battery

The LNNB is almost entirely in a 'pencil and paper' format. Its administration involves question and answer, drawing, copying and execution of motor movements, reading words and text, completion of two-dimensional puzzles, and so on. All scores are conveniently recorded in a single booklet and are then either analysed manually or by computer.

There are 279 test items in total, and the battery takes on average two to four hours to complete.

Test components

Clinical scales

These scales are empirically derived from the test items.

Motor
Rhythm
Tactile
Visual
Receptive speech
Expressive speech
Reading
Writing
Arithmetic
Memory
Intellectual Processes
Intermediate memory

Subsidiary scales

These profiles and scales are derived from a reordering of the original test items.

Pathognomic
Right hemisphere
Left hemisphere
Profile elevation
Impairment
Power
Speed

Interpretational profiles

These profiles and scales are derived from a reordering of the original test items.

Factor items
Localisation
Analysis of test items

References

Birchwood, M., Hallett, S. & Preston, M. (1988) *Schizophrenia: An Integrated Approach to Research and Treatment*. London: Longmans.

Flor-Henry, P. (1969) Psychosis and temporal-lobe epilepsy: a controlled investigation. *Epilepsia*, **10**, 365-395.

Green, P. (1986) *Disturbances in Speech Comprehension in Schizophrenics and Cerebral Lesioned Patients*. Unpublished PhD Thesis: University of Birmingham.

Hallett, S. (1987) *Defective Interhemispheric Integration in Children at Risk for Schizophrenia*. Unpublished PhD Thesis: University of Birmingham.

Incagnoli, T., Goldstein, G. & Golden, C. J. (1986) *Clinical Applications of Neuropsychological Test Batteries*. New York: Plenum Press.

Jones, R., Tranel, D., Benton, A., *et al* (1992) Differentiating dementia from 'pseudodementia' early in the clinical course: utility of neuropsychological test. *Neuropsychology*, **6**, 13-21.

Kapur, N. (1988) *Memory Disorders in Clinical Practice*. London: Butterworths.

Lezak, M. (1983) *Neuropsychological Assessment* (2nd edn). New York: Oxford University Press.

Luria, A. R. (1966) *Higher Cortical Functions in Man*. New York: Basic Books.

Parsons, O. A. & Farr, S. P. (1981) The neuropsychology of alcohol and drug abuse. In *Handbook of Clinical Neuropsychology* (eds S. B. Filskov & T. J. Boll). New York: Wiley Interscience.

Richardson, J. T. E. (1990) *Clinical and Neuropsychological Aspects of Closed Head Injury*. London: Taylor and Francis.

Snoek, J., Jennett, B., Adams, J. H., *et al* (1979) Computerised tomography after recent severe head injury in patients without acute intracranial haematoma. *Journal of Neurology, Neurosurgery and Psychiatry*, **42**, 215-225.

Walsh, K. (1985) *Understanding Brain Damage*. Edinburgh: Churchill Livingstone.

Wilson, J. T. E. (1990) Significance of MRI in clarifying whether neuropsychological deficits after head injury are organically based. *Neuropsychology*, **4**, 261-269.

6 Neuropathology
Philip Luthert

Techniques • *Cerebrovascular disease* • *Infectious diseases* •
Neurodegenerative disease • *Epilepsy* • *Tumours* • *Space-occupying lesions
and cerebral oedema* • *Secondary metabolic disorders* • *Inheritable
metabolic disorders* • *Schizophrenia* • *Demyelinating disorders* •
Developmental disorders • *Hydrocephalus* • *Perinatal neuropathology* •
Head injury • *Conclusions*

An understanding of neuropathological processes is essential in order to appreciate the many organic disorders that may be seen in day-to-day psychiatric practice. As the techniques used to study the brain become more sophisticated and sensitive, it seems probable that the number of conditions with a clear organic basis will increase.

Techniques

The postmortem examination and psychiatry

Old age psychiatry provides the clearest example of the role of postmortem examination in contemporary practice. With the growing prospect of therapies for dementing illnesses, and with the better understanding of their genetic basis, it is becoming more crucial that disorders presenting with cognitive decline are accurately diagnosed. In addition, postmortem examination should be a routine element in clinical audit. This becomes even more important in the context of research into potential therapies and in correlating pathology with neuroimaging data.

Research is probably the area where postmortem studies of patients with psychiatric disorders are of most value, but care must be taken to ensure that consent is obtained for tissue to be used for research purposes, as well as simply ascertaining the cause of death. In schizophrenia, although neuroimaging studies may have provided the impetus, the value of neuropathological examination in clarifying the organic nature of at least some cases cannot be overestimated. Likewise, it is to be hoped that further neuropathological study of mental handicap will bring about enhanced understanding in this important area.

An ever-growing range of techniques from the neurosciences are extending into neuropathology. Advances will, however, only come about by the coordinated efforts of patients, relatives, clinicians, and pathologists. Although asking for consent is often difficult, when handled appropriately the 'research postmortem' can often be seen by the family as a positive aspect of bereavement. It is hard to see how rapid, major advances in organic psychiatry will be forthcoming without the facility to examine tissue from those affected by these conditions.

Occasionally, postmortem examination of the brain is of importance in forensic cases. It may, for example, clarify whether intellectual decline following trauma was due to a head injury or to some other process.

Surgical biopsies and psychiatry

There are relatively few indications in psychiatry for a biopsy to be taken, although this may change. It has, for example, been suggested that skin or nasal mucosa biopsy may be of value in the diagnosis of Alzheimer's disease. In storage disorders (see p. 211) it is now generally possible to reach a diagnosis by analysing peripheral blood or by culturing fibroblasts, although histochemistry and/or electron microscopy of suction rectal biopsies may be of value in certain conditions.

Basic pathological processes

Nerve cells react to injury in relatively few ways and, although, some manifestations of neuronal pathology are rather more characteristic of one disorder than another (this applies particularly to intraneuronal inclusions – see later), virtually none should be considered 'disease specific'. Changes include:

(1) neuronal death
(2) dendritic retraction or 'pruning'
(3) axonal degeneration or swellings
(4) 'sprouting' of new neuronal processes
(5) chromatolysis
(6) inclusion formation.

During their development, neurons can migrate to the wrong position or, presumably, become incorrectly connected.

Astrocytes typically react to a wide variety of insults by increasing their number (hyperplasia) and/or their size (hypertrophy). The extent and branching complexity of their processes increases, and the content of intermediate filament protein, glial fibrillary acidic protein (GFAP), also rises. These changes are often known as 'gliosis' or 'astrocytosis'.

Oligodendrocytes, contrary to initial beliefs, do appear to show reactive changes, but these seem to be of much less importance than those of astrocytes. They are also specific targets in some diseases, for instance multiple sclerosis and progressive multifocal leucoencephalopathy.

Endothelial cells of the blood-brain barrier can react to disease by proliferation (angiogenesis), as is seen in relation to the growing edge of high-grade tumours, or by losing their blood–brain barrier properties and becoming permeable to non-transported solutes, including protein. The associated cerebral oedema may be life-threatening.

Ependymal cells, lining the ventricular system, do not play a major role in the neuropathology of adults.

Examining the structure of the nervous system

Routine macroscopical (naked-eye) examination of the brain normally takes place after fixation in formalin. The demands of the coroner or researcher may, however, sometimes necessitate slicing of the fresh brain. The firm, fixed brain gives a false impression as to the consistency of fresh brain, which is remarkably soft and wobbly. Externally the leptomeninges, cranial nerves and vessels can be assessed, as can the degree of any atrophy or swelling. Slicing reveals the ventricular system and any space-occupying or any other focal abnormality.

Routine histology has, of necessity, to be selective. This does not usually present a difficulty with focal pathology or when the expected disorder has a characteristic distribution, but it is a problem if one is trying to determine whether a given condition is associated with organic pathology or not. A great deal of information can be gleaned from a straightforward haematoxylin and eosin preparation, but more specific stains are an essential part of the examination of most cases. Silver stains are valuable in displaying neuronal structure and some inclusions, and myelin stains assist in the examination of white matter.

Increasingly, immunohistochemistry is being used. In this technique, an antibody is raised to a specific antigen, applied to the section and then excess is washed off. Antibody that has bound to the antigen on the section is then visualised in a variety of ways. A common example is an antibody to GFAP, which is used to demonstrate gliosis.

Cerebrovascular disease

Approximately 15% of all deaths in the UK are caused by cerebrovascular disease, and the prevalence of disability from such disease in the general population is approximately 350/100 000. Most stroke occurs during the seventh decade, but up to 25% occur below the age of 65. Over 60% are thrombotic (associated with arteriosclerosis), 15% haemorrhagic, and 15% embolic (usually associated with mitral stenosis, atrial fibrillation or mural thrombus following myocardial infarction).

Hypertension

Hypertensive cerebrovascular disease is a common source of morbidity and mortality. Treatment of hypertension is associated with a reduced risk of some of the associated disorders such as spontaneous intracerebral haemorrhage, but there is a potential risk of significantly reducing cerebral blood flow.

Atheroma formation

Hypertension is associated with increased atheroma formation and hence a higher risk of cerebral thromboembolic disease. Similarly, arteriolosclerosis, a hyaline change in the walls of arterioles, is probably accelerated. (Diabetes is also an important risk factor for these changes.)

Spontaneous intracerebral haemorrhage

In hypertensive people, haemorrhage occurs mainly in the region of the deep grey matter and internal capsule. It is believed to be the result of rupture of microaneurysms (Charcot–Bouchard aneurysms) that are found on the penetrating lenticulostriate branches of the middle cerebral artery in increased numbers in hypertension.

Hypertensive encephalopathy

This is a feature of accelerated or malignant hypertension and results from hypertension-induced failure of autoregulation (a process whereby changes in arteriolar tone normally maintains constant cerebral blood flow over a wide range of arterial pressures). There may be multiple small cerebral haemorrhages (also seen in the retina – see Chapter 4, p. 118) and cerebral oedema.

Lacunar disease (or state)

This is characterised by multiple small to medium-size holes, often in relation to perivascular spaces, in white (*état criblé*) and grey (*état lacunaire*) matter (particularly in relation to the basal ganglia). These appear to be small infarcts or enlarged perivascular spaces.

Binswanger's disease

This is a progressive disorder arising from vascular insufficiency and resulting fibre loss and gliosis of the deep white matter. Patients present with a moderately rapidly progressive dementia. The white-matter changes can be detected by magnetic resonance imaging (MRI) and minor changes may be seen in controls.

Cerebral infarction

The term 'cerebral infarction' is generally applied to circumstances where brain tissue is essentially destroyed because of reduced supply of oxygen. This may be because of lowered tension of oxygen in circulating blood or because of reduced blood flow. The two are often combined, as impaired myocardial function is a consequence of systemic hypoxia.

Global ischaemia/hypoxia

Global reduction in oxygen supply to the brain may be total, and in this circumstance the degree of damage depends on the rapidity and effectiveness of reperfusion. Causes include reduced cardiac output and carbon monoxide poisoning. Incomplete reduction, as may be seen during an episode of profound hypotension, often leads to a characteristic pattern of damage in which the areas lying between the boundaries of the major arterial territories (especially between anterior and middle cerebral arteries) are most severely affected. These so-called 'boundary-zone infarcts' are typically wedge-shaped, with the apex in the white matter. On occasion, global hypoxia, or profound cerebral oedema due to some other cause, may lead to cessation of cerebral blood flow, but the patient is kept alive by mechanical means. At postmortem, the brain has become generally softened and necrotic, an appearance known as 'respirator' brain.

Lesser degrees of generalised hypoxia/ischaemia may result in the death of susceptible neurons, with preservation of the remainder and of glial and vascular elements. Cerebellar Purkinje cells and the pyramidal cells of Sommer's sector of Ammon's horn in the hippocampus are often affected in this way. The same pattern of 'selective vulnerability' is seen in epilepsy and hypoglycaemia.

Focal ischaemia/hypoxia

Strokes are responsible for one-third of deaths in industrialised countries and a major source of morbidity, requiring extensive support. Over 60% of 'strokes' are caused by cerebral infarction; the remainder are haemorrhagic (see below). Causes of focal ischaemia are listed in Box 6.1.

Thrombotic stroke is usually associated with focal motor deficit, generally hemiplegia. This is sometimes preceded by headache and malaise and often develops over several hours. Loss of consciousness occurs in only 50%. The middle cerebral artery is the most vulnerable to thrombosis, particularly the lenticulostriate arteries which supply the internal capsule. Initially, muscle tone is reduced with normal or reduced tendon reflexes, although the Babinski sign is positive. Sensation is usually normal, but hemianopia may occur and thalamic involvement may lead to burning unilateral pain and hyperalgesia. The head and eyes are typically turned away from the lesion. Epileptic seizures occur in about 20%.

Occlusion of any of the major arteries of the brain gives rise to infarcts with fairly consistent localisation corresponding to the inner parts of the respective vessel's distribution (see Chapter 1, Fig. 1.3, p. 5), the outer portion being

Box 6.1   Causes of focal cerebral ischaemia

Atheroma/thrombosis of neck and/or cranial vessels
Emboli from:
  proximal atheromatous vessels
  mural thrombus in the heart
  valvular vegetations
  fractures (fat)
  venous circulation if cardiac septal defect, etc.
  medical intervention, e.g. cardiac bypass or massive air embolus
  metastases
  nitrogen bubbles (the 'bends')
Arterial spasm following subarachnoid haemorrhage
Arteritis (infective or collagen-vascular disease)
Endarteritis obliterans (as in chronic meningitis)
Venous or sagittal sinus occlusion

Note increased risk in thrombotic haematological disorders

protected by overlapping supply from adjacent vessels. Note that, unlike the major arteries supplying the cortex, the penetrating arteries that supply deep grey-matter structures do not have any such anastomotic arrangement.

The exact time course of the evolution of an infarct varies greatly from case to case but a resumé is given in Box 6.2.

Treatment includes prevention of further thrombotic stroke with aspirin, and surgery if localised carotid occlusion is detected. Rehabilitation is aimed at regaining as much lost motor and language function as possible. Major depressive disorders occur in about 20% of sufferers.

**Box 6.2   Time course of events following focal occlusion of a
cerebral vessel**

< 12 hours: virtually no macroscopical or microscopical changes by
  conventional methods
12–24 hours: increasing swelling of damaged area with loss of normal
  staining of brain
1–3 days: softening of the brain becomes more marked; inflammatory
  cell response (neutrophils then macrophages); neuronal cytoplasm
  homogeneous and ghostly, eosinophilic or dark
1–2 weeks: macrophage response becomes marked, new capillaries
  form and astrocytosis develops
Months–years: tissue destruction with remaining astrocytic scar or
  cavity formation

Transient ischaemic attack

Transient ischaemic attacks last less than 24 hours. Brief loss of consciousness is followed by several hours of confusion, difficulty in finding words, and weakness of a limb. They tend to recur, and one in five die in the first five years after diagnosis, most by myocardial infarction. They are thought to be caused by platelet thrombi released from ulcerated plaques in the internal carotid arteries. Treatment is preventive, with aspirin, and carotid surgery where discrete narrowing is detected.

Intracranial haemorrhages

These are classified according to site, although in an individual case blood may extend beyond this. Most act as space-occupying lesions if they are large enough. As with haemorrhage at other sites, bleeding diatheses must be considered.

Extradural haemorrhage

This typically arises following trauma to the side of the head over the pterion, where the skull is thin and there is laceration of the middle meningeal artery. Classically a short, lucid interval is followed by a rapid descent into coma and, without treatment, death.

Subdural haematomas

Subdural haematomas may be divided into acute, subacute and chronic. The former tend to be associated with severe trauma. The latter, believed to arise from the rupture of bridging veins passing from the surface of the brain to the superior sagittal sinus, may occur following minor injury, especially in patients where stretching of these vessels is more likely (e.g. where there is cerebral atrophy or following shunting of hydrocephalus). Debilitated patients seem to be especially at risk. Chronic subdural haematomas lie within fibrous membranes, and the fluctuation of consciousness may relate to re-bleeding more than osmotic shifts of fluid into the membrane-lined cavity.

Subarachnoid haemorrhage

This arises following rupture of a berry aneurysm (90% of cases), from a leaking vascular malformation, or from extension of haemorrhage elsewhere within the cranium. The sudden onset of headache, photophobia and meningism result from irritant blood in the subarachnoid space. This also provokes arterial spasm, which is often severe enough to produce extensive cerebral infarction and, in survivors, may clog the subarachnoid space and arachnoid granulations sufficiently to cause hydrocephalus.

Other types of aneurysm include mycotic (fungal), fusiform (usually basilar and related to atheroma) and dissecting (usually traumatic). Rupture can occur during vigorous exertion, such as coitus, but up to a third arise during sleep. The characteristic presentation is the sudden development of very severe diffuse or occipital headache, usually associated with vomiting. On arrival at hospital one-third of sufferers are confused and a further third comatose. In some cases there may be several days of less severe headache and dizziness before haemorrhage. Smoking, hypertension and oral contraception after the age of 35 increase risk.

Diagnosis is confirmed by finding blood in the CSF and in the meningeal spaces on CT scan, which may also reveal calcification in an arteriovenous malformation. The source of haemorrhage is investigated by arteriography.

Initial treatment is symptomatic if the patient is conscious, or supportive if in coma, and aimed at reducing cerebral oedema and the prevention of arterial spasm. Blood in the meningeal spaces causes arterial spasm, and this may lead to anoxic damage. The drug nimodipine has recently been found to improve outcome, possibly by reducing spasm, and is now given routinely. Prevention of further haemorrhage by surgical clipping is possible where an accessible aneurysm is the cause. Unfortunately surgery also leads to arterial spasm and more direct trauma, particularly to frontal and limbic structures, and neurobehavioural sequelae of varying severities are common. Less common causes of subarachnoid haemorrhage include blood dyscrasias (leukaemia, thrombocytopenia, haemophilia, anticoagulant treatment), neoplasm (primary or secondary), infection (bacterial, viral), vasculitis (lupus, polyarteritis) and thrombotic infarct.

Intracerebral haemorrhage

This is a complication of systemic hypertension and congophilic angiopathy (see below). It can also arise following trauma and as a result of raised intracranial pressure. If the patient survives the acute event, recovery can be fairly good.

Multi-infarct dementia

Multi-infarct dementia arises through multiple small infarcts of the brain. While there is an association with hypertension, the disorder can occur in non-hypertensive patients. There is also an association with atheromatous cardio-vascular and cerebrovascular disease, and infarction is believed to be caused by arteriolar thrombosis. Multi-infarction accounts for approximately 20% of dementia, although mixed states, with Alzheimer's disease, are common.

Infectious diseases

Infections of the central nervous system (CNS) remain an important group of conditions and, with the increasing spread of HIV infection and the clinical

---

Box 6.3   Routes of infection

Direct spread
  Middle ear/sinus infection
Through defect
  Open skull fracture
  Meningomyelocele
  Ventricular shunt
Haematogenous
  Iatrogenic
    growth hormone (Creutzfeldt-Jakob disease)
    blood transfusion (HIV)
  Transplacental
    toxoplasmosis, rubella, cytomegalovirus, listeria, syphilis
  Embolic
    from subacute bacterial endocarditis
  Others
    meningococcus and other bacterial
    infections, many viral infections, malaria, etc.
Retrogradely, up neuronal axons
  Rabies

---

use of immunosuppressants, the range and frequency of many conditions appear to be increasing. Routes of infection are listed in Box 6.3.

Intracranial infections may be conveniently considered according to which anatomical area is primarily affected, although in many instances there may be overlap.

Epidural abscess

This is normally associated with local vertebral pyogenic infection.

Subdural empyema

This is usually associated with local sepsis and may lead to sinus thrombosis.

Meningitis

Acute bacterial meningitis

Acute bacterial meningitis may affect individuals of any age (see Table 6.1), and, untreated, is frequently fatal. Specific organisms, low glucose, high protein concentrations and numerous polymorphs are seen in the cerebrospinal fluid (CSF). The meninges may appear relatively normal very early in the disease, but later a purulent exudate fills the sulcal subarachnoid space.

Table 6.1 Common causes of acute bacterial meningitis

Age group	Bacillus
Neonates	E. coli
	Group B streptococci
Young children	Haemophilus influenzae
	Neisseria meningitidis (meningococcus)
Young adults	Neisseria meningitidis
Any age	Streptococcus pneumonia
	(pneumococcus)

The brain may become swollen. Survivors may be left with cranial nerve palsies and/or hydrocephalus.

Acute viral meningitis

This is generally a benign, self-limiting disease. Common causes include the enteroviruses (ECHO, polioviruses and Coxsackie) and mumps. The CSF glucose level is generally normal, but protein levels are raised and there is lymphocytosis. A degree of meningitis is generally also seen in cases of encephalitis (see below).

Chronic bacterial meningitis

This is seen with Mycobacterial infection and, more historically, in tertiary syphilis. The base of the brain is often most affected and the meninges appear thickened. Rarely a tuberculoma may mimic a tumour. Histologically, collagenous meningeal thickening, chronic inflammatory cells, granulomas and endarteritis obliterans are seen. An important differential diagnosis is cerebral sarcoid.

Fungal meningitis

This is commonly caused by Cryptococcus and is most often seen in the context of immunosuppression. Aspergillus and Candida albicans are other relatively common pathogens.

Differential diagnosis

It is important to remember neoplastic (usually carcinomatous or secondary to systemic lymphoma) and chemical causes.

Parenchymal CNS infections

Cerebral abscess

Bacterial infections (often anaerobic and arising from local or haematogenous spread) are the main causes of cerebral abscess. There is central liquefaction of cerebral tissue, with usually a thin wall and intense surrounding oedema. Fungi and amoebae may also be responsible. The prognosis is generally poor, but it is essential that this potentially curable space-occupying lesion should be distinguished from a cerebral tumour. Recently, in the context of immunodeficiency, toxoplasma abscesses have become relatively frequent. The main differential is primary cerebral lymphoma, which also presents with multiple space-occupying lesions in immunosuppressed individuals.

Viral encephalitis

Viral encephalitis may result in relatively little or totally devastating degrees of damage. Macroscopically there may be some congestion and swelling of the brain or, in the case of herpes simplex (type 1) encephalitis, there may be massive, bilateral, usually asymmetrical necrosis of medial temporal structures and sometimes other parts of the limbic system. Other viruses produce different, characteristic patterns of damage. Polioencephalomyelitis affecting lower, and to a lesser degree upper motor neurons, herpes zoster affecting dorsal root ganglia, and so on.

The microscopic features of some viral encephalitides are described in Box 6.4.

Box 6.4   Histological features of viral encephalitis

Neuronal loss
Neuronophagia (dying neurons surrounded by phagocytes)
Inflammation
  Acute, polymorph infiltration followed by monocyte/macrophages, lymphocytes and plasma cells, microglial and astrocytic response
Inclusions
  Cowdry type A: intranuclear, cytomegalovirus or measles
  Intranuclear in progressive multifocal leucoencephalopathy
  Intracytoplasmic in rabies (Negri bodies)

Specific forms of viral encephalitis are described below.

Subacute sclerosing panencephalitis (SSPE)   This results from a persistent infection with an abnormal form of the measles virus where, as the name suggests, cortical damage occurs, with white-matter damage. Inclusions are found in neurons and oligodendrocytes.

Progressive multifocal leucoencephalopathy (PML)   This is the result of an opportunist infection with a papovavirus (JC virus usually). Multiple foci of demyelination with fuzzy edges (compare with multiple sclerosis - see p. 213), often in showers, may coalesce. Large oligodendrocytes with inclusions and bizarre-looking astrocytes are seen.

Perivenous encephalomyelitis   This is a rare autoimmune disorder usually seen following a viral infection (e.g. measles) or after vaccination (e.g., historically, smallpox). Myelin loss occurs around veins and this is usually associated with a chronic perivenular inflammatory cell infiltrate. Unlike PML, where virus is present within the brain, no virus is found in perivenular demyelination. A particularly severe form of this disorder is known as haemorrhagic leucoencephalitis.

HIV encephalitis   This is seen in about 25 % of HIV-positive patients examined neuropathologically. Nodules with multinucleated giant cells are the most characteristic feature. Cortical neuronal loss has been documented. An HIV leucoencephalopathy with pallor and gliosis of the white matter is also described. Occasionally there may be pallor of the long tracts of the spinal cord. A wide range of opportunist infections and primary cerebral lymphoma are also often seen in these patients.

Other causes of encephalitis

Miscellaneous causes of encephalitis and related conditions include encephalitis lethargica, Behçet's disease, paraneoplastic syndrome (usually associated with small-cell carcinoma of the bronchus), Rickettsiae infection, malaria, toxoplasmosis, and bacterial infection (e.g. in association with subacute bacterial endocarditis). Encephalitis lethargica was epidemic in the late 1920s, and the survivors suffered from Parkinsonism. It was possibly caused by the influenza virus.

Neurosyphilis

Syphilis may affect the CNS in a number of ways. After an initial, asymptomatic phase, meningeal, vascular or parenchymatous lesions develop. Meningeal and vascular varieties lead to raised intracranial pressure, sudden-onset focal cerebral symptoms and limb weakness, and paraesthesia where the spinal cord is involved.

The parenchymatous disorder may be tabetic, involving the dorsal columns of the spinal cord and brainstem, leading to pain, paraesthesia, ataxia, loss of proprioception (leading to a stamping gait) and impaired pupillary reflexes. The pupils are small, often irregular in shape, and respond to accommodation but not to light (the Argyle-Robertson pupil). The paretic form involves personality change, global cognitive impairment, and seizures. Optic atrophy may also occur in association with the tabetic and parenchymatous forms.

Differential diagnosis

Presenting symptoms are similar to meningitis but confusional states are commoner despite the fact that pyrexia is often less severe. Cranial nerve signs and features of brainstem disorder, such as marked sleep disturbance, may also be present. Local or diffuse inflammatory reactions in the CNS are commonly infectious but may occur in autoimmune disorders such as systemic lupus erythematosus. Toxoplasma and cytomegalovirus infection is most likely to occur in individuals with impaired immunological responses (e.g. due to treatment with immunosuppressants or in acquired immune deficiency syndrome). Neurosyphilis has been termed clinically 'the great imitator'.

Multifocal brain infection may follow septicaemia, systemic infections such as tuberculosis, and embolism, usually from an atheromatous plaque or a valvular vegetation in endocarditis.

Neurodegenerative disease

The clinical presentations and management of these diseases have been covered in Chapter 4 – see pages 145–148.

General principles

Except in the familial cases, the aetiology of neurodegenerative disorders is unknown, yet they constitute a colossal health problem. In the absence of aetiological markers of the disorders, the different entities are defined clinicopathologically. Pathological characterisation is according to the distribution of nerve-cell loss and associated gliosis, together with the absence or presence (and distribution) of inclusions or extracellular deposits.

Alzheimer's disease

Alzheimer's disease is the commonest neurodegenerative disease and the commonest cause of dementia. Currently, little distinction is made between presenile cases and those arising in the more elderly, which were previously classified simply as senile dementia. The histology is much the same, as indeed it is in all cases of Down's syndrome living beyond the third decade.

Macroscopically there is reduction in brain weight in comparison with 'normal' age-matched controls (especially in presenile cases), together with widening of sulci in a fronto-temporo-parietal distribution and enlargement of the lateral and third ventricles. There may be pallor of the locus coeruleus.

Microscopically the classic, but non-specific, hallmarks are plaques and tangles (Table 6.2).

Table 6.2 Comparison between plaques and tangles

Senile plaques	Neurofibrillary tangles
Site	
Hippocampus, amygdala, PHG, neocortex	Hippocampus (especially AH), amygdala, PHG, neocortex, locus coeruleus, nucleus of Meynert, raphé nuclei
Components	
Extracellular amyloid ($+/-$ core), microglia, swollen nerve cell processes (neurites)	Intracellular paired helical filaments (PHF); PHF also seen in plaque neurites and neuropil threads
Biochemistry	
βA4 protein a major component of plaque amyloid	Abnormally phosphorylated tau protein is present in PHF
Also seen in:	
Ageing, DS	Ageing, DS, dementia pugilistica, PEP, PSNP, others

PHG, parahippocampal gyrus; AH, Ammon's horn; DS, Down's syndrome; PEP, postencephalitic Parkinson's disease; PSNP, progressive supranuclear palsy.

Plaques are characterised by the deposition of βA4 protein in the extracellular space. This may aggregate further to form amyloid with or without a central core. Plaques often reach about 0.2 mm across. Nerve cell processes (neurites) around the plaque become swollen and tortuous, and may accumulate paired helical filaments (PHF) in their cytoplasm. Reactive microglial and astrocytic elements complete the complex picture of a classic plaque. βA4 protein is an abnormal fragment of the amyloid precursor protein, the gene for which is on chromosome 21.

Neurofibrillary tangles, on the other hand, form within nerve cell bodies, particularly in the pyramidal cells of the hippocampus, where they are flame-shaped. In rounder cells they may be more whorl-like. Tangles are also composed of PHF, the paired helical nature of which is discernible only by electron microscopy. PHF are also seen in the dendrites of tangle-bearing neurons as neuropil threads.

The PHF are probably composed largely of abnormal cytoskeletal components. PHF structures are stained with antibodies to phosphorylated neurofilaments, but of particular importance seems to be an abnormally phosphorylated form of tau. Tau is a microtubule-associated protein (MAP) that is involved in stabilising the polymers of tubulin that form microtubules.

The number and neocortical extent of plaques and tangles is greater in Alzheimer's disease than in 'normal' ageing, but the boundaries are indistinct. The βA4 protein that is a major constituent of the amyloid in plaques is also seen in the amyloid that is deposited in meningeal and cortical blood vessels (Congophilic angiopathy).

Other abnormalities include eosinophilic ovoid structures seen in relation to pyramidal cells in Ammon's horn known as 'Hirano bodies'. In the same cells small pale spherical structures with a dark core called granulovacuoles are often seen.

There is much speculation as to the possible cause of non-familial (sporadic) Alzheimer's disease. Suggestions include aluminium toxicity, blood–brain barrier defect, infection by virus or prion-like agent (see below) and head injury.

Pick's disease

Macroscopically, cases of Pick's disease show dramatic frontal or temporal atrophy (with so-called knife-edge gyri), or both.

Microscopically, round, argyrophilic intraneuronal inclusions (Pick bodies) and swollen cortical pyramidal cells (Pick cells) are seen together with nerve cell loss and gliosis. Some cases are familial but little is known about the possible pathogenesis. Pick bodies stain with the same antibodies as tangles but do not contain PHF.

Huntington's disease

The macroscopic hallmark of this autosomal dominant condition is striatal atrophy, with flattening or even concavity of the outline of the head of the caudate. There is also cortical atrophy.

There are no specific microscopic abnormalities, although the large striatal neurons are relatively well preserved in comparison with the small and medium-sized ones. Gliosis can be quite marked.

Creutzfeldt-Jakob disease

This rare dementia is notable for being transmissible and for the enigmatic nature of the transmissible agent, which is difficult to inactivate by conventional means. There is no compelling evidence that the agent contains nucleic acid; in fact infectivity is associated with a protein (prion protein). Scrapie in sheep, and in cattle as bovine spongiform encephalopathy, is a related animal pathogen. Gerstmann–Straüssler syndrome is poorly delineated from familial forms of Creutzfeldt-Jakob disease. A variety of abnormalities of the prion gene have been documented in familial cases.

There may be no macroscopic abnormalities, or the brain may appear atrophic.

Histologically, one sees the triad of nerve cell loss, gliosis and spongiform change - numerous small to medium-sized vacuoles within the neuropil, which may coalesce. Rarely plaques, without obvious abnormal neurites, may be seen, and antibodies to prion protein may be used on sections to detect these deposits more readily.

Parkinson's disease

Pallor of substantia nigra and locus coeruleus with the presence of Lewy bodies (eosinophilic, haloed intraneuronal inclusions) in the above nuclei, the nucleus of Meynert, the dorsal motor nucleus of the vagus and sympathetic nuclei are seen in the disease. There is usually nerve cell loss in areas where the inclusions are seen.

It is now increasingly appreciated that many demented patients (with or without Parkinsonism) have the subcortical pathology of Parkinson's disease, together with similar inclusions (cortical Lewy bodies) with less well defined haloes in the cortex (especially parahippocampal gyrus). This condition is known as diffuse Lewy body disease. The presence of a Parkinson's disease-like disease in drug-abusers exposed to the synthetic drug MPTP has strengthened the argument for the importance of an environmental cause of the disease.

Other degenerative disorders

There are many other important neurodegenerative disorders.

Motor neuron disease shows mainly upper and lower motor neuron and tract loss, with some patients exhibiting dementia.

Multiple system atrophy is a term embracing three 'patterns' of pathology which often coexist in varying proportions in any one case, the patterns being:

(1) striatonigral degeneration
(2) olivopontocerebellar atrophy
(3) autonomic degeneration (Shy–Drager syndrome).

Progressive supranuclear palsy shows tangles in brainstem nuclei composed of mainly straight, rather than paired helical, filaments (compare with Alzheimer's disease). There are also a variety of cerebellar degenerations.

Epilepsy

While it is often difficult to distinguish one from the other, it is useful to divide the pathology of epilepsy into changes 'causing' epilepsy and those arising from it. In the absence of the former, the epilepsy is said to be 'idiopathic' or 'primary', and in the presence of a 'cause' it is known as 'secondary' or 'symptomatic' (see Chapter 4, pp. 125–129).

Almost any insult to the nervous system may lower the threshold for seizures. Apart from metabolic abnormalities, structural lesions are particularly likely to be associated with fits if they are:

(1) cortical
(2) close to the motor strip
(3) slow-growing/evolving.

Tumours, abscesses and malformations are typical examples of such lesions. Some individuals appear to have a genetic predisposition to have seizures in response to structural lesions.

Most patients with epilepsy (primary or secondary) show no changes that could be considered a consequence of repeated fits. Following prolonged status epilepticus, however, there may be diffuse brain swelling, and in some individuals chronic changes are found. At the most dramatic there may, in children, be atrophy of an entire cerebral hemisphere. More commonly, medial temporal structures, including the hippocampus (especially Sommer's sector, part of CA1 of Ammon's horn), amygdala and parahippocampal gyrus, may show loss of nerve cells. These changes are sometimes known as mesial temporal sclerosis (MTS). Neocortex, thalamus and the cerebellum may also be involved. MTS may be seen following febrile convulsions and it seems probable that this damage, arising from ictal activity, may then go on to 'cause' temporal lobe epilepsy in later life.

Abnormal electrical activity *per se*, as well as secondary factors such as global cerebral ischaemia, hyperthermia and acidosis, contribute to seizure-induced nerve cell death. It is of interest that Sommer's sector shows selective vulnerability in epilepsy, global cerebral ischaemia/hypoxia and hypoglycaemia. Finally, contusional damage arising from seizure-related head injury may be seen.

Tumours

Primary neoplasms of the CNS and meninges are relatively uncommon, producing about one-twentieth of the disability caused by cerebrovascular disease. About half of the primary neoplasms of the CNS derive from neuroepithelial cells, gliomas being the most common; mesodermal tumours account for a quarter, with meningioma the commonest; ectodermal tumours (including pituitary adenoma and craniopharyngioma), vascular and a variety of rarities make up the remainder.

Tumours of the CNS present clinically either by producing localised disturbance of brain function, due to local pressure effects or focal epilepsy, or generalised impairment of higher function, usually by raising intracranial pressure. Raised intracranial pressure typically presents as a worsening headache followed by drowsiness or confusion and vomiting. Papilloedema is the characteristic sign. The course is usually slowly progressive, although sudden deterioration can occur, following haemorrhage into and sudden enlargement of the tumour. A wide variety of headaches can occur, typically with a progressive increase in severity. Postural headache – headache on awakening relieved by adopting an upright posture – is said to be characteristic. Epileptic seizures can be the first sign and may be focal/partial or complex partial with or without secondary generalisation. A range of neuropsychiatric features may be produced, including lethargy, depression, irritability, abulia and personality change. Focal or generalised cognitive impairment can occur.

Temporal lobe and limbic tumours may lead to schizophreniform and affectiform psychoses. Tumours of the brainstem may present with cranial nerve signs, and lead to reduced arousal and impairment in the sleep-wake cycle. Hypothalamic tumours may, in addition, lead to altered appetite and thirst, passivity or rage, and endocrine disorders.

Primary cerebral tumours

The distribution of primary cerebral tumours (Box 6.5) varies between children and adults. The former are afflicted with mainly infratentorial tumours (cerebellar astrocytoma, medulloblastoma and ependymoma).

Adults mainly suffer from supratentorial tumours (astrocytomas, or occasionally other gliomas and primary cerebral lymphomas). Primary cerebral tumours characteristically have a diffuse growing edge, and astrocytomas, in particular, tend to be cystic.

Astrocytomas

Astrocytomas are composed of cells with eosinophilic cytoplasm and many processes that generate a fibrillary background. These processes contain glial fibrillary acidic protein (GFAP), an intermediate filament protein. The nuclei are generally hyperchromatic and oval. These tumours grow diffusely and are often cystic.

The labels benign and malignant are less readily applied to primary CNS tumours than to those elsewhere. The confined space within the skull and the diffuse growth of an astrocytoma make these tumours very difficult to treat, although patients with astrocytomas will do better than those with the high-grade

---

Box 6.5   Common primary cerebral tumours

Gliomas
    Astrocytoma
    Anaplastic astrocytoma
    Oligodendroglioma
    Ependymoma
    Glioblastoma multiforme
Primitive tumours
    Medulloblastoma
Lymphoid tumours
    Primary cerebral lymphoma
    (formerly microglioma)

counterpart, the anaplastic astrocytoma. Here there are more mitoses, the cells are more pleomorphic, and necrosis is seen. Despite the 'malignancy' of these tumours and the even more anaplastic glioblastoma multiforme (where endothelial cell hyperplasia and pseudopallisading necrosis are often seen), these tumours hardly ever metastasise outside the CNS.

Other primary neuroectodermal tumours

Oligodendrogliomas have round, uniform, small nuclei which are often surrounded by a pale zone ('fried egg' appearance) in sections. These tumours may grow slowly, and calcification is often a feature.

Ependymomas have rather more oval nuclei and a tendency to form rosettes, sometimes around blood vessels.

The medulloblastoma is the commonest form of primitive neuroectodermal tumour (PNET) and affects young children, particularly boys. Sheets of cells with little cytoplasm may occasionally show evidence of differentiation into either astrocyte- or neuron-like cells. These tumours are radiosensitive but the effects of radiation on the young nervous system are giving cause for concern, as intellectual and behavioural problems may appear later in life.

Primary cerebral lymphoma

This is seen sporadically and in the context of immunosuppression. Such lymphomas are generally of the B-cell type, and may be associated with the presence of many 'reactive' microglial cells, hence the old term 'microglioma'.

Tumours of the meninges, pituitary and skull

Meningiomas are common, generally benign, tumours arising predominantly from arachnoidal cells of the leptomeninges. Particularly if they are frontal and slow growing they may reach great size. They normally separate readily from the underlying brain but may extend into sinuses and skull without being considered malignant. They can occur at a wide variety of sites, including the ventricles, and may occasionally grow over the surface of the brain. Hence they may display a wide variety of clinical presentations. Olfactory and anterior falx/sagittal meningiomas may present with the development of a frontal lobe syndrome, ranging from abulia to reduced impulse and temper control, behavioural disinhibition and fatuousness. Meningiomas exerting direct pressure on the cortex commonly lead to focal epileptic disturbances, and very large and presumably slow-growing tumours may remain clinically silent until the development of seizures. Ventricular meningiomas may at an early stage lead to raised intracranial pressure.

Other ventricular tumours include colloid cysts and choroid plexus papillomas.

Pituitary adenomas are now classified by the hormones they produce and secrete rather than according to their tinctorial properties. The majority produce adrenocorticotrophic hormone, prolactin or growth hormone. Non-secreting tumours are not uncommon. Compression of the optic chiasm may produce a bitemporal homonymous hemianopia. Malignant tumours of the anterior pituitary are rare.

Craniopharyngioma is a non-malignant, slowly growing neoplasm which develops in childhood and adolescence but may not present clinically for many years: the commonest symptoms arise from pressure on the optic chiasm and pituitary, invasion of the hypothalamus, midbrain and third ventricle. Hence the commonest presenting features are visual, endocrine and behavioural, particularly abulia, and concentration and memory disorders.

Skull tumours are not common but include benign 'ivory' osteomas, chordomas (arising from the clivus) and, rarely, osteosarcoma (complicating Paget's disease). Clearly secondary tumours, including myeloma, may involve the skull. A variety of other conditions, for instance histiocytosis X and fibrous dysplasia, also affect the skull.

Secondary tumours of the nervous system

Metastases are usually from carcinomas and tumours of lung and, in women, breast. They are generally multiple, have a well defined edge, a necrotic centre, and lie at the junction between grey and white matter. Malignant meningitis may complicate carcinomatosis or systemic lymphoreticular malignancies, which rarely cause discrete parenchymal deposits (unlike primary cerebral lymphoma).

Complications

Non-metastatic complications of systemic malignant disease are:

(1) peripheral neuropathy (including of the autonomic nervous system)
(2) cerebellar cortical degeneration
(3) limbic 'encephalitis' (hippocampal damage)
(4) Eaton–Lambert syndrome (myasthenia-like).

Space-occupying lesions and cerebral oedema

Space-occupying lesions

Space-occupying lesions cause:

(1) local damage
(2) herniations of portions of brain from one intracranial compartment to another
(3) interference with CSF flow
(4) a rise in intracranial pressure.

Table 6.3 Consequences of space-occupying lesions

Site lesion	Herniation	Consequence
Cerebral hemisphere	Subfalcial or cingulate	–
	Medial temporal or uncinate	Third-nerve palsy, occlusion of the posterior cerebral artery, haemorrhage in the midbrain
	Tonsillar	Compression of medulla and death
Cerebellar hemisphere	Upward through tentorium	–
	Down through foramen magnum (tonsillar) (i.e. 'coning')	Compression of medulla and death

The latter occurs when the CSF and vascular compartments can no longer compensate for the expanding lesion's volume and leads to a reduction in cerebral perfusion pressure. This can eventually lead to cessation of effective cerebral perfusion, brain death and, if the patient is kept alive on a ventilator, so-called 'respiratory brain'.

Space-occupying lesions may interfere with the flow of CSF, especially in the posterior fossa. Other consequences are summarised in Table 6.3.

Cerebral oedema

Oedema is defined as an increase in the extravascular water content of the tissue. It may arise due to breakdown of the blood–brain barrier (vasogenic oedema) or swelling of cells (cytotoxic oedema), as may occur in liver failure. Its major consequence is the rise in intracranial pressure resulting from the intracranial space it occupies. Cerebral tumours and abscesses are major causes of vasogenic cerebral oedema. Other disorders, such as cerebral ischaemia, can result in both vasogenic and cytotoxic forms.

Secondary metabolic disorders

Liver failure

Liver failure, from whatever cause, imposes a metabolic burden on the nervous system. The precise nature of the crucial biochemical abnormality remains unclear, but excess circulating nitrogenous compounds, including ammonia and a possible false transmitter–octopamine – seem important. Acutely, there is swelling of astrocyte processes, and large, pale, irregular astrocyte nuclei (Alzheimer type-II astrocytes) are seen postmortem in patients surviving beyond the initial fulminant stage.

In hepatolenticular degeneration (Wilson's disease) it is debatable as to which changes are attributable to the hepatic problems and which result directly from the abnormal copper metabolism.

Reye's syndrome in children is another specific example of hepatocerebral pathology.

Alcoholism

In addition to the well known diet-related problems encountered by alcoholics, it now appears that ethanol has a direct toxic action upon the nervous system. Some of the pathological entities associated with alcoholism are:

(1) foetal alcohol syndrome
(2) cerebellar atrophy
(3) cerebral atrophy
(4) peripheral neuropathy
(5) Wernicke's encephalopathy
(6) Korsakoff's psychosis
(7) Marchiafava–Bignami syndrome
(8) amblyopia
(9) central pontine myelinolysis.

Wernicke's encephalopathy is an acute condition with ophthalmoplegia, ataxia and disorientation. There is cerebral oedema and capillary engorgement and/or haemorrhage in regions adjacent to the third and fourth ventricles, including the colliculi. The chronic form of thiamine deficiency, which may arise consequent to, or independent of, Wernicke's encephalopathy is Korsakoff's psychosis, and although shrinkage of the mammillary bodies is the most striking external feature, damage of the dorsomedial nuclei of the thalamus correlates better with the short-term memory loss.

Central pontine myelinolysis is often the result of rapid correction of hyponatraemia and can be seen in a variety of conditions. The name describes the pathology.

Other complications relate to liver failure and head injury.

Diabetes

The CNS complications of diabetes are largely secondary.to vascular disease or to therapy (i.e. hypoglycaemia). The former may present as a stocking-glove-distribution peripheral neuropathy (accumulated small ischaemic lesions make distal disease more prominent) or as cerebral thromboembolic disease. Prolonged hypoglycaemia, from whatever cause, leads to extensive cerebral neuronal destruction similar to that seen in global cerebral ischaemia/hypoxia.

Other endocrine disorders

Despite the dramatic behavioural symptoms seen in some adults with hypothyroidism and abnormalities of steroid metabolism, consistent structural CNS abnormalities are not reported. Reduced brain weight and cerebrovascular abnormalities are reported in childhood myxoedema.

Intoxications

Alcoholism is discussed above. A comprehensive account of neurotoxicology is not practicable here, but a summary of some conditions is given below. Clearly, familiarity of the effects of these agents is paramount in addiction and occupational medicine.

Aluminium is undoubtedly neurotoxic and a major feature in dialysis dementia. Despite the presence of increased amounts of aluminium in the lesions of Alzheimer's disease, an aetiological role in this disease remains to be proven.

Chemotherapeutic agents may be profoundly neurotoxic when given accidentally or sometimes therapeutically via the intrathecal route.

Lead in its inorganic forms tends to produce an acute encephalopathy in children and a predominantly motor peripheral neuropathy in adults. Organic lead compounds cause an acute encephalopathy. Irritability, lethargy, depression and headache develop in the early stages, associated with gastrointestinal disturbance. Prolonged exposure, or high dose, leads to encephalopathy, somnolence or mania, and confusion followed by stupor, coma, convulsions and death. High concentrations of lead in children's teeth have been found to be associated with cognitive disabilities and behavioural disturbance, and this has led to legislation on lead emissions from motor vehicles.

Mercurial compounds are also neurotoxic in both inorganic and organic forms and produce cerebellar damage. Methyl mercury also produces damage to primary sensory areas. Fine tremor of the limbs is associated with depression and a mixed neurotic (neurasthenic) syndrome including fatigue, irritability, apprehension and headache. Acute poisoning by, for example, mercury-containing pesticides, can lead to an acute cerebellar syndrome including marked ataxia.

Methyl-phenyl-tetrahydropyridine (MPTP) appeared as a contaminant of a synthetic recreational drug and causes loss of neurons from the substantia nigra; affected individuals present with a Parkinsonian syndrome.

Opiate overdose, either clinical or self-administered, may leave survivors with extensive cerebral destruction of the global ischaemic/hypoxic type following respiratory depression.

Carbon monoxide inhalation leads to hypoxia, due to the reduced capacity of the blood to carry oxygen as the concentration of methaemoglobin rises. There may also be other effects on cerebral metabolism. Headache, irritability, dizziness and confusion occur in the early stages, with cerebral oedema and coma at higher concentrations. On recovery from acute poisoning there may be cognitive impairment of varying severity, particularly memory disorder. Lesions are particularly common in the basal ganglia (detectable on CT scan), which become calcified in time.

Solvent abuse with hexacarbons can cause a peripheral neuropathy. Details of any CNS pathology are not clear.

Dietary deficiency

A list of dietary deficiency states with CNS complications is given in Table 6.4. Disorders of the nervous system can arise from a variety of dietary deficiencies, the commonest relating to vitamin deficiencies, particularly the B vitamins. Diagnosis is usually confirmed by finding a low serum level of the relevant vitamins.

Thiamine deficiency

Thiamine is an important cofactor in the metabolism of carbohydrate. A diet deficient in carbohydrate and thiamine, particularly over a prolonged period, leads to beriberi, a disorder involving polyneuropathy (axonal degeneration with secondary demyelination) and cardiac failure. While commonest in malnourished children, it can develop at any age and is seen in the developed world in association with conditions leading to anorexia and neglect (e.g. alcohol abuse or major depression). Features of a mixed sensory and motor neuropathy can occur alone or with cardiac failure. Treatment is by parenteral thiamine and adequate diet.

Wernicke's encephalopathy develops where thiamine deficiency is particularly severe and acute. Vomiting and feelings of unreality rapidly progress to a confusional state associated with ataxia and ophthalmoplegia (of lateral gaze in particular). It is most commonly associated with the dietary neglect found in alcohol dependence, but it also occurs in other conditions, particularly where persistent vomiting is a feature. Untreated, the condition is rapidly fatal, and even after treatment (with parenteral thiamine) residual brain damage is common. The usual picture is Korsakoff's syndrome (learning/memory disorder associated with confabulation), which may be

Table 6.4 The consequences of neurological dietary deficiency

Deficiency	Consequence
Vitamin B_{12}	Subacute combined degeneration of the spinal cord
Nicotinic acid	Pellagra (with swollen cortical neurons)
Thiamine	See under 'Alcoholism'
Vitamin E	Peripheral and cranial nerve problems
General	Almost certainly interferes with development of the young brain

associated with marked abulia. These features arise from petechial haemorrhagic damage to grey matter surrounding the third ventricle.

Nicotinic acid deficiency

Nicotinic acid acts as a co-enzyme in cellular oxidation processes. The vitamin is produced endogenously, and tryptophan is a precursor. Chronic deficiency leads to pellagra, a disorder said to be characterised by diarrhoea, dermatitis and a varied psychiatric picture, ranging from depressive or manic disorders to paranoid confusional states or admixtures. Diplopia, dysarthria and ataxia can also occur. The earliest features to develop are diarrhoea associated with desquamation and thickening of skin exposed to light. The disorder can arise from dietary deficiency or as a result of impairment of tryptophan metabolism or absorption (e.g. in Hartnup's disease or phaeochromocytoma). Treatment is by giving high-dose parenteral nicotinic acid and by treating any metabolic disorder.

Cyanocobolamin deficiency (B_{12})

Vitamin B_{12} deficiency leads to megaloblastic anaemia, white-matter degeneration in the lateral and posterior spinal cord, and cerebral atrophy. Anaemia is often asymptomatic, and the commonest presenting features are paraesthesia and numbness of the toes, with later involvement of the hands, progressing proximally. A sense of having on tight socks and gloves is said to be characteristic. Weakness and unsteadiness of gait generally develop later and urinary retention or incontinence can also occur. A variety of psychiatric features have been reported, including depression, paranoid psychosis, confusional states, amnestic syndromes, and more global cognitive impairment. Physical signs include impaired sensation (touch and proprioception particularly), ataxia and nystagmus. The deficiency is generally related to malabsorption, often due to gastric pathology impairing intrinsic factor release. Treatment is by intramuscular B_{12}, with subsequent maintenance injections.

Folic acid

Deficiency of this vitamin most commonly occurs in association with malabsorption syndromes and through the use of antagonistic drugs (particularly phenytoin and phenobarbitone). Clinical features include megaloblastic anaemia and peripheral neuropathy, irritability and depression. Global cognitive impairment is generally a later development. Treatment is by treating causative conditions and by giving oral folic acid.

Inheritable metabolic disorders

There are too many inherited disorders of the nervous system for a full description here, but a general classification is presented, together with a more detailed description of a few commoner conditions.

Lysosomal storage disorders

In these, generally autosomal recessive, conditions, reduced activity of a lysosomal enzyme leads to the accumulation of one or more substances which may interfere with neuronal function or myelination, or both. Many of these, and other inherited metabolic disorders, can now be diagnosed from biochemical assays of white blood cells, cultured fibroblasts, or cultured cells from amniotic fluid. In others histochemistry or electron microscopy of skin or rectal biopsy may be required. These conditions are often further divided clinically according to the age at onset. Examples of those predominantly affecting grey matter are listed in Table 6.5.

Metachromatic and Krabbe's leucodystrophies are considered below under the leucodystrophies, but they are also lysosomal storage disorders.

Miscellaneous conditions affecting mainly grey matter

Wilson's disease

Hepatic and striatal pathology characterise this autosomal recessive disease of copper handling. Shrinkage and discoloration of the corpus striatum is seen macroscopically, with neuronal loss and gliosis histologically. Superimposed may be features of hepatic encephalopathy.

Leigh's disease

This, probably heterogeneous, condition arises as a consequence of failure of glycolytic metabolism. Adult forms are rarer than those presenting in infancy or early childhood. Symmetrical lesions of brainstem nuclei are most often seen, although many parts of the CNS may be involved. Histologically the

Table 6.5 Examples of lysosomal disorders affecting grey matter

Group/disorder	Example	Enzyme deficiency
Gangliosidosis	Tay-Sachs disease	Hexosaminidase
Ceroid lipofuscinosis	Batten-Kufs' disease	Not known
Mucopolysaccharidoses	Hurler's syndrome	α-1-iduronidase
Niemann-Pick disease		Sphingomyelinase
Gaucher's disease		Glucocerebrosidase

Table 6.6 The leucodystrophies

Name	Genetics	Features
Metachromatic leucodystrophy	AR	Arylsulphatase A deficiency. Metachromatic granules in urine
Krabbe's leucodystrophy	AR	Galatocerebroside β-galactosidase deficiency. Multinucleate globoid cells seen
Adrenoleuco-dystrophy	XLR	Adrenal abnormalities also. Excess very-long-chain fatty acids
Pelizaeus–Merzbacher disease		Preservation of myelin around blood vessels
Sudanophilic leucodystrophy	Variable	General term for cases of leucodystrophy where no more specific features are present

AR, autosomal recessive; XLR, X-linked recessive.

lesions resemble those of Wernicke's encephalopathy, which has a similar pathogenesis. Lactate tolerance tests are often abnormal.

Leucodystrophies

These conditions are characterised by extensive degeneration of myelin. The term 'metachromatic' relates to the ability of the storage product to change the colour of certain dyes.

The main types of leucodystrophy are listed in Table 6.6. Other, even rarer, familial disorders of white matter include Canavan's disease, Cockayne's syndrome and Bassen–Kornzweig syndrome.

Schizophrenia

The neuropathology of schizophrenia was for many years rather unsatisfactory and hard to interpret. Studies were poorly controlled and no consistent pattern emerged. Now, however, there is a substantial body of knowledge indicating that there is definite organic pathology in at least some sufferers.

The main change is that the lateral ventricles are abnormally large, especially in the temporal lobe, where there appears to be less grey matter than normal. Brain weight and size are reduced. The hippocampus and anterior parahippocampal gyrus seem to be the most severely affected regions and there is the suggestion that the left side is more involved than the right. The degree of these changes relates more closely to negative symptoms than to positive aspects of the disease (Chapter 5, pp. 159–163). Some studies also suggest that there are cytoarchitectural changes, implicating disordered nerve-cell migration in development. This, the paucity of gliotic reaction and the failure to demonstrate progressive loss of cerebral substance in imaging studies, has led to the notion that the changes occur early in development and become unmasked later in life.

Demyelinating disorders

Demyelination is the loss of myelin with relative preservation of axons. It may arise following direct damage to the myelin sheath or secondary to oligodendrocyte pathology. A summary of demyelinating conditions is given in Box 6.6

Multiple sclerosis

Multiple sclerosis is the most common cause of demyelination and although the details of its pathogenesis remain obscure, genetic, environmental and autoimmune factors appear to be of importance.

The neuropathology of multiple sclerosis is essentially that of the chronic phase of the disease, as patients rarely die with acute lesions. An acute, rapidly progressive form of the disease (Marburg type) is, however, recognised. The term 'Dévic's disease' is sometimes applied to the combination of optic-nerve and cord lesions.

Macroscopically, the plaques in multiple sclerosis range from 1 mm to a few cm across, and although they are most readily found in the white matter adjacent to the lateral ventricles, often by veins, it is often smaller lesions in cerebellar, visual and spinal pathways that are of the most clinical significance. True peripheral nerves, as opposed to the optic nerve, which is of CNS origin, are not affected. Chronic plaques have a well defined edge and are a translucent grey. They are mainly found in the white matter but they can extend into grey matter as well.

Microscopically, plaques contain few or no oligodendrocytes and there is relative preservation of axons. In long-standing lesions, however, there is loss of axons as well as myelin. The associated gliosis is responsible for the 'sclerotic'

Box 6.6   Demyelinating conditions

Multiple sclerosis
Progressive multifocal leucoencephalopathy
Central pontine myelinolysis
Long-standing cerebral oedema
Marchiafava–Bignami syndrome
B_{12} deficiency
Leucodystrophies

nature of plaques in the fresh brain. In acute plaques one sees inflammatory cells at the plaque edge and perivascular lymphocytic cuffs may be present. Remyelination is generally not apparent, although limited remyelination may take place at the plaque edge.

Developmental disorders

Genetic and environmental factors (toxins, irradiation, drugs, infections, etc.) lead to a wide array of developmental abnormalities, some of which are described below. Any classification is likely to be arbitrary, and here a largely anatomical approach has been taken. In addition, in any individual case, more than one such abnormality may be present. One group of genetically determined disorders is described separately under 'The phacomatoses'.

Defects of the neural tube

Here, the terminology relates to the structures that have failed to be enclosed within the normal skeletal confines of the CNS, and the commonest examples of this are spinal. The posterior portions of the vertebrae involved do not fuse (spina bifida) and

(1) in a meningocele, dura and arachnoid protrude backwards under the skin
(2) in a meningomyelocele, dura, arachnoid and spinal cord protrude backwards under the skin
(3) in an encephalocele, brain herniates through a defect, which is most commonly occipital.

While not necessarily a developmental problem, this is a useful place to consider syringomyelia and hydromyelia. The former is an abnormal longitudinal cavity in the spinal cord that is separate from the central canal, and the latter an enlargement of the central canal itself. The two may not always be readily distinguishable. Syrinxes arise following trauma or in association with tumours or a wide range of developmental abnormalities. The cervicothoracic region is most often affected. Syringobulbia is the analogous condition in the brainstem.

Missing elements

Anencephaly, in which a mass of vascular tissue is present instead of the brain, is said to be the most frequent cerebral malformation. Less dramatic, and compatible with life, are agenesis of the corpus callosum and cerebellar hypoplasia or aplasia. In the Dandy-Walker malformation, the vermis is partly replaced by a cyst.

The above are malformations, but portions of brain may be lost, having been formed, by destructive processes, usually infective or ischaemic. These tend to occur later in pregnancy. Massive destruction leaves little more than a CSF-filled sac (hydranencephaly) or, if more focal, porencephalic cysts. (Hydrocephalus is discussed separately below.)

Abnormal size

Micrencephaly (brain more than 2 standard deviations smaller than average) may be seen with or without other abnormalities and may be familial. Intrauterine infections and X-irradiation are important environmental causes.

Megalencephaly (brain more than 2.5 standard deviations bigger than average) may be seen with or without an associated storage disorder. Patients may show mental retardation or epilepsy.

Architectural abnormalities

In holoprosencephaly, the lateral ventricles are fused, and associated facial abnormalities may include a single mid-line eye (cyclops).

In the Arnold–Chiari malformation (Chiari's type 2 malformation), spina bifida is associated with elongated cerebellar tonsils which protrude through the foramen magnum, a kinked medulla, and hydrocephalus, together with other abnormalities. In the Chiari type 1 malformation only the tonsillar abnormality is present.

There are a variety of types of abnormality of gyrus formation, most of which seem to arise because of failure of the normal migration of nerve cells from the periventricular region to the neocortex. In lissencephaly, the surface of the brain is smooth with no gyri (agyria), and in pachygyria there is less extensive failure of gyrus formation. In polymicrogyria the cortex is abnormally layered; it is thickened and has a characteristic pattern of narrow, irregular, gyrus-like ridges on the surface.

Ectopic grey matter is seen adjacent to the ventricular surface when migration of some neurons fails completely.

Vascular abnormalities

Arteriovenous malformations are relatively common, usually affect the meningeal vessels, and tend to present in young adults with subarachnoid haemorrhage or epilepsy. Other vascular malformations include those seen in the phacomatoses, discussed below.

The phacomatoses

These conditions (Table 6.7) are manifest by a variety of malformations and neoplastic disorders affecting skin and nervous tissues. Many have a genetic basis.

Table 6.7 The phacomatoses

Disorder	Prevalence	Clinicopathological features
von Recklinghausen's neurofibromatosis	1/3000	*Café au lait* spots Cutaneous neurofibromas, including plexiform type Lisch nodules (in iris) Mental retardation Intracranial tumours Autosomal dominant (chromosome 17)
Bilateral acoustic neurofibromatosis	$1/10^6$	Multiple intracranial and spinal tumours (i.e. central), mainly Schwannomas and neurofibromas Gene deletion on chromosome 22
Tuberose sclerosis	1/15 000	Cutaneous lesions (shagreen patch, subungual angiofibromas, etc.) Glial nodules (tubers) in cortex and adjacent to ventricle Rhabdomyomas of the heart Mental retardation and epilepsy
von Hippel–Lindau disease	Rare	Vascular malformation of retina Haemangioblastoma (often cerebellar) Pancreatic, adrenal and renal cysts and tumours Autosomal dominant
Sturge–Weber syndrome	Rare	Strawberry naevus/port-wine stain on face Angiomatous malformation of meningeal vessels with calcification Mental retardation and epilepsy Not hereditary
Ataxia telangiectasia	Rare	Telangiectasia of skin and conjunctiva Progressive ataxia from childhood IgA deficiency and thymic hypoplasia Autosomal recessive

Hydrocephalus

Hydrocephalus is an increase in CSF volume and is readily demonstrated in life as enlarged ventricles on CT scan. There are many causes (Box 6.7) and they can be conveniently divided into those in which there is loss of cerebral substance (usually associated with widening of sulci) and those in which ventricular pressure is increased due to obstruction. (Ventricular dilation secondary to increased CSF production is very rare.) The most common causes tend to vary at different ages. In children it may be associated with enlargement of the head and thinning of the skull.

Box 6.7   Examples of causes of hydrocephalus

Raised pressure type
    Stenosis of cerebral aqueduct
    Posterior fossa malformation (e.g. Arnold–Chiari, Dandy–Walker)
    CSF path blocked by space-occupying lesion (e.g. tumour)
    Obstruction of movement of CSF through subarachnoid space or
        across arachnoid granulations (e.g. following meningitis or
        subarachnoid haemorrhage)

Loss of substance type
    Neurodegenerative diseases, especially Alzheimer's disease, etc.
    Global ischaemia with long-term survival (adults and neonates)
    Extensive multiple sclerosis

Perinatal neuropathology

Perinatal brain damage is an important cause of mental handicap, and some of the commoner pathologies seen are described below. Appreciation of the haemorrhagic complications of childbirth has grown markedly with the increasing use of neonatal scanning techniques.

Subependymal plate haemorrhages

These haemorrhages are a common complication of prematurity. They arise in the germinal matrix tissue in the lateral wall of the lateral ventricles. Haemorrhage may extend into the substance of the brain or into the ventricular system.

Periventricular leucomalacia

Periventricular leucomalacia, also a complication of prematurity, is the result of ischaemia/hypoxia affecting the deep white matter near the angle of the lateral ventricle.

Hypoxic/ischaemic encephalopathy

This is the commonest form of brain damage seen in full-term infants and is often associated with a difficult labour. Changes include widespread destruction of grey and white matter, often with marked thinning of the cortex at the depths of sulci, giving a mushroom appearance to the gyri (ulegyria).

Birth trauma

Birth trauma may lead to tearing of the tentorium cerebelli or falx, superficial haemorrhage, or cord/plexus injuries.

Kernicterus

Kernicterus arises from bilirubin crossing the blood-brain barrier and is now fortunately less frequently seen, although premature babies are an important high-risk group. Basal ganglia and other deep grey matter structures are discoloured yellow.

Infections of the neonate and infant

These infections differ from those in older children and adults. Rubella, cytomegalovirus, syphilis and toxoplasmosis are now joined by HIV as important congenital infections.

Head injury

Cerebral trauma is a common cause of morbidity and mortality, and is associated with a wide range of types of damage. The pathology seen can be divided into:

(1) that arising from direct impact
(2) that arising from acceleration/deceleration injury, as seen in a road traffic accident
(3) changes secondary to associated systemic changes, such as hypoxia.

In any individual case a combination of these pathologies may be seen.

Direct impact injuries

Direct impact is likely to cause superficial damage to the scalp and, if severe enough, may be associated with a skull fracture. The latter is not, necessarily, a good indicator of the degree of cerebral damage. Depressed skull fractures are clearly more damaging, and the risks of meningitis and post-traumatic epilepsy are greatly increased if the fracture is open and the dura has been breached. There may be an extradural and/or subdural haemorrhage. Penetrating injuries from sharp objects or bullets clearly breach the skull and may cause considerable parenchymal damage.

Contusional damage is common following direct impact injuries and typically occurs where the inside of the skull is rougher and at the poles, that is, over:

(1) frontal poles
(2) inferior (orbital) aspect of frontal lobes
(3) temporal poles
(4) occipital poles.

The contusions consist of haemorrhagic patches of damage at the tops of gyri. They may be associated with laceration of the brain and in severe cases extensive subarachnoid and/or intracerebral haemorrhage. Damage is often more severe over the aspect of the brain opposite the site of impact. For instance, a fall onto the back of the head may show greatest damage over the frontal poles. This pattern of injury is known as *contre coup*. In survivors of contusional damage, the chronic changes are of superficial pitting at the tops of gyri, with broken down blood often leaving an orange discoloration.

Acceleration/deceleration injuries

Where the head is suddenly accelerated or decelerated, the soft substance of the brain is subjected to shearing forces as more mobile portions shift relative to more fixed regions, or as different parts of the brain move in opposite directions. The resulting tearing may disrupt blood vessels, but in sustained acceleration/deceleration there may be extensive shearing of axons. This may be macroscopically manifest as tears in the corpus callosum or the dorsolateral quadrant of the pons. A more diffuse damage, known as diffuse axonal injury, may take place throughout much of the white matter and is recognised histologically by the presence of axonal retraction balls. In survivors, special stains reveal degenerate myelin in areas of damage. This type of damage may be of importance in causing a persistent vegetative state. At the other extreme, repeated relatively minor head injury may lead to dementia pugilistica or 'punch-drunk syndrome'.

Secondary changes

As with most cerebral injuries, cerebral oedema may develop following head injury and lead to a further increase in intracranial pressure and perfusion failure. Injuries elsewhere in the body may exacerbate the latter by causing hypoxia and hypotension, and cerebral ischaemia is not uncommon in such trauma cases. Fat embolism may arise in cases where long bones are fractured. Patients deteriorate after about three to four days and macroscopically multiple, often haemorrhagic, lesions are seen throughout the white matter. In penetrating injuries or where there is an open fracture, meningitis may develop and epilepsy may be a long-term complication. Neuropsychological consequences of head injury are discussed in Chapter 5.

Conclusions

Organic pathology of the brain impinges on many aspects of contemporary psychiatry, and it seems certain that there will be a considerable increase in our understanding of the pathology of neural cells. The volume of information currently accumulating is already reaching overwhelming proportions, and the briefest outline has been given here. For the interested reader some current neuropathology reference texts are listed below.

Further reading

Davis, R. L. & Robertson, D. M. (1991) *Textbook of Neuropathology* (2nd edn). Baltimore: Williams and Wilkins.

Esiri, M. M. & Oppenheimer, D. R. (1989) *Diagnostic Neuropathology*. Oxford: Blackwell Scientific.

Hume Adams, J. & Duchen, L. W. (1992) *Greenfield's Neuropathology* (5th edn). London: Edward Arnold.

7 Neuroendocrinology

Stephen Gilbey & Alexander Macrae

The diffuse endocrine system ● Regulation of endocrine function ●
Hormone receptors ● Regulation of hormone action ● Receptor
abnormalities and endocrine disease ● The endocrine brain ●
The hypothalamus ● The pituitary gland ● Hormone actions and
psychiatry ● Conclusions

The diffuse endocrine system

Complex organisms sense changes in their internal and external environments, and mount coordinated endocrine, autonomic and behavioural responses, usually to maintain a homeostatic balance. The endocrine system has evolved to meet this need.

Endocrine glands such as the pituitary, thyroid, or adrenal glands are ductless glands secreting chemical messengers (hormones) into the bloodstream, affecting remote target organs. The diffuse endocrine system is a network of cells that are present in nearly all tissues, show secretory features (i.e. storage of products in secretory granules and release when stimulated), and have an 'endocrine' relationship with surrounding cells.

Highly organised interactions exist between secretory cells within endocrine glands, or between neurons, as in the hypothalamus, or between endocrine cells and their local autonomic neurons (e.g. islets of Langerhans, adrenal medullary tissue). Thus the concepts of local, autocrine and paracrine, hormone and neurotransmitter actions have evolved, in which, at the cellular level, the distinction between the endocrine and autonomic nervous systems becomes blurred. Paracrine effects concern the action of a hormone on neighbouring cells, either following secretion into the surrounding interstitial fluid and interaction with receptors on the target cell, or by a neurotransmitter effect mediated through an organised synapse. Autocrine effects concern the action of a secreted hormone on the cell that has secreted it. This is an ideal mechanism for appropriate negative feedback: a substance secreted by a cell may act to limit further hormone release. Thus local neurotransmitters can act in a paracrine or autocrine manner to affect endocrine function, and other local factors not previously thought to impinge on the endocrine system, such as cytokines, may interact with endocrine cells.

Although the endocrine system is controlled at all levels from the individual cell upwards, it is mostly the central nervous system that senses the relevant signals and translates them into hormonal secretion (see 'The endocrine brain', p. 233). Even peripheral organs such as the endocrine pancreas, in which glucose-insulin and glucagon secretion would appear to be independent of the central nervous system, receive an autonomic innervation which is an important influence on function (viz. the cephalic phase of insulin secretion).

Control systems in the neuroendocrine brain are complex. All neuroendocrine responses are tempered and influenced by the surrounding neuroendocrine environment.

Endocrine systems are based largely on feedback mechanisms. Afferent signals are sensed by receptors linked to or on endocrine cells, which then release neurotransmitters or hormones which act on the end-organs to restore homeostasis. Upon this is superimposed rhythmicity, which permeates all aspects of life and behaviour, whether diurnal (eating, sleeping), menstrual or seasonal (fertility), or reflecting different ages (e.g. puberty). To this may be added programmed cell death (apoptosis), the normal function of which dictates the life span of individual cells, and the malfunctioning of which may lead to premature cell death or uncontrolled cell survival and proliferation.

Regulation of endocrine function

The aim of endocrine research is to understand malfunction, to replace hormones where appropriate, and to develop pharmacologically useful agonists and antagonists. Circulating hormones need to be characterised and measured. Tissues producing hormones need to be identified and their control mechanisms understood. At the cellular level the identities of individual cell types producing hormones, the identification of receptor type, action and effects, and the interaction between local neurons controlling endocrine function, are all areas under investigation.

Hormone production: control of gene transcription

As new polypeptide hormones or receptors are discovered, the genes on which these are encoded may now be established. There are three main advantages of doing this:

(1) The basis of inherited endocrine disease may be revealed.
(2) The control of gene expression may be explored. All genes encoding peptides share a similar structure. Relatively simple molecular biological techniques may be used to identify:
    (a) the structure and processing of relevant DNA sequences
    (b) DNA sequences that control gene transcription in response to extracellular signals (e.g. binding of the steroid–receptor complex or activation of cyclic adenosine monophosphate (cAMP))
    (c) the interaction of different (transcription) factors influencing gene expression.

(3) Direct measurement of gene expression may be possible using complementary DNA (cDNA) probes to measure messenger RNA (mRNA) either by the Northern blotting technique (which provides a quantitative estimation of the quantity of a particular mRNA present in extracts of tissue) or by *in-situ* hybridisation techniques (which use cDNA to measure RNA in tissue slices, enabling both quantification and identification of the cells involved, by microscopy).

Laboratory investigations

Cell culture techniques enable cloned and manipulated sequences of DNA to be attached to 'reporter' genes (e.g. conferring antibiotic resistance) and introduced, using viruses, into cell lines. Expression of the reporter gene can be detected chemically, and this can be used to identify the cells in which the DNA has been successfully introduced (fused) into the recipient cell's DNA. This simple basic model can be used for a wide variety of purposes, such as investigating which sequences of DNA are essential for the expression of a particular gene, or for the screening of a wide variety of candidate DNA sequences to identify which encodes for a particular polypeptide.

Alternative processing of a common precursor to give different hormones

Polypeptide hormones are synthesised initially as larger precursors, to be processed, for example by cleavage at pairs of dibasic amino-acid residues, before secretion. This process can be extended to give rise to differing 'mixes' of products in different tissues. Thus, in the anterior lobe of the pituitary, post-translational processing gives rise to adrenocorticotrophic hormone (ACTH) and β-lipotrophin (LPH) as its products. In the intermediate lobe of the pituitary, further processing leads to the production of α-melanocyte-stimulating hormone (α-MSH), corticotrophin-like intermediate lobe peptide (CLIP), γ-lipotrophin, and β-endorphin, all products with radically differing biological effects (Fig. 7.1).

Calcitonin and calcitonin gene related peptide (CGRP) are also products of the same gene that have different actions. Calcitonin is a product primarily of medullary cells of the thyroid. Its major identifiable actions are to reduce osteoclast activity and renal calcium loss, thereby reducing bone turnover and tending to decrease serum calcium. The physiological importance of this action in man is unclear, although its therapeutic value in diseases characterised by high bone turnover (e.g. Paget's disease of the bone) is well established. CGRP is produced in closely related forms (α and β), mainly by neurons in the central and peripheral nervous system. It is a powerful vasodilator and may have an important role in sensory nerve transmission. Calcitonin and CGRP have distinct receptors with differing tissue distribution. Calcitonin and the two CGRPs are products of the same gene on chromosome 11. Thus

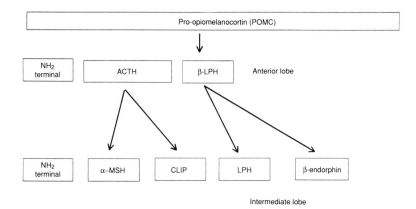

Fig. 7.1 Processing of POMC, in the anterior lobe of the pituitary, with further processing in the intermediate lobe to give products with very different biological effects, from the single common precursor.

alternative processing of a common RNA transcript gives rise to either calcitonin or CGRP, depending on the site of production.

Hormones with similar actions produced by different genes: aberrant gene expression in disease

Parathyroid hormone-like peptide (PTHrP) is a 141-amino-acid peptide that shares a homology with the NH_2 terminal of the 84-amino-acid polypeptide hormone parathyroid hormone (PTH) (Fig. 7.2). PTH and PTHrP have similar actions on bone, kidney and gut, leading to phosphaturia and hypercalcaemia, and appear to act on the same receptor. PTHrP is encoded for on chromosome 12, while PTH is encoded for on the related chromosome 11. PTHrP can be measured in tissue and in the circulation by radioimmunoassay, and gene expression quantified using cDNA probes and Northern blotting to give a measure of messenger RNA content of tissue or *in-situ* hybridisation of tissue slices to demonstrate the site of mRNA production. In its pathological guise, PTHrP is a product of tumour cells (notably neuroendocrine tumours of the pancreas and squamous-cell cancer of the lung), and a major cause of the hypercalcaemia of malignancy. The normal physiological role of PTHrP is

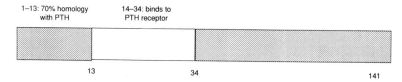

Fig. 7.2 Structure of PTHrP: amino acids 1-13 have a 70% homology with PTH; amino acids 14-34 bind to the PTH receptor.

not known. There is some evidence that it is secreted in relatively high quantities by the lactating breast and in the placenta. Thus its physiological action may be restricted to materno–foetal and neonatal calcium homeostasis; its secretion by tumour cells represents inappropriate de-differentiation.

Co-storage of cell products

As with the one neuron – one neurotransmitter concept in neuroanatomy, the one endocrine cell – one physiologically relevant product principle in endocrinology no longer holds. Many endocrine cells have been shown to store more than one endocrine product, not necessarily the product of the same gene. This principle is important in the neurons of the central nervous system, where co-localisation of neurotransmitters within neurons (e.g. catecholamines and neuropeptide neurotransmitters) is likely to have important implications with respect to autocrine and paracrine functions.

The co-production of the hormones insulin and islet amyloid polypeptide (IAPP, or amylin) in the islet β-cell illustrates the importance of this phenomenon. The islets of Langerhans in the pancreas of patients with type 2 (non-insulin-dependent) diabetes have been known for 80 years to contain amyloid tissue. The insolubility of this amyloid resulted in a delay until 1985 before its constituent peptide was extracted and identified as a novel peptide with considerable homology to CGRP. IAPP was identified as a normal product of pancreatic β-cells, encoded for on chromosome 12, and stored in the same secretory granules as insulin. This implies strongly that it is released with insulin in response to the same stimuli. *In vitro*, IAPP inhibits the release of insulin from islet cells. Thus IAPP appears to be an ideal example of an endocrine product whose main physiological role may be as an autocrine hormone, feeding back on the β-cell to prevent excessive cell stimulation. The physiological significance of this mechanism is unknown: it may curb excessive insulin action and hypoglycaemia (IAPP also appears to inhibit insulin action at the liver and skeletal muscle); it may avoid β-cell 'exhaustion' and diabetes.

Hormone receptors

Hormones and neurotransmitters act through specialised receptors, which trigger cellular responses. Hormone receptors may be divided according to their site: cell membrane, cytoplasmic, and nuclear.

Cell membrane receptors

Receptors for polypeptides, proteins, glycoproteins, and catecholamines are located in the cell membrane. These receptors may now be sequenced, the genes encoding them identified, and hence their DNA and messenger RNA cloned. Cell membrane receptors have characteristic secondary structures characterised by different domains:

(1) for ligand binding (the NH_2 terminal of the polypeptide chain)
(2) for interaction with effector systems (e.g. with G-proteins or ion channels; the COOH terminal)
(3) to determine membrane localisation and orientation
(4) with intrinsic catalytic properties (e.g. tyrosine kinase activation by the insulin receptor).

Families of similar receptors thus have a similar basic architecture: for instance G-protein-linked receptors such as the adrenergic receptor have a structure that encompasses a seven-pass transmembrane component.

Second-messenger systems

Peptide hormone receptors are linked to intracellular processes by a number of alternative mechanisms. These can be ion-channel linked, G-protein linked, or catalytic.

Receptors linked to ion channels

Ion-channel-linked receptors are classically associated with rapid, synaptic transmission. A neurotransmitter receptor may be directly linked to an ion channel: Na^+, K^+, Cl^-, or Ca^{2+}. Binding of a hormone causes the ion channel either to open or to close, thereby creating rapid changes in cross-membrane potential, and either enabling or preventing depolarisation of the cell, thus converting a neurotransmitter signal to electrical activity. The acetylcholine receptor at the neuromuscular junction opens in response to acetylcholine binding and allows a rapid influx of cations, thus depolarising the muscle cell. Voltage-gated ion channels typically link electrical activity to neurotransmitter release. GABA and glycine act on ion channels that allow rapid influx of negative ions, stabilising cell membranes and having a net inhibitory effect. Thus voltage-gated Ca^{2+} channels lead to a rapid increase in intracellular Ca^{2+} in response to depolarisation of the cell membrane (see Chapter 3, pp. 73–81).

Receptors linked to G proteins

G-protein-linked receptors transmit the signal from a hormone or neuro-transmitter ligand either to neighbouring cell membrane ion channels, or to intracellular enzymes (Fig. 7.3). A hormone binds to its cell surface receptor, and alters the conformation of its intracellular component. This in turn binds to a regulator protein binding guanosine triphosphate (GTP) (a G protein). If the net effect is enzyme activation, this is called a stimulatory

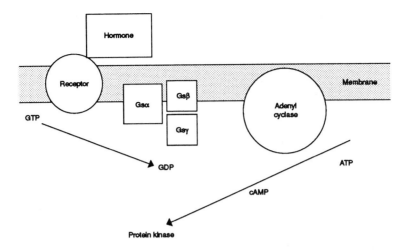

Fig. 7.3 G-protein-linked cell membrane receptor, and the activation of adenyl cyclase to produce cAMP from adenosintriphosphate (ATP), and thereby protein kinase activation.

(Gs) protein. The Gs protein is composed of three subunits: Gsα is normally bound to guanosinediphosphate (GDP). The β and γ subunits of Gs are tightly bound and anchor Gs to the plasma membrane. When GSα is activated in response to alteration of the hormone receptor conformation, it binds GTP in place of GDP. This is associated with a dissociation of GSα from the β and γ subunits, and its binding to an adenyl cyclase molecule, which in turn is activated, leading to the formation of intracellular cyclic adenosine monophosphate (cAMP) in response to the initial hormone–receptor binding. Almost immediately GTP is hydrolysed to GDP, the Gsα subunit reverts to its previous conformation and binds to the β and γ subunits again, ready for activation. The purpose of this sophisticated second-messenger system is thought to be amplification of the signal engendered by hormone–receptor binding. The system can be regulated, notably by the cholera toxin, which alters the α subunit so that it no longer binds GTP. Thus Gs-protein-dependent hormone receptors can be identified as such by the inhibition of their effect by cholera toxin *in vitro*.

Other G proteins inhibit adenyl cyclase, activate other second messengers (Box 7.1) such as phospholipase c (thereby mobilising intracellular calcium), and regulate ion channels. These diverse effects depend on the presence of differing α subunits.

Clonal abnormalities of G-protein function in endocrine tumours Abnormalities of G proteins may be of pathological significance. Proto-oncogenes are genes involved in the regulation of gene transcription that may become oncogenes (i.e. implicated in uncontrolled cell proliferation) in some pathological circumstances. Some oncogenes (e.g. ras) are known to be G-protein subunits.

Box 7.1 Second-messenger activation by membrane-bound hormone receptors, classified by their actions

Adenyl cyclase activation
ACTH
Beta adrenergic effects
Calcitonin
HCG
LH/FSH
Glucagon
Histamine[1]
LHRH
MSH
PTH
Prostaglandin E1
Serotonin
TSH

Adenyl cyclase inhibition
Adenosine
Alpha$_2$ adrenergic
Dopamine[1]
Opiates
Insulin
Prostaglandin E2
Opiates

Control of phosphoinositide turnover/intracellular calcium flux
Alpha$_1$ adrenergic
Angiotensin II
GnRH
TRH
Arginine vasopressin

Guanylate cyclase activation
Atrial natriuretic peptide

1. Different receptor subtypes may have differing effects mediated by differing second-messenger systems.

Somatic mutations in Gsα have been shown to be associated with the development of endocrine tumours, notably a subset of growth-hormone-producing pituitary tumours. These mutations appear to be inhibiting GTP hydrolysis and stabilising Gsα in the active GTP-bound state, leading to a state of continuous Gs activation and chronic cell stimulation and, presumably, proliferation.

Catalytic receptors

Catalytic receptors do not operate via second-messenger systems but are transmembrane receptors in which extracellular binding of a hormone has direct effects on intracellular metabolism. The insulin receptor is a typical example: the extracellular α subunit is linked to the transmembrane β subunit. Binding of insulin to the α subunit activates β subunit tyrosine kinase, which transfers a phosphate from adenosine triphosphate (ATP) to tyrosine residues on intracellular proteins, thus triggering a cascade of intracellular phosphorylation. The insulin receptor amplifies its own activity by phosphorylating itself once activated.

Intracellular and nuclear receptors

Small, lipid-soluble hormones act on cytoplasmic and nuclear receptors. Receptors for steroid hormones, thyroid hormones, retinoic acid and vitamin D share structural characteristics, act through similar mechanisms, and form a superfamily of receptors. Binding of a steroid to its unbound receptor in the cytoplasm leads to transfer of the resulting complex to the nucleus. There the hormone-bound receptor (in contrast to the unbound receptor) binds avidly to hormone response sequences of DNA, thereby controlling the initiation of gene transcription by promoter elements (Fig. 7.4).

Thus steroid receptors bind to DNA and directly influence mRNA transcription. Regulation of this effect may be by DNA binding, interaction with competing factors regulating transcription, and by tissue-specific differences in the response to the steroid–receptor complex (i.e. the same steroid hormone may bind to the same steroid receptor but cause dramatically different transcriptional effects, depending on the tissue involved).

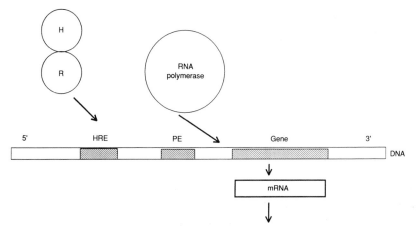

Fig. 7.4 A steroid hormone-receptor (HR) complex binds to DNA, thereby enabling initiation of gene transcription. HRE is the hormone-responsive element, and PE is the promoter element.

The expression or otherwise of steroid receptors is of prognostic importance in tumours (notably breast cancer) and can be exploited therapeutically by the use of the anti-oestrogen tamoxifen, a non-steroidal agent that competes with oestrogen for its receptor.

Regulation of hormone action

Receptor subtypes

The development of radioligand binding assays has enabled the characterisation of different receptor subtypes within tissues. The classic example of this was the recognition of α- and β-adrenergic receptors, followed by subdivision of each into 1 and 2 subtypes, with the promise of more to be discovered (e.g. the recently identified β_3-adrenergic receptor, which may mediate the stimulatory effect of adrenergic compounds on peripheral thermogenesis and metabolic rate generally).

Different receptor subtypes lead to different biological effects following the binding of the same agonist. They may be characterised by these effects and by differing binding affinities to different forms of a class of agonists (e.g. adrenaline and noradrenaline). In the case of polypeptide hormones and neurotransmitters, substitution of a few amino acids or truncation of the polypeptide may significantly change the biological effect of the agonist.

New receptor subtypes are constantly being discovered. Once the existence of a receptor subtype has been deduced from biochemical studies, its molecular weight, amino-acid sequence, and its structure may be studied. Its differential effects may be studied biochemically. Differences between different tissues in its expression may be studied using bioassays, binding studies, or, once its messenger RNA has been cloned, *in-situ* hybridisation and Northern blotting.

Receptor down-regulation

Down-regulation is a characteristic feature of hormone receptor physiology: continued stimulation of a receptor will lead to attenuation of its effect. This may occur in different ways.

Down-regulation of receptor number

This may occur as a consequence of decreased receptor synthesis, increased receptor breakdown, or movement of the receptor to an inactive site (e.g. internalisation). Insulin classically decreases the number of its own receptors (homologous regulation); although the mechanism is not clear, it is possibly by altering receptor synthesis, possibly by altering receptor half-life. Corticosteroids act to increase insulin receptor numbers (heterologous regulation).

Receptor desensitisation

A tissue continuously exposed to a hormone may lose its responsiveness to that hormone: desensitisation or tachyphylaxis. This classically occurs with adrenergic receptors: β_2-adrenergic receptors act by stimulating cAMP formation by a G-protein-dependent mechanism. Activated β_2 receptors are themselves phosphorylated by a kinase which is unrelated to the effect on cAMP. This alters the configuration of the receptor, blocking its interaction with its Gs protein, limiting its action (homologous desensitisation).

Heterologous desensitisation of the β_2-adrenergic receptor may occur in response to other hormones such as prostaglandin E1; this occurs by a different mechanism but also involves interference with G-protein effects.

Regulation at the level of the receptor: 11-hydroxysteroid dehydrogenase

The presence of 11-hydroxysteroid dehydrogenase (11-OHSD) activity close to steroid receptors explains a conundrum in endocrine physiology: why do glucocorticoids, which circulate at much higher concentrations than mineralocorticoids, not continuously activate mineralocorticoid receptors in the kidneys and cause excessive sodium retention and hypokalaemia?

The reason appears to be that in tissues that are responsive to mineralocorticoids (notably the kidneys), the microsomal enzyme 11-OHSD (which is dependent on nicotinamide-adenine-dinucleotide phosphate (NADP)) inactivates circulating cortisol by converting it to (inactive) cortisone, thus preventing binding to steroid receptors (Fig. 7.5). Liquorice inhibits 11-OHSD dehydrogenase, thereby interfering with this process, and causes a syndrome of apparent mineralocorticoid excess. Congenital 11-OHSD deficiency, giving rise to a similar syndrome of apparent mineralocorticoid excess, has been described. Recognition of the importance of this enzyme has led to the discovery that it exists in different isoforms in many tissues that express glucocorticoid receptors; its expression may regulate the response to cortisol at many sites.

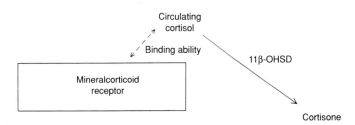

Fig. 7.5 Enzymatic regulation of steroid receptor binding by 11-hydroxysteroid dehydrogenase 11β-OHSD converts cortisol to inactive cortisone.

Regulation by binding proteins: insulin-like growth factor binding proteins

Insulin-like growth factor I (IGF-I) is produced in the liver and in other tissues on which growth hormone (GH) has an action. IGF-I mediates most or all of the biological effects of GH and feeds back on the hypothalamopituitary axis to inhibit GH synthesis. As implied, IGF-I is similar to insulin, having a 60% homology with proinsulin, and the IGF-I receptor has a similar structure to the insulin receptor. This may be reflected in a physiologically important functional overlap: insulin can have GH-like effects when present in high quantities, and GH-like effects may be insulin's major action *in utero* (hence macrosomia in children of diabetic mothers). IGF-II shows homology with IGF-I, but has a different receptor, which is quite dissimilar in structure from the insulin receptor. The biological actions of IGF-II are less well defined but are more likely to be related to development, especially in the foetus.

Insulin-like growth factors are unusual polypeptide hormones in that they are bound, in the circulation, to a family of IGF binding proteins (IGFBP), of which at least five (IGFBP-1–5) are known to exist. IGFBP-1 binds to both IGF-I and IGF-II, and is present at particularly high concentrations in the foetus. The major circulating IGFBP complex has three components: IGFBP-3; an acid-labile subunit; and IGF-I or IGF-II (Fig. 7.6). IGF-I and IGFBP-3 need to be present as a complex before the combining with the acid-labile subunit. IGFBP-1 expression is closely related to that of GH and IGF-I: it shows a marked diurnal variation, and an increase during childhood to a peak during puberty and a gradual decline in adult life. Thus regulation of gene expression, synthesis, and circulating concentrations of different IGFBPs are closely related to the IGFs that they preferentially bind.

Binding proteins with similar physiological functions exist for other growth factors, and have recently been described for growth hormone. Thus binding proteins do not exist solely to transport hormones to target tissues: regulation of the synthesis of binding proteins may be an important part of the regulation of growth factors or hormones.

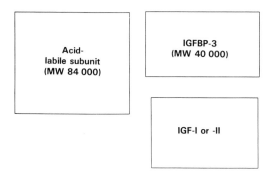

Fig. 7.6   The composition of IGFBP-3, with molecular weight (MW) of the subunits.

Table 7.1 Hormone resistance syndromes

Hormone	Associated syndrome
Insulin	Diabetes
	Lipodystrophy
	Acanthosis nigricans
	Polycystic ovaries/hyperandrogenism
	Hypertriglyceridaemia
Thyroxine	
'Generalised' resistance	Euthyroid with elevated thyroxine with normal TSH
'Central' resistance	Hyperthyroid with elevated thyroxine and TSH
Parathyroid hormone	Pseudohypoparathyroidism
Androgens	Testicular feminisation
Growth hormone	Dwarfism
Vitamin D	Vitamin D resistant rickets

Receptor abnormalities and endocrine disease

Abnormalities in receptor number, structure, and function represent a rich source of endocrine disease.

Complete absence of receptors leads to a complete failure of end-organ response. Abnormalities of receptor structure, for instance owing to point mutations in the relevant gene, lead to increased concentrations of circulating hormone as well as end-organ malfunction. Thus insulin resistance syndromes (Table 7.1) lead to diabetes, and massively elevated insulin requirements following the development of pancreatic failure. High concentrations of insulin in the circulation can lead to idiosyncratic consequences: notably polycystic ovaries (probably due to growth factor-like actions of insulin on gonadal tissue), and 'pseudo-acromegaly' (thought to be due to a spill-over effect of insulin on IGF-I receptors).

Receptor defects due to point mutations are heterogeneous: practically every family with defective insulin or thyroid receptors that has been studied has a different point mutation in the gene(s) encoding the receptor. This heterogeneity may be of relevance to the inheritance of psychiatric disorders.

The endocrine brain

The endocrine brain provides an interface between the central and peripheral nervous system and the endocrine and metabolic *'milieu intérieur'*. It coordinates the endocrine system, behaviour and development in order to ensure growth, survival, and reproduction. This is achieved by a complex control system in which endocrine and neural elements overlap so much as to be practically indistinguishable. The classic principles of the control of the

---

Box 7.2   Experimental investigation of neurotransmitter function

Synthesis and storage
Immunocytochemistry: evidence of intracellular storage
In-situ hybridisation: evidence of synthesis
Messenger RNA measurement (Northern blotting): evidence of synthesis

Demonstration of action
Changes in neurotransmitter content in experimentally deranged states (e.g. following adrenalectomy, thyroidectomy)
In-vitro effects on cell culture or tissue preparations
In-vivo responses following systemic or local administration (e.g. by intrahypothalamic or intracerebroventricular injection)
In-vivo responses to local or systemic blockade using specific antagonists or monoclonal antibodies

---

pituitary and thereby more distant endocrine glands by hypothalamic neurons and/or releasing hormones are well recognised; details of paracrine and autocrine relationships between the cells in these glands remain poorly understood and the subject of intensive research (Box 7.2).

The importance of the hypothalamopituitary axis in clinical areas such as the control of reproduction, growth and development, or fluid balance, is unquestioned and its manipulation of recognised clinical significance. In other areas, such as food intake or the control of peripheral metabolism, a physiological role for the hypothalamus and its efferent pathways is strongly suggested by animal experiments and by the consequences of gross pathology, but its precise role in man and the possibilities for pharmacological intervention remain unclear.

Neurotransmitters

Neurons communicate by the release of neurotransmitters (Chapters 2 and 3). To be recognised as a neurotransmitter, a hormone (or any product of a neuron) must:

(1) be synthesised in neurons
(2) be released when neurons are activated
(3) have a biological action which can be reproduced by the exogenous administration of the putative neurotransmitter and blocked by the administration of antagonists, or monoclonal antibodies
(4) have a self-limiting biological effect.

The hypothalamus

The hypothalamus is composed of anatomically distinct 'nuclei': clusters of neurons that have distinct yet complex functions, linked by bundles of nerve fibres. These neurons provide a network of afferent and efferent pathways that enable the hypothalamus to act as a link between higher cerebral centres and the brainstem, coordinating visceral, endocrine, and behavioural functions.

A single hypothalamic nucleus has a number of functions (e.g. the Paraventricular nucleus)

The paraventricular nucleus (PVN) is a small area of the hypothalamus, containing approximately 15 000 neurons, and it illustrates the functional complexity of such centres, many of which contain more than one neurotransmitter. The PVN is a site for the reception of afferent signals from the brainstem, higher cerebral centres, and other hypothalamic nuclei, processing of this input, and afferent output to the anterior and the posterior pituitary, together with effects on autonomic function and behaviour.

Control of the posterior pituitary

Neurons synthesising oxytocin and vasopressin connect the magnocellular portion of the PVN (and the supraoptic nucleus) with the posterior pituitary. The peptides are then released, controlling parturition and lactation, and fluid and electrolyte balance.

Control of the anterior pituitary

The parvocellular portion of the PVN contains a large number of neurons synthesising polypeptide hormones controlling anterior pituitary function. Thus corticotrophin-releasing factor (CRF) and thyrotrophin-releasing hormone (TRH) are synthesised in the PVN, transported to the median eminence, and released into the hypothalamopituitary portal circulation to stimulate hormone release by ACTH- and TSH-releasing cells respectively.

Control of autonomic function

Neurons within the PVN can be shown (by lesioning, or by the direct injection of neurotransmitters) to affect feeding behaviour, peripheral thermogenesis, gastrointestinal function (e.g. gastric acidity) and the cardiovascular system (blood pressure, pulse rate).

Single hypothalamic neurotransmitters have multiple biological effects

The biological action of neurotransmitters in the endocrine brain depends entirely on the context and the site of their release, as well as the particular receptor upon which they impinge. A single hypothalamic neuropeptide may combine the functions of a hormone released into the hypothalamopituitary circulation, a local neurotransmitter involved in direct cell–cell communication, and an autocrine or paracrine modulator of the actions of other neurotransmitters, such as catecholamines.

Neuropeptide Y (NPY) in the PVN provides a useful model for the complexity of action of individual neurotransmitters. NPY is present in many neurons, but is not synthesised in cell bodies in the PVN. NPY-containing neurons in the PVN originate either from the brainstem (in which neurons it is stored with catecholamines) and from the arcuate nucleus (no co-localisation with catecholamines). In the PVN the actions of NPY include a powerful action on food intake, and a role in controlling CRF and TRH release. Elsewhere in the central nervous system, injected NPY affects pulse rate and blood pressure (with differing effects depending on the site of administration), sexual activity, and release of luteinising-hormone releasing hormone (in oestrogen-primed animals). There is evidence for release of NPY into the hypothalamo-pituitary portal circulation, and for synthesis and action of NPY in the control of hormone synthesis in the anterior pituitary.

The hypothalamus and behaviour

The complicated and interconnecting control systems within the hypothalamus control endocrine and autonomic function in an integrated fashion. The hypothalamic control of behaviour is an integral part of this, enabling the establishment of a pattern of feeding, sleeping, grooming, and sexual activity that maximises metabolic and reproductive efficiency for a given species. In addition, the hypothalamus, with its connections with the sympathetic nervous system, plays a central role in the adaptation to both acute and chronic stress, both of which may have a profound effect on the endocrine system.

Gross lesions of the hypothalamus may be implicated in pathological weight gain, anorexia, hypersomnia, and sexual dysfunction.

The hypothalamus and feeding

The hypothalamus appears to be of central importance in converting nutritional requirements to feeding behaviour. Early work suggested that there was a peripheral, satiety area of the hypothalamus, and a central, feeding area. Thus stimulation of the feeding area caused feeding, and its destruction inhibited feeding. It is now clear that the neuroanatomy of feeding centres is more complex than this; nevertheless, control systems and neurotransmitters can be divided fairly clearly into stimulators and inhibitors of feeding behaviour.

Table 7.2 Principal hypothalamic neurotransmitters influencing feeding

Stimulate feeding	Inhibit feeding
Neuropeptide Y	Corticotrophin-releasing factor
Noradrenaline (α_2-adrenergic)	Serotonin
Opioids	Neurotensin
Galanin	Cholecystokinin
Growth-hormone releasing factor	

Feeding is functionally linked to other behaviour such as reproductive activity and to higher functions such as memory (presumably the memory of how to obtain food is of survival value).

Serotonin is an inhibitor of feeding (Table 7.2), and serotonin uptake inhibitors (which may also have antidepressant effects) are in clinical use as short-term weight-reducing drugs. Cholecystokinin was the first satiety neurotransmitter identified.

Neuropeptide Y is the most potent appetite-stimulating neurotransmitter yet discovered. Development of effective antagonists to the appetite-stimulating action of NPY would be of enormous clinical value. However, NPY is a widespread neurotransmitter in the sympathetic nervous system, where it is a potent vasoconstrictor, and has a considerable number of differing effects within the central nervous system (e.g. increasing or decreasing blood pressure, depending on the site of injection). Thus an NPY antagonist would either have to be delivered to precisely the correct site in the hypothalamus, or be designed to act on an NPY receptor with specific effects on appetite, if such a specific receptor exists. Thus the search for new NPY receptors (three have already been described) is a high priority.

The role of neuropeptides controlling feeding illustrates an important aspect of the integrated nature of hypothalamic control: neurotransmitters that increase feeding when injected into the hypothalamus also tend to increase gastric acidity, decrease alternative forms of behaviour (e.g. grooming, sexual activity), and have the appropriate effects on peripheral metabolism. Thus anorectic neurotransmitters tend to decrease peripheral lipolysis and glycogenolysis and increase energy stores, while appetite-stimulating neurotransmitters have the opposite effect, mobilising peripheral energy stores. In rodents these effects are reflected in thermogenesis: hypothalamic neurotransmitters influence thermogenesis through the sympathetic nervous system and β_3-adrenergic receptors.

The pituitary gland

The posterior pituitary (neurohypophysis)

The posterior pituitary has a separate embryological origin from the anterior pituitary, and forms a single functional subunit with two hypothalamic nerve

> **Box 7.3   Stimuli for release of posterior pituitary hormones**
>
> *AVP*
> Decreased plasma osmolality
> Volume receptors (atria, carotid bodies, others)
> Atrial peptides
> Stress and nausea
>
> *Oxytocin*
> Suckling reflex
> Labour

tracts. In the pituitary these two tracts come into contact with fenestrated capillaries, allowing the relatively free passage of neurotransmitters/hormones from nerve to circulation.

The nerve bodies for these tracts arise in two hypothalamic nuclei: the supraoptic and paraventricular nuclei (PVN), which secrete primarily arginine vasopressin (AVP) and oxytocin (Box 7.3). These neurotransmitters are not restricted to the neurohypophysis: both have a widespread distribution within the neuroendocrine system and have important functions. Thus AVP-containing cells within the PVN radiate to the brainstem, spinal cord, and higher brain centres, influencing autonomic function and higher cerebral function (e.g. memory) independently of the neurohypophysis.

The intermediate lobe

This is derived from Rathke's pouch, and is largely vestigial in adults, in whom its functional significance is the subject of controversy. The lobe is thought to be responsive to dopamine in humans, and its main function is the release of melanocyte-stimulating hormone (MSH). This is probably of little relevance in humans, but important in species in which adaptive changes in skin pigmentation are needed for survival.

The anterior pituitary (adenohypophysis)

Hypothalamic nuclei are linked to the anterior pituitary by the hypothalamo-hypophyseal portal circulation. Afferent information is processed by hypothalamic nuclei, and converted into neurotransmitter signals (Table 7.3). These neurotransmitters (pituitary-hormone releasing factors) are released by hypothalamic nuclei at the median eminence, where a rich plexus of nerves terminates close to a primary capillary plexus. In addition, cells of the neurohypophysis and intermediate lobe pass through the median eminence, while nerves from the hypothalamus terminate in the median eminence and influence secretion of releasing factor.

Table 7.3 Hypothalamic and pituitary hormones

Pituitary	Hypothalamic	Hypothalamic nucleus
LH/FSH	Gonadotrophin releasing hormone	Pre-optic area Mediobasal hypothalamus
POMC (ACTH)	Corticotrophin releasing hormone Arginine vasopressin	Paraventricular nucleus
TSH	Thyrotropin releasing hormone	Paraventricular nucleus
Prolactin	*Stimulation*: TRH? Vasoactive intestinal polypeptide?	
	Inhibition: Dopamine	Arcuate, paraventricular nuclei
Growth hormone	*Stimulation*: GHRH	Arcuate, periventricular nucleus
	Inhibition: Somatostatin	Paraventricular nucleus

A number of 'classic' releasing factors are now recognised. A clear understanding of the nature of these and the control of their release has been critical for an understanding of neuroendocrinology and hypothalamopituitary disease. However, it should be noted that:

(1) new 'releasing factors' may yet be discovered
(2) there is considerable functional overlap between different systems; thus both AVP and corticotrophin-releasing factor (CRF) exert an important influence on ACTH release by the pituitary; AVP may indeed have a greater claim to being *the* CRF than CRF itself
(3) other neurotransmitters impinge on these control systems at every level, from interactions within hypothalamic nuclei, to reciprocal innervation at the level of the median eminence, to paracrine and autocrine relationships between different populations of cells in the anterior pituitary
(4) a single hypothalamic releasing factor may be important in a number of different systems; thus CRF appears to be an important stress-related inhibitor of appetite as well as having effects on ACTH secretion.

Control of pituitary hormone release: growth hormone

Growth hormone (GH) has two main functions: the control of tissue growth, largely mediated through its stimulation of peripheral production of the insulin-like growth factor IGF-I, and the regulation of lipid and carbohydrate metabolism. The control of GH demonstrates the complexity of intrinsic rhythms and feedback, and the involvement of several overlapping neurotransmitters at several different levels (Fig. 7.7); there is the implication that manipulation of these neurotransmitters (e.g. the cholinergic and the galaninergic systems) could be exploited therapeutically.

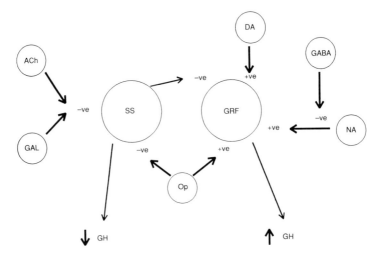

Fig. 7.7   GRF, somatostatin (SS) and galanin (GAL) control of GH release (ACh, acetylcholine; DA, dopamine; NA, noradrenaline; Op, opioids).

GH is secreted in intermittent surges

The surges of GH secretion are interspersed with periods of little or no secretion. The most important feature in humans is the nocturnal surge in secretion during slow-wave (stage 3/4) sleep, which can be altered by delaying the onset of deep sleep or inverted by reversing the sleep–wake cycle.

GH release varies with age and sex

Basal and stimulated GH secretion shows a marked rise at the time of puberty, and subsequently declines with age. Physiological and stimulated serum GH levels are generally higher in premenopausal women than in postmenopausal women, or men.

Hypothalamic neuropeptides control pituitary GH secretion

The secretion of GH reflects the net effect of its stimulation by growth hormone releasing hormone (GRF) and its inhibition by somatostatin (SS). GRF is present in high concentrations in the arcuate nucleus of the hypothalamus with cell processes directed to the median eminence and the hypothalamohypophyseal portal circulation. SS-containing cell bodies in the hypothalamus are found predominantly in the periventricular preoptic/anterior hypothalamic area and also project to the median eminence. Both peptides exert their effects by means of specific cell membrane receptors, acting on membrane-bound adenyl cyclase via inhibitory or stimulatory G-proteins. Infusion studies with GRF in male rats have indicated that it determines the height of GH peaks, while

SS influences their frequency. The precise mechanisms controlling GRF secretion are not known, but they include GABA-ergic, α-adrenergic, and opioid pathways.

Somatostatin inhibits GH release

Somatostatin has a direct, inhibitory, influence on the production of GH by the anterior pituitary. SS also exerts a tonic inhibitory influence on GH: a decrease in the release of SS precedes the rise in GRF associated with episodic peaks in GH secretion, and the administration of SS antibody to rats leads directly to a rise in GH which can be blocked by antibody raised to GRF.

Somatostatin is controlled by cholinergic pathways

Acetylcholine inhibits the release of SS by rat hypothalamic cells. Muscarinic cholinergic agonists stimulate basal GH release and potentiate GH responses to growth-hormone releasing hormone. Muscarinic antagonists cause reductions in GH levels during deep sleep, and in the GH responses to a wide variety of stimuli, including GRF. The inhibitory effects of atropine on GH secretion are reversed by antisomatostatin antibodies. Conversely, stimulation of the cholinergic pathway by the acetylcholinesterase inhibitor pyridostigmine potentiates GH response to provocative stimuli in all but GH-deficient individuals.

Feedback influences on GH secretion

The control of GH secretion involves feedback loops at several levels:

(1) Growth hormone regulates its own secretion   This may in part reflect direct effects of GH on GRF production as well as feedback by circulating IGF-I. Repeated administration of GRF, or treatment with exogenous GH, results in a diminishing GH response, although responses to other GH-secreting stimuli such as hypoglycaemia and arginine are preserved. IGF-I inhibits pituitary GH synthesis directly *in vitro*, and may also stimulate SS production.

(2) GRF appears also to regulate its own secretion   Intracerebroventricular administration of GRF at low doses inhibits GH secretion, and this is blocked by the antibody to somatotrophin release inhibiting factor (SRIF), suggesting it is due to GRF stimulating SRIF production or release. Sex differences can be demonstrated in the GH feedback responses: female rats showed a small fall in hypothalamic GRF and no rise in SS, when exposed to GH, in contrast to male rats in whom the responses were significantly greater.

Other hormones influence GH responses

Thyroid hormones and corticosteroids exert an important influence on GH secretion and production. Hypothyroidism causes a profound suppression of GH production in the pituitary. Corticosteroids increase GH production and release. However, in chronic hypercortisolism this is over-ridden by an inhibitory effect on GH production.

Galanin: a locally acting neurotransmitter involved in the hypothalamic control of GH release

Galanin is a 29-amino-acid neuropeptide first discovered in 1983. There are several lines of evidence for its involvement in GH secretion.

(1) Anatomical evidence Galanin immunoreactivity is high in the hypothalamus (particularly the paraventricular and supraoptic nuclei), with a high concentration of terminals in the median eminence.

(2) Pharmacological evidence Administration of galanin into the central nervous system in male and ovariectomised female rats produces rapid and dose-dependent increase in plasma GH levels. This would appear to be a central action: much higher intravenous doses are required to produce a rise in GH, and galanin has no effect on GH release by cultured anterior pituitary cells.

(3) Galanin and GH secretion in man Galanin affects GH secretion in man: infusion of male volunteers with synthetic porcine galanin at pharmacological doses causes a rise in circulating GH. The GH response to GH releasing hormone is potentiated by simultaneous galanin infusion; this is blocked by infused somatostatin. The GH response to galanin infusion is suppressed by pretreatment with the anticholinergic agent pirenzepine.

Hormone actions and psychiatry

Technical details of the control of behaviour patterns by certain parts of the brain, such as the control of feeding behaviour by the hypothalamus, and the part played in this by different neurotransmitters, are gradually being unravelled, at least for experimental animals. A notable feature of this system is its complexity, manifested in the bewildering degree of functional overlap between different neurotransmitters.

Quite clearly, the hormonal environment can modulate behaviour. In the case of the influence of sex hormones on reproductive behaviour, this is of importance for the survival of species. On a more subtle and as yet poorly understood level, there is an apparent interaction between the endocrine and immune systems which may provide a link between 'stress', the immune

Table 7.4 Psychiatric manifestations of endocrine disorders

Hormonal abnormality	Manifestations
Corticosteroid	
excess	Depression, euphoria, psychosis
deficiency	Lethargy, apathy, memory impairment
Thyroxine	
excess	Anxiety, depression, psychomotor agitation, apathy
deficiency	Slowing of intellectual function (reversible in adults), memory loss, depression, dementia, psychosis, hypomania (after commencement of thyroid treatment)
Androgen	
excess	Aggression
deficiency	Decreased libido
Gonadotrophin flux	Premenstrual syndrome? Depression?
Catecholamine excess	Anxiety, hyperventilation
Hyperparathyroidism	Confusion, psychosis, depression
Hypoparathyroidism	Intellectual impairment, depression
Hyperinsulinism	Behavioural effects of hypoglycaemia

system, and susceptibility to disease. This raises the possibility that specific and identifiable neuroendocrine abnormalities may underlie common psychiatric disorders. Knowledge of this inter-relationship remains sketchy, although many drugs used for psychiatric disorders act through neuro-transmitter systems (e.g. tricyclic antidepressants). Nevertheless, the extent to which gross abnormalities of circulating hormones can lead to recognisable patterns of abnormal behaviour hint at their potential significance in the physiological control of behaviour (Table 7.4).

Endocrine manifestations of psychiatric disorders

A further indication of the interaction between the hormonal environment, behaviour, and psychiatric disorder is the extent to which patients with severe psychiatric disorders have abnormalities of dynamic tests of the endocrine system.

The most clearly defined examples are centred on the endocrine consequences of severe depression, and are thought to be largely due to increased hypothalamic CRF. This is of particular importance in the differential diagnosis of Cushing's syndrome, where depression can give rise to spuriously elevated corticosteroids which are not suppressible by exogenous dexamethasone. Patients with anorexia nervosa also have demonstrable hormonal abnormalities (Table 7.5), and as a general principle all dynamic tests of endocrine function should be interpreted with caution in patients with severe psychiatric disorders.

Table 7.5 Endocrine manifestations of psychiatric disorders

Disorder	Hormone abnormality
Depression	Reduced GH response to levodopa Hypercortisolism, impaired suppression of cortisol by exogenous dexamethasone, with (appropriate) decreased response of ACTH to CRF Blunted TSH response to TRH
Anorexia nervosa	Hypercortisolism (with preserved diurnal rhythm) Impaired osmotic regulation of arginine, vasopressin Menstrual disturbances (impaired gonadotrophin secretion, low oestradiol) Sick euthyroid (low total T4, normal free T4, low T3)

Conclusions

Neuroendocrinology represents a rapidly developing field of scientific knowledge greatly enhanced by the impact of recent developments in the understanding of the molecular basis of cell biology, and with the added potential of unravelling the genetic basis of congenital disorders, whether due to single or multiple gene defects.

Although the development of psychotropic drugs affecting neurotransmitter systems has become increasingly prolific and sophisticated, detailed knowledge of the interaction between the endocrine environment, behaviour, susceptibility to systemic illness, and psychiatric disease remains strikingly rudimentary. Further research may unravel the basis of some common psychiatric disorders, as well as enabling a more targeted approach to the development of new pharmacological agents.

Further reading

Alberts, B., Bray, D., Lewis, J., *et al* (1989) *Molecular Biology of the Cell*. New York: Garland.

Bolander, F. F. (1989) *Molecular Endocrinology*. San Diego: Academic Press.

Franklyn, J. A. (1991) Syndromes of thyroid hormone resistance. *Clinical Endocrinology*, **34**, 237–245.

Herington, A. C. (1991) Insulin-like growth factors: biochemistry and physiology. *Baillière's Clinical Endocrinology and Metabolism*, **5**, 531–553.

Lightman, S. L. & Everitt, B. (1987) *Neuroendocrinology*. Oxford: Blackwell Scientific.

Lyons, J. L., Landis, C., Harsh, G., *et al* (1990) Two G-protein oncogenes in human endocrine tumours. *Science*, **249**, 655–659.

Maclean, D. B. & Jackson, I. M. D. (1988) Molecular biology and regulation of the hypothalamic hormones. *Baillière's Clinical Endocrinology and Metabolism*, **2**, 835–869.

Stewart, A. F. & Broadus, A. E. (1990) Parathyroid hormone related proteins: coming of age in the 1990s. *Journal of Clinical Endocrinology and Metabolism*, **71**, 1410–1415.

Walker, B. R. & Edwards, C. R. W. (1991) 11β hydroxysteroid dehydrogenase and enzyme mediated receptor protection: life after liquorice? *Clinical Endocrinology*, **35**, 281–289.

Westermark, A. A., Johnson, K. H., O'Brien, T. D., *et al* (1992) Islet amyloid polypeptide - a novel controversy in research. *Diabetologia*, **35**, 297–303.

Wilson, J. D. & Foster, D. W. (1992) *Williams's Textbook of Endocrinology*. New York: Harcourt Brace Jovanovitch.

8 Clinical neurophysiology
Hilary Morgan

Electroencephalography • The normal EEG • The abnormal EEG •
The effects of treatment • Acute and chronic intracerebral pathology •
Epilepsy and the EEG • EEG and episodic behavioural changes •
Major psychiatric disorders and the EEG • Sleep and the EEG •
Mapping • Event-related potentials • Evoked potentials

Clinical neurophysiology, which concerns the application of physiology to neurology and psychiatry, arose as a direct result of the pioneering work of scientists such as Adrian, Bronk, Caton, Matthews and Grey Walter (Brazier, 1961). The discipline defines abnormal function of the central nervous system and neuromuscular function by comparison with normal control data, and allows correlation of these divergences with pathology. Changes in function shown for specific anatomical sites within the nervous system, particularly by electromyography (EMG), nerve conduction (NC) and evoked potentials (EP), can help to localise pathology. The information complements that from other techniques, such as X-rays and computerised tomography (CT), which reveal structural abnormalities. In relatively rare instances the neurophysiological change itself can indicate the pathological aetiology or clinical diagnosis.

The prognostic implications of neurophysiology have not yet achieved the pre-eminence of its diagnostic applications, but objective and quantitative information is of value in monitoring progress and assessing outcome. A discerning clinician needs to be critically aware of the specificity and sensitivity of the studies which are possible in this evolving specialty.

Electroencephalography

In 1935, at a meeting of the Physiological Society, Adrian and Matthews attached leads from electrodes on Adrian's head to an amplifier and ink-writing oscillograph, and confirmed the psychiatrist Hans Berger's discovery that electrical rhythms of the human brain were accessible through the intact skull. Since Berger's publication in 1929, the *Electroencephalogram of Man*, electroencephalography (EEG) has passed through the phase of expansion, followed by the overoptimistic expectations of its clinical use in psychiatry, and is now recognised as a valuable investigative tool if selectively applied.

This chapter describes those EEG features which are of most value for patient management, and merely draws attention to studies where statistical correlations of EEG findings within particular patient groups, or disease entities, are relevant to psychiatry.

The EEG records potential differences over the scalp. These minute electrical signals, of the order of millionths of a volt, are amplified and then displayed by means of an oscilloscope or chart recorder. The physiological basis of the EEG is complex and not yet fully understood, although some experimental facts are known and form the basis of present hypotheses. At a cellular level, within the cortex the pyramidal cells are influenced by afferent inhibitory and excitatory connections via their dendrites, with resulting conduction of neuronal potential changes as axon spikes. Axon spikes affect postsynaptic membranes of target cells, producing changes in potential of longer duration. The sum of many such postsynaptic electrical changes is thought to be the basis of scalp EEG activity, resulting from an effect of the vertical orientation of pyramidal neurons and the extension of their apical dendrites to the surface.

Specific waveforms within the EEG probably result from the synchronisation of groups of cortical neurons, modulated by activity within thalamocortical projections. Hypersynchronisation of cortical activity results in EEG spikes, defined as transient waves lasting less than 70 ms. These discharges, to be differentiated from axonal microcellular spikes, can reflect epileptic changes and form the basis of the major contribution which the EEG plays in the diagnosis and management of epilepsy.

The normal EEG

Electroencephalographic activity contains a spectrum of frequencies, responding to physiological as well as pathological changes in cerebral function. The designation of Greek letters for the major frequency bands results from historical practice, thus:

delta   below 3.5 cycles per second or hertz (Hz) (usually 0.1 – 3.5 Hz)
theta   4 – 7.5 Hz
alpha   8 – 13 Hz
beta   above 13 Hz (usually 14 – 40 Hz)

Internationally accepted electrode placements, as shown in Fig. 8.1, allow standardised patterns of connections between recording electrodes, or montages, from different laboratories. The letters describing these electrode positions denote frontopolar, frontal, central, temporal, parietal and occipital areas; even numbers refer to those on the right side, and odd numbers to those on the left of the head. The EEG activity recorded represents the potential differences between pairs of electrodes. A standard clinical trace usually comprises about 16 channels, in which montages are chosen to provide an overall assessment of EEG activity. By convention, electrode connections over the right side are displayed before those from the left, whether the montage is an anteroposterior or transverse row.

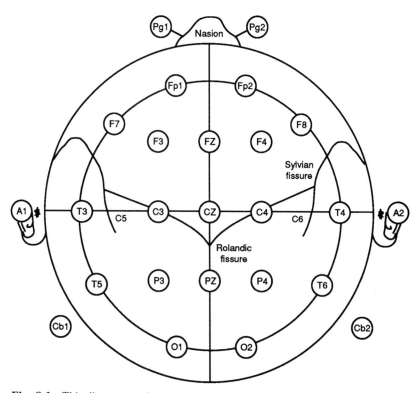

Fig. 8.1 This diagrammatic representation of the head shows the international 10 - 20 system of electrode placements. The letters stand for frontopolar (Fp), frontal (F), temporal (T), central (C), and occipital (O). The measurements are made at standard distances (10% or 20%), related to the bony landmarks of the nasion and inion. Even numbers refer to the right, and odd numbers the left side of the head.

The voltage of the EEG activity is usually between 10 and 100 μV. There is a marked attenuation through the skull, cortically recorded activity being about 500 – 1 500 μV. Internationally agreed definitions of the main EEG frequencies allow the clinician to recognise deviations from patterns of normality. EEG maturation both in the foetus and throughout life involve frequency and waveform changes. There are gradual alterations from a posterior basic rhythm of about 4 Hz at six months, to 6 Hz at one year, 8 Hz at three years, and 10 Hz at ten years, but wide normal variation exists. The frequency of the dominant occipital alpha activity tends to slow in the elderly, apparently reflecting underlying cerebral pathology, either vascular or degenerative, the absence of which is thought to account for the preservation of normal 10 ± 0.9 Hz activity even into the ninth decade of life.

Figure 8.2 shows a normal EEG with alpha activity as the dominant rhythm over the posterior quadrants. The low- and high-frequency filters, referred to as the time constant (TC) and high filter (HF), are indicated on all the EEG examples in the accompanying figures. Alpha activity is temporarily blocked

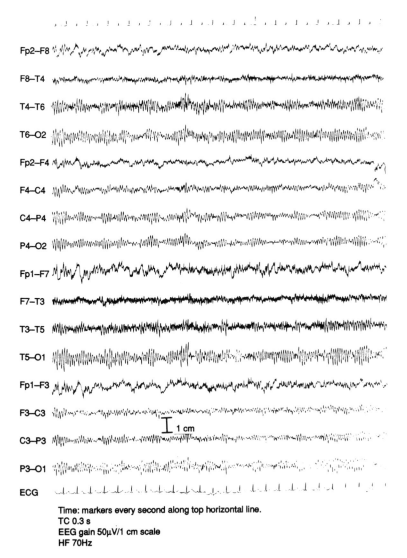

Time: markers every second along top horizontal line.
TC 0.3 s
EEG gain 50μV/1 cm scale
HF 70Hz

Fig. 8.2 The dominant occipital rhythm in this EEG is alpha activity. The paper speed is at 1.5 cm/s.

by eye opening as well as a variety of alerting stimuli, and its frequency can be 'driven' by rhythmically flashing light, as shown in Fig. 8.3.

Slow activity, in the theta and delta range, is normal in the young, and during sleep. The changing frequencies of the EEG during drowsiness and sleep are a continuing source of clinical and research interest. Moruzzi and Magoun, in 1949, suggested that the sleep – waking cycle was controlled by the reticular formation and a non-specific excitatory reticular activating system. Cholinergic mechanisms are known to be implicated, and systemic injections of cholinolytics

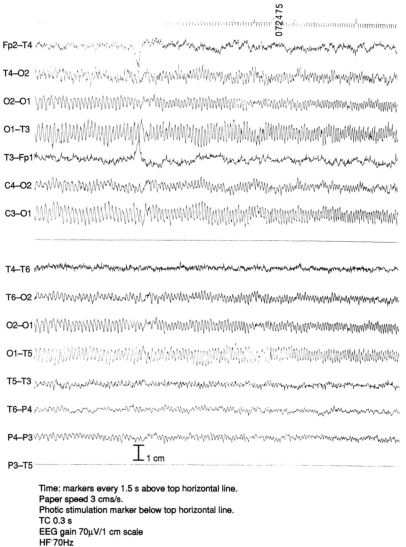

Fig. 8.3 The rhythmic alpha activity in this EEG changes its frequency, and becomes progressively faster as the photic stimulus rate is steadily increased.

induce slow delta-wave activity in the EEG. Afferents rich in acetylcholinesterase originate in the brainstem, and this system was thought to be the sole activating mechanism affecting the neocortical EEG. Recent evidence has shown that other structures are also important, in particular the cholinergic nucleus basalis, which is the major source of corticopetal cholinergic afferents. The fact that patients with Alzheimer's disease have a marked decrease in neurons within the nucleus basalis, together with EEG slowing found to be related to the severity of the dementia, has stimulated a hunt for some effective method of treating, or influencing, the development of this condition.

Some alterations in the EEG, for example slow waves due to drowsiness, sleep, overbreathing and crying, are physiologically normal features in babies, children and young adults, but would be regarded as abnormal in an adult.

The abnormal EEG

Normality or otherwise in the EEG depends on differentiating the observed waveforms, in respect of frequencies and distribution, from those recognised as occurring in EEGs recorded in normal subjects of similar age and sex. A slow, dominant, occipital rhythm with generalised slow-wave activity in the theta and delta range might be normal for a baby under one year, but would be grossly abnormal for an adult.

Transient waveforms of sharp outline, defined by their duration as either sharp waves or spikes, are abnormal characteristics under most conditions, although they may be normal in sleep. 'Paroxysmal' or epileptiform features usually consist of a mixture of transient spikes, or sharp waves with slow frequencies. An example is shown in Fig. 8.4.

Pathological EEG features may be revealed or enhanced by 'activation' procedures such as hyperventilation for three minutes, photic stimulation, sleep, or sleep deprivation. Figure 8.5 shows 'paroxysmal' complexes induced by photic stimulation, a phenomenon known as photic sensitivity. The interictal discharges of 'benign rolandic epilepsy' of childhood, and complex partial seizures arising in the temporal areas, are usually enhanced by sleep.

Metabolic effects

Many metabolic disorders, and hypothermia, are associated with similar EEG changes in the main frequencies, often with slowing of the dominant occipital rhythmic alpha activity and a diffuse increase in underlying slow waves.

In renal failure there is a correlation between the amount of slowing affecting the EEG and the level of consciousness: alpha frequencies are replaced with increasing theta and delta waves, there may be bursts of rhythmic slow waves, and an exaggerated arousal response to noise or other stimuli. Seizures may be associated with sharp waves, spikes, and complex discharges. The latter may be defined as the combination of a single slow wave with a sharp wave or spike.

Patients on chronic haemodialysis have sometimes developed a slowly progressive dementia, with speech disturbance, involuntary movements, myoclonus, and convulsions. The EEGs exhibit bursts of high-amplitude, slow, triphasic, and sharp waves, as well as complexes. Toxic levels of aluminium in the dialysate have been recognised in this condition, and preventive measures can now be taken to avoid the problem.

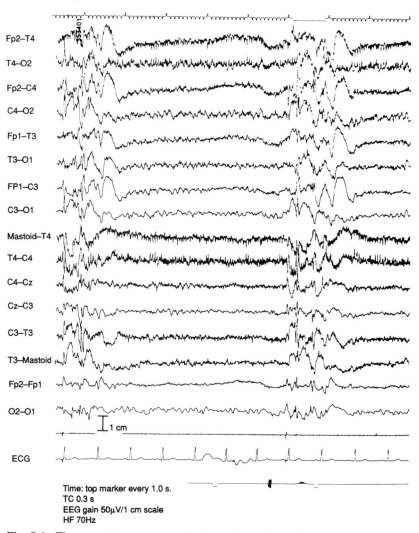

Fig. 8.4 These spontaneous generalised complex spike and slow-wave discharges are an example of interictal EEG abnormality.

Predominantly frontal triphasic slow waves, and generalised slow activity, may be seen in renal failure and also occur in hepatic failure. The degree of EEG slowing parallels the level of consciousness as the encephalopathy worsens, but may lag behind the clinical improvement following treatment. Other metabolic disturbances, including hypercalcaemia, hypocalcaemia and hypoglycaemia, produce slow activity, with episodic, bilaterally synchronous, rhythmic delta waves and epileptiform features in the EEG. Varying focal sharp activity may be seen with hypocalcaemia, particularly in infants. In hyperglycaemia the trace may be surprisingly normal until there is clouding of consciousness.

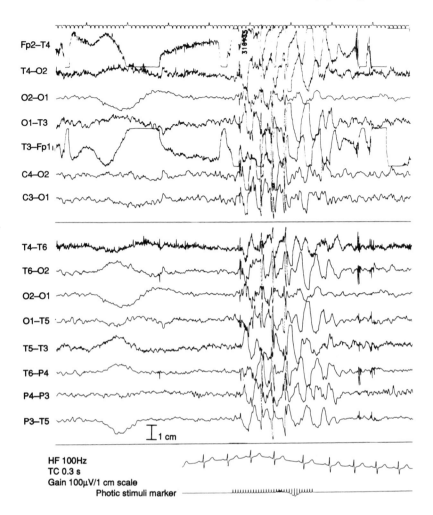

Fig. 8.5 EEG complex discharges in this record have been triggered by the use of photic stimulation. The rate of photic stimulation is shown on the lower horizontal marker channel.

EEG changes due to toxic states

Hypoxia

Hypoxia can have a profound effect on the EEG, the persistence of which will depend on the degree of permanent cerebral ischaemic damage. The changes are also similar to those described with metabolic disorders, progressing from slowing of the occipital rhythm to increasing amounts of theta and delta frequencies. With severe clinical change there is likely to be a reduction in the amplitude of all activity, known as 'cortical suppression'. At first this occurs intermittently, producing periodic reduced-amplitude EEG activity, separated by runs of normal-amplitude mixed frequencies of similar duration – the 'burst-suppression effect'. Progressive reduction in the amplitude of the bursts, and increased duration of the periodic suppression, terminates as an iso-electric or 'flat' EEG trace.

Pathological changes in the cortex due to hypoxia may give rise to seizures and epileptiform discharges, and myoclonic jerking often accompanies the bursts of cortical activity. When there is gross disruption of brainstem – cortical pathways, the EEG shows a lack of the normal transient changes caused by arousal stimuli, one manifestation being an unusual, invariant, rhythmic alpha-like activity, the so-called 'alpha coma', which signifies a poor prognosis. The EEG is of value in the differentiation of such a state from the clinically similar presentation of the 'locked in' syndrome due to widespread motor paralysis, when normal occipital frequencies show a transient blocking response to stimuli and reveal the presence of cognitive cortical function.

Alcoholism

This can give rise to seizures in the withdrawal period, whether it is relative after a heavy drinking bout, or total during enforced withdrawal. There is a heightened sensitivity to flicker stimulation (see Fig. 8.5) and myoclonus, as well as lowered magnesium levels, and there may be delirium tremens.

Photosensitivity seen in the EEG 6 – 30 hours after a drinking bout usually subsides rapidly, and any persistent EEG abnormality itself amounts to no more than diffuse irregularity and excess fast activity. When there is a history of chronic epilepsy, however, the trace often shows epileptiform abnormality, with focal or generalised spikes or sharp waves and complexes. The relative lack of such features in alcohol withdrawal seizures contrasts with the effect of barbiturate withdrawal, when EEG epileptiform disturbance is often significant.

Subacute and chronic encephalopathies in alcoholism include Wernicke's pontine myelinolysis, cerebellar degeneration, as well as Machiafava – Bignami disease, with pericallosal parenchymatous tissue damage and laminar cortical sclerosis. Variable EEG changes are reported in these disorders, but none is specific. Frequent epileptiform abnormality, such as repetitive localised spike discharges at about one per second, known as periodic lateralised epileptiform discharges (PLEDS), and other spikes or sharp waves are reported in the subacute toxic states.

The effects of treatment

Anaesthesia produces a progression of cerebral changes, with frontal then generalised fast activity in the early stages, with loss of alpha and sometimes paroxysmal activity at this point. An increase in the amplitude and amount of slow activity, that is theta and delta frequencies, is followed by a burst-suppression effect. With excessive cerebral depressant effects due to overdoses of hypnotics and sedative agents, the EEG is also increasingly dominated by slow activity. The voltage then diminishes and periods of suppression become longer until an iso-electric trace occurs.

Therapeutic levels of barbiturates produce excess fast activity, slow activity, and EEG changes characteristic of drowsiness or sleep. This is usually most prominent in the first few days, but can persist for several weeks.

There is some correlation between the drug level and the degree of slowing for several hypnotics and sedatives, including anticonvulsants such as phenytoin, but the relationship is not absolute and there are individual idiosyncratic effects. After long-term use, withdrawal is associated with generalised paroxysmal complex spike activity, especially on photic stimulation.

The neuroleptic drugs, including phenothiazines, thioxanthenes, and butyrophenones, produce minor increases in alpha frequencies at therapeutic levels, but slow waves, paroxysmal complex activity and frank convulsions at higher doses. Therapeutic levels of the tricyclic antidepressants slow the alpha activity, increase slow waves, and may cause paroxysmal slow and sharp wave or spike complexes with convulsions. Acute toxicity also produces complex EEG changes as well as seizures.

Lithium causes frequent and marked EEG abnormalities. The degree of disturbance tends to correlate with the blood levels, but this is certainly not an invariable finding. Unlike most other drug effects there may be focal slow waves, which can be confused with localised alterations due to cerebral pathology. The long-term sequelae of lithium intoxication include episodic EEG features, which bear some resemblance to those found in Creutzfeldt – Jakob disease.

The benzodiazepines produce a significant increase in fast activity, persisting for up to two weeks after the drug has been stopped. An example of the diffuse fast activity induced by these agents is shown in Fig. 8.6. Antiepileptic drugs cause increased slow-wave activity. Carbamazepine is related to the tricyclic antidepressants and can give rise to slow and paroxysmal complex disturbances.

The EEG and electroconvulsive therapy

While the EEG trace before the administration of electroconvulsive therapy (ECT) has not usually been an accurate predictor of therapeutic efficacy, the use of quantitative EEG analysis may be more helpful. In one study of elderly depressed patients, the presence of normal interhemispheric coherence in the delta frequency band was associated with a better response to ECT than the finding of lower coherence values.

Monitoring seizures during ECT, to see whether there has been a generalised spike and wave discharge of adequate duration (25 – 90 seconds), plays a major part in assuring therapeutic efficacy and safe delivery of treatment. Computer analysis of selected EEG parameters has been shown to be superior to visual assessment. In addition, such quantification has been applied to the investigation of the relative efficacy of unilateral versus bilateral ECT.

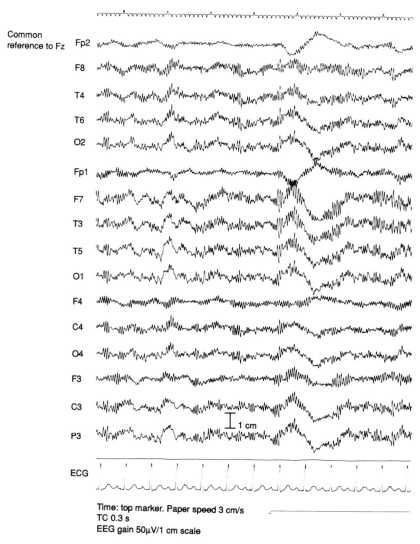

Fig. 8.6 The dominant rhythm in this EEG is beta activity, which is due to medication. The montage consists of several electrodes, each of which is connected to one common reference electrode in the mid-frontal region (Fz). The paper speed is at 3.0 cm/s.

The EEG has been used to investigate possible mechanisms of action in ECT. Theories investigated have included kindling processes, resolution of hemispheric dysfunctions, anticonvulsant effects, and diencephalic stimulation. In one such study of patients with schizophrenia and schizoaffective disorder, the EEG data gave tenuous support for the sensitisation theory, and contradicted the dominant accentuation theory. It was proposed that the combined clinical, neuropsychological and neurophysiological data were compatible with the idea of a restoration of equilibrium between the hemispheres.

After ECT, slow waves appear in the EEG, usually increasing in proportion to the number of sessions, although there is wide individual variation. Generalised, irregular, slow waves and bilaterally synchronous bursts may persist for at least a month after a course of treatment, and some authors quote a maximum of four months. The contributory effects of medication on the EEG need to be noted in these patients, as lithium can cause generalised, localised and focal slow activity, and the tricyclic antidepressants may induce complex discharges, including photosensitivity, as well as convulsions.

Acute and chronic intracerebral pathology

Infections

Meningitis and encephalitis

The degree of EEG slowing seen in patients with meningitis is dependent on the extent to which the cerebral hemispheres are involved, and there are no specific abnormalities. During the acute phase of an encephalitis, the EEG almost invariably shows diffuse slow activity, often with episodic, bilaterally synchronous and symmetrical bursts of rhythmic slow waves. The latter probably reflect abnormality affecting the subcortical grey matter. When the process is subacute, and white matter is affected, the EEG is often more significantly affected by slow waves.

Viral processes affect the EEG in a similar manner. In the acquired immune deficiency syndrome (AIDS) there may be focal or generalised slow waves in the EEG. However, the pathological processes differ, and the EEG merely reflects the changes in cerebral function.

Herpes simplex encephalitis causes the unusual appearance of episodic discharges, recurring every one to three seconds, as well as variable focal slow waves over the temporal areas. The discharges are not invariably present, but commonly occur within 2 - 15 days of the onset of the illness. It is therefore worth repeating the EEG on more than one occasion. Such periodic EEG discharges, in a patient with seizures and an acute febrile illness, is highly suggestive of the diagnosis.

Other infective processes

A non-specific increase in slow waves recorded diffusely over almost all areas of the scalp is also seen in the EEG of patients with other disorders, including rarer infections such as neurosyphilis, several parasitic infestations, as well as the paediatric condition known as Reye's syndrome which sometimes follows infection.

Creutzfeldt - Jakob disease

Although previously thought to be the result of a slow virus, the aetiology of this condition is under review following the discovery of prion proteins. This diffuse degenerative disorder of subacute onset is characterised by dementia and myoclonus. Periodic stereotyped repetitive discharges in the EEG at a rate of about one per second, although not invariably present, particularly in the early stages of the disease, are strongly suggestive of the diagnosis. These may be revealed by alerting stimuli or waking the patient from sleep, and the rate may 'follow' the frequency of photic stimulation.

In Heidenhain's variant of the disease, the EEG shows predominant abnormality over the occipital areas. There is a gradual increase in slow waves, and a reduction in amplitude of all activity as the disorder progresses.

Figure 8.7 shows repetitive discharges approximately every second in a patient whose post-mortem findings confirmed Creutzfeldt - Jakob disease. Repetitive discharges are also seen in the EEG shown in Fig. 8.8, taken during the later stages of this patient's illness. The background frequencies have diminished and the trace is relatively low amplitude and featureless. Myoclonic jerks have caused much associated muscle artefact in this EEG.

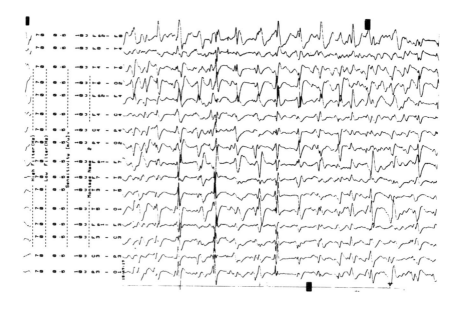

Fig. 8.7 This trace shows the generalised repetitive, bilaterally synchronous discharges, seen in the EEG of a patient with Creutzfeldt - Jakob disease, as later confirmed by post-mortem.

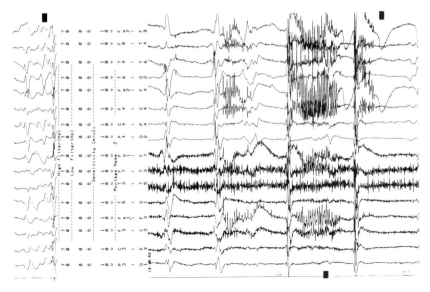

Fig. 8.8 Deterioration in background activity can be seen in this EEG, recorded at a later stage in the illness. The discharges are at times accompanied by muscle artefact due to the myoclonic jerks.

Subacute sclerosing panencephalitis

This is a slowly progressive disease of childhood believed to be caused by the measles virus. There is intellectual deterioration, convulsions, especially of myoclonic type, and neurological manifestations including extrapyramidal or pyramidal signs. The characteristic EEG consists of high-amplitude, repetitive, bilaterally synchronous and symmetrical, polyphasic sharp-wave and slow-wave complexes, which occur every 4 – 15 seconds. Each discharge is often accompanied by an involuntary 'myoclonic' jerk, but the slow relaxation phase of the movement is not entirely typical of myoclonus.

An example of the characteristic repetitive EEG findings is shown in Fig. 8.9. The associated myoclonic movements are shown on the EMG arm and leg polygraphic channels.

Early in the disease the EEG may not exhibit repetitive discharges, but the pattern is likely to evolve with time, together with increasing slow-wave activity. Later in the course of the illness sleep patterns become disrupted, and sleep staging is no longer possible.

Cerebrovascular disorders

Thrombosis, haemorrhage, emboli

While the advent of CT scanning has largely supplanted the EEG in the assessment of acute strokes, an EEG can sometimes prove more sensitive in

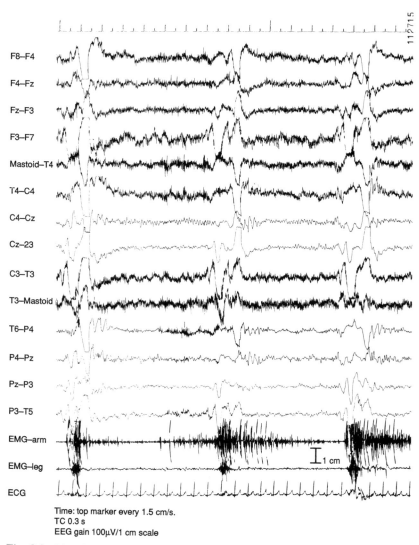

F8–F4

F4–Fz

Fz–F3

F3–F7

Mastoid–T4

T4–C4

C4–Cz

Cz–23

C3–T3

T3–Mastoid

T6–P4

P4–Pz

Pz–P3

P3–T5

EMG–arm

EMG–leg

ECG

Time: top marker every 1.5 cm/s.
TC 0.3 s
EEG gain 100μV/1 cm scale

Fig. 8.9 Myoclonic jerks, seen in the limb electromyograms, are associated with repetitive EEG discharges at a slow rate in this example of an EEG from a child with subacute sclerosing panencephalopathy.

the very early stages, when only magnetic resonance imaging (MRI) – if available – may be more informative. Slow-wave activity in the EEG is usually focal when there is cortical damage, with episodic bilaterally synchronous delta waves more commonly seen when there is a disturbance of subcortical function. The preservation of faster activities, especially in middle cerebral artery disease, indicates neuronal survival in the affected area and hence a better prognosis.

Internal carotid artery thrombosis, with marked neurological deficits such as hemiplegia, causes delta-wave activity over the affected hemisphere. This is likely to be most prominent over the temporal area, and may be followed by moderate voltage reduction. This is sometimes described as a 'depression' rather than as a suppression of cortical activity. The relative contributions of slow activity and depression are thought to reflect the degree of parenchymal damage, extremely slow activity followed by decreasing amplitude indicating extensive infarction.

With middle cerebral occlusion there may be similar slow-wave EEG changes, as well as seizure discharges, especially when 'watershed' areas are involved. An example is shown in Fig. 8.10, with slow and sharp waves over the right posterior temporal area. Background abnormalities may provide the clinician with more useful information than focal slowing, as preservation may be associated with a better prognosis.

Haemorrhage involving middle cerebral artery territory may cause less impressive EEG changes, only increasing as coma supervenes. However, the role of the EEG in the differential diagnosis of haemorrhage and infarction remains controversial. Statistical differences between the EEGs of groups of people with these conditions have been of limited value in the interpretation of an individual recording. The localisation of slow waves in the EEG varies with the site of thrombosis, usually occurring over the ipsilateral frontal area following anterior cerebral artery thrombosis, but the parieto-occipital area after posterior cerebral lesions.

Embolic lesions produce a variety of changes in the EEG which cannot effectively distinguish the pathological process. When there is 'watershed' ischaemia the EEG is often generally disorganised, with excess slow activity. A particular feature in comatose patients may be repetitive localised spike discharges, known as PLEDS. These are not invariably associated with focal clinical seizures, but herald a generally poor prognosis.

Transient ischaemic attacks

The EEG during an ischaemic episode is likely to show localised slow-wave activity, but between episodes there may be no indication of any abnormality. For this reason a prolonged telemetric or ambulatory trace can be of help in the differential diagnosis of transient neurological dysfunction. There is a lack of specificity in the diagnosis of the vessels involved that detracts from the value of the EEG in such disorders.

In transient global amnesia the EEG has been reported to be almost invariably normal both between and during an attack, with only one report of predominantly temporal slow waves occurring in some patients. This fact is of value in differentiating other causes, such as partial or minor epileptic seizures.

Migraine

Acute hemiplegic migraine may mimic cerebrovascular damage, especially if vasospasm has occurred. The EEG shows marked localised slow-wave

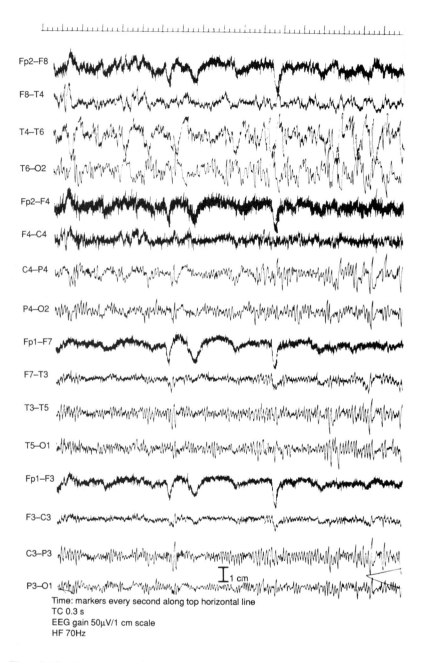

Fp2–F8

F8–T4

T4–T6

T6–O2

Fp2–F4

F4–C4

C4–P4

P4–O2

Fp1–F7

F7–T3

T3–T5

T5–O1

Fp1–F3

F3–C3

C3–P3

P3–O1

1 cm

Time: markers every second along top horizontal line
TC 0.3 s
EEG gain 50μV/1 cm scale
HF 70Hz

Fig. 8.10 Focal, phase reversed, slow waves are seen over the right temporo-occipital area of this EEG. The patient had suffered a cerebrovascular accident. Some of the slow waves have an associated sharp component, forming complexes.

activity. Although the EEG of a migrainous subject may be mildly abnormal, with brief bursts of moderately slow-wave and complex activity between attacks, the appearance is non-specific. Intermittent photic stimulation frequently produces an occipital following response that extends above 20 flashes per second, the 'H' response, a finding which tends to support the diagnosis.

Trauma

There is a close correlation between clinical and EEG findings in acute post-traumatic comatose states. The correlation is greater in the early stages, and serial traces are more valuable than a single trace. Classification of the EEG changes according to the severity of the disturbance can be based on the relative amounts of normal alpha as opposed to abnormal slow theta and delta frequencies. The presence or absence of brainstem damage can be assessed using waveform morphology and its response to extraneous stimuli. Depending on the level of the damage sustained within the brainstem, there may be unreactive 'alpha-like' activity, or variably responsive delta waves. Burst-suppression is only found when cerebral hypoxia has been sustained in addition to the trauma, unless there is an added effect due to medication or hypothermia. Complicating changes due to metabolic derangement have also to be considered.

Early seizure activity, often in association with clinical attacks, only occurs in the EEG of patients with severe cerebral damage. The appearance of such EEG activity is correlated with a reportedly threefold increase in the mortality rate. Epileptic status in adults, although less so in children, is a particularly adverse event. PLEDS occur rarely, except when there is a subdural haematoma.

There has been much study of the relationship of EEG findings and outcome, whether it be death, severe disability, moderate disability, or good recovery. The presence of sleep or sleep-like potentials indicates relatively intact cortical function in the acute stage, and these potentials have been used to assess the likely outcome. Important parameters for good outcome are the presence of spindles, and reactivity with alerting response stimuli. Decrease or loss of spindles, with diminished or absent reactivity, are features noted in prolonged coma. Decrease of spindles not only indicates deepening coma, but may also herald a prolonged comatose state. However, if other indicators such as reactivity, alternating patterns with time, high voltage, and symmetry of activities remain unchanged, the loss of spindles is less serious. When medication, particularly with barbiturates, has been introduced, there is additional suppression of cortical activity. Under this currently less favoured regime, the level of medication is usually adjusted to produce burst-suppression, and the additional effect of therapy must be borne in mind when assessing prognosis.

In the more prolonged coma states, the re-emergence of circadian rhythms in the EEG, together with sleep patterns, are favourable prognostic signs. In the late stages there is less informative clinical and EEG correlation. However, in the 'apallic' state – characterised clinically by an awake but unaware condition – following prolonged coma, recovery is usually associated with an increase in the frequency of slow activity, and reappearance of alpha waves. While the EEG reflects the degree of acute cerebral damage, it is much less helpful in detecting those at risk of post-traumatic epilepsy, and there is no clear correlation between early epileptiform discharges and the later development of seizures.

Chronic trauma

The chronic progressive encephalopathy occurring in boxers – the 'punch-drunk' state or 'dementia pugilistica' – produces relatively non-specific EEG abnormalities. The degree of abnormality does not correlate directly with the severity of the clinical state, and a normal EEG does not exclude the presence of an encephalopathy.

Space-occupying lesions

Tumour, abscess, subdural haematoma

The accuracy of the CT scan in diagnosing brain tumours is about 96%, and the EEG localises no more than 76%, without specific differentiation of gliomas from other tumours. However, the physiological changes reflected in the degree of EEG abnormality can provide useful clinical information. In particular it may indicate the possibility of seizures, or of non-convulsive seizure activity. Severe slow-wave disturbance may give warning of unsuspected secondary cortical changes in lesions primarily affecting the posterior fossa. In general terms, the more rapid the tumour growth, and its secondary effects due to distortion, the greater the amount of EEG slow activity. Conversely, when the tumour is slow growing, as is the case with many meningiomas, there may be virtually no EEG abnormality. It is particularly important to realise that a normal EEG cannot exclude an intracerebral neoplasm, contrasting strongly with the virtual exclusion of a very rapidly changing lesion such as an abscess, in which extremely slow focal delta waves are usually recorded.

Pathological space-occupying lesions cause local or focal slow-wave activity, as well as reduction of normal activity over a similar area. Thus alpha frequencies, and fast activity, may be diminished over the affected hemisphere. There may also be episodic sharp waves, spikes, or complexes of slow and sharp waves, which do not invariably signify a liability to seizures.

The CT scan is the investigation of choice in the diagnosis of an acute subdural haematoma, but in a patient presenting with chronic behavioural or neurological changes, the EEG may alert the physician to the possibility of a chronic subdural collection. Classically there is an asymmetry, with reduced amplitude activity on the affected side, but more often the EEG shows an increase in localised irregular slow activity, sometimes with sharp waves or other complex activity. Once again there is no pathological specificity, and a CT scan will be needed.

Dementia and cerebral atrophy

The repetitive complexes seen in Creutzfeldt – Jakob disease have already been described. In Huntington's disease the EEG is often, but not invariably, of reduced amplitude. Studies of CT scanning and EEG have shown poor correlation of EEG changes with the degree of atrophy, but a tendency for these to parallel the severity of the dementia. When discriminant-function analysis of group figures is analysed, EEG features may correlate as accurately with dementia as the CT scan, abnormalities being present in as many as 86% of cases. The degree of functional brain impairment reflected in the EEG changes, rather than the extent of atrophy in the CT scan, is also a better predictor of early mortality.

Current methods of investigation using the newer imaging techniques, together with qualitative neuropsychological analysis, have allowed recognition of several distinct disorders grouped within the non-Alzheimer's forms of cerebral atrophy. These include dementia of the frontal-lobe type (DFT), motor neuron disease, lobar atrophy and Lewy-body disease. The precise status of DFT in relation to Pick's disease requires clarification, but on clinical and pathological criteria it is distinct from Alzheimer's. The EEG is normal although cerebral blood flow is selectively reduced in the anterior cerebral hemispheres. Lobar atrophy, causing aphasia and changes in the dominant hemisphere, and the atrophy affecting parieto-occipital cortex, may show relatively non-specific localised slow-wave EEG changes. The dementia of Lewy-body type is increasingly recognised in patients previously thought to have multi-infarct or vascular dementia, although the definitive diagnosis may often only be made post-mortem. The EEG in any individual will be varyingly abnormal in relation to the degree and localisation of the cortical changes, and is therefore of relatively little help.

Mental handicap

The EEG does not have a specific role in these disorders, almost always displaying excess slow-wave activity in the more severely affected. However, it may provide useful information regarding the occurrence of seizures, their type, and progressive changes with time. In infantile subjects, the specific pattern of high-amplitude, chaotic, mixed slow-waves and spikes known as hypsarrhythmia may be revealed. This pattern is highly associated with the brief clinical seizures of serious prognosis for neurological and intellectual outcome, termed 'salaam spasms'. Serial traces in older patients may show a changing focus due to tuberose sclerosis, for example, or increasing slow activity and slowing of the dominant occipital rhythm with the onset of

Alzheimer's disease. There are also rare conditions, such as Angelman's disease, when the EEG waveforms – frontal rhythmic slow waves and occipital complexes – can be almost diagnostic.

Miscellaneous degenerative cerebral disorders

The EEG changes in a number of degenerative disorders, while not being specific, have a distinctive morphology which can be of diagnostic assistance. The photically induced complexes occurring at very slow rates of flicker (1 per second) in late infantile neuronal ceroid lipofuscinosis should alert the clinician to this possible cause of progressive neurological deterioration. The repetitive discharges seen in the chronic infective disorders have been mentioned, but complexes in association with progressive neurological disease can also aid the differential diagnosis. Complex discharges and myoclonus occur in essential hereditary myoclonic epilepsy and dyssynergia cerebellaris myoclonica. The latter condition starts in childhood, with ataxia, tremor and sometimes a progressive dementia.

Although the pathological processes in multiple sclerosis affect subcortical rather than cortical areas, the EEG may show fluctuating multifocal slow-wave activity of moderate severity. However, evoked potentials (see below) are of more use in the differential diagnosis.

Epilepsy and the EEG

The synchronous firing of many cells, whether focally or as a generalised event, can be recorded as spikes by 'microcellular' EEG as well as on the scalp. Physiological and clinical manifestations of these events are complex, being dependent on other inhibitory as well as excitatory influences. Animal research has shown that the primary events can, in the longer term, generate 'mirror foci', which may then lead to secondary, independent seizure activity over the contralateral hemisphere.

The clinical diagnosis of epilepsy, in which there is a recurring liability to seizures, must rest primarily on a careful history and an eye-witness account of the attacks. The EEG can be helpful in categorising the type of epilepsy, and the International Classification of Epilepsy (shown in outline in Table 8.1) incorporates EEG findings for some conditions. In certain instances, where clinical doubt remains, the EEG can provide confirmatory or supportive evidence. In general terms, an EEG during an attack is of more help than an interictal recording. Where there is a major or generalised attack, the trace can be expected to show specific abnormalities. Conversely, a normal EEG during a generalised or major attack is strong evidence against the diagnosis. While the absence of scalp EEG changes in apparent partial seizures may indicate pseudoseizures, it can also be due to very localised EEG discharges, only detectable by specialised techniques such as sphenoidal, depth or foramen ovale recordings.

Table 8.1 The international classification of epileptic seizures (ICES) (1981 revision)

Clinical seizure type	EEG seizure type	EEG interictal expression
I Focal (partial, local) seizures		
Focal seizures can be classified into one of the following three fundamental groups:		
A. Simple focal seizures		
B. Complex focal seizures		
1. With impairment of consciousness at onset		
2. Simple focal onset followed by impairment of consciousness		
C. Focal seizures evolving to generalised tonic–clonic convulsions (GTC)		
1. Simple evolving to GTC		
2. Complex evolving to GTC (including those with simple focal onset)		
A. Simple focal seizures (consciousness not impaired)		
1. With motor signs	Local contralateral discharge starting over the corresponding area of cortical representation (not always recorded on the scalp)	Local contralateral discharge
(a) Focal motor without march		
(b) Focal motor with march (Jacksonian)		
(c) Versive		
(d) Postural		
(e) Phonatory (vocalisation or arrest of speech)		
2. With somatosensory or special sensory symptoms (simple hallucinations, e.g. tingling, light flashes, buzzing)		
(a) Somatosensory		
(b) Visual		
(c) Auditory		
(d) Olfactory		
(e) Gustatory		
(f) Vertiginous		

Continued

Table 8.1 *Continued*

Clinical seizure type	EEG seizure type	EEG interictal expression
3. With autonomic symptoms or signs (including epigastric sensation, pallor, sweating, flushing, piloerection and pupillary dilation)		
4. With psychic symptoms (disturbance of higher cerebral function). These symptoms rarely occur without impairment of consciousness and are much more commonly experienced as complex focal seizures		
(a) Dysphasic		
(b) Dysmnesic (e.g. *déjà vu*)		
(c) Cognitive (e.g. dreamy states, distortions of time sense)		
(d) Affective (fear, anger, etc)		
(e) Illusions (e.g. macropsia)		
(f) Structured hallucinations (e.g. music, scenes)		
B. Complex focal seizures (with impairment of consciousness; may sometimes begin with simple symptoms)		
	Unilateral or, frequently, bilateral discharge, diffuse or focal in temporal or frontotemporal regions	Unilateral or bilateral generally synchronous focus; usually in the temporal or frontal regions
1. Simple focal onset followed by impairment of consciousness		
(a) With simple focal features (A.1 - A.4) followed by impaired consciousness		
(b) With automatisms		
2. With impairment of consciousness at onset		
(a) With impairment of consciousness only		
(b) With automatisms		

C. *Complex focal seizures evolving to secondarily generalised seizures (These may be generalised tonic – clonic, tonic, or clonic)*

Above discharges become secondarily and rapidly generalised

1. Simple focal seizures (A) evolving to generalised seizures
2. Complex focal seizures (B) evolving to generalised seizures
3. Simple focal seizures evolving to complex generalised seizures

II Generalised seizures (convulsive or non-convulsive)

A. *1. Absence seizures*
  (a) Impairment of consciousness only
  (b) With mild clonic components
  (c) With atonic components
  (d) With tonic components
  (e) With automatisms
  (f) With autonomic components
  (b) to (f) may be used alone or in combination

Usually regular and symmetrical 3 Hz but may be 2 – 4 Hz spike- and slow-wave complexes and may have multiple spike- and slow-wave complexes. Abnormalities are bilateral

Background activity usually normal although paroxysmal activity (such as spike- or spike and slow-wave complexes) may occur. The activity is usually regular and symmetrical

2. Atypical absence
May have:
  (a) Changes in tone that are more pronounced than in A.1
  (b) Onset and/or cessation that is not abrupt

EEG more heterogeneous; may include irregular spike- and slow-wave complexes, fast activity or other paroxysmal activity. Abnormalities are bilateral but often irregular and asymmetrical

Background usually abnormal; paroxysmal activity (such as spikes or spike- and slow-wave complexes) frequently irregular asymmetrical

Continued

Table 8.1 *Continued*

Clinical seizure type	EEG seizure type	EEG interictal expression
B. Myoclonic seizures		
Myoclonic jerks	Polyspike and wave, or sometimes spike and wave or sharp and slow waves	Same as ictal
C. Clonic seizures	Fast activity (10 Hz or more) and slow waves; occasional spike and wave patterns	Spike and wave or polyspike and wave discharges
D. Tonic seizures	Low voltage, fast activity or a fast rhythm of 9–10 Hz or more decreasing in frequency and increasing in amplitude	More or less rhythmic discharges of sharp and slow waves, sometimes asymmetrical. Background is often abnormal for age
E. Tonic–clonic seizures	Rhythm at 10 Hz or more decreasing in frequency and increasing in amplitude during tonic phase, interrupted by slow waves during clonic phase	Polyspike and waves or spike and wave, or sometimes, sharp and slow wave discharges
F. Atonic seizures		
(Astatic) combinations of the above may occur (e.g. B and F, B and D)	Polyspikes and wave flattening or low-voltage fast activity	Polyspikes and slow wave

III Unclassified epileptic seizures

Includes all seizures that cannot be classified because of inadequate or inconsistent data and some that defy classification in hitherto described categories. This includes some neonatal seizures (e.g. rhythmic eye movement, chewing, and swimming movements)

A normal EEG between attacks does not exclude a diagnosis of epilepsy. An EEG is only diagnostic of epilepsy when 'paroxysmal' or epileptiform activity occurs in association with a clinical seizure, but the particular form of EEG activity is not always specific for the type of seizure.

Ictal EEG abnormalities

Generalised seizures

Major tonic – clonic attacks (grand mal)   The initial EEG changes during a major tonic – clonic seizure consist of a desynchronisation, or drop in voltage, lasting a few seconds. There is generalised very fast activity, followed by rhythmic activity at approximately 10 Hz, of rapidly increasing amplitude. In most circumstances, without muscle relaxants, the EEG activity is largely obliterated by muscle artefact at this stage. Rhythmic activity gradually slows to about 4 Hz, when an alternating polyspike and slow-wave appearance develops in association with the clonic phase of the attack.

Figures 8.11a and 11b show the EEG changes during the tonic and clonic phases of a major seizure. Major seizures patterns are not seen during the first five or six months of life, when the EEG patterns are varied and often only consist of rhythmic runs of activity in the alpha, theta or delta wave bands.

Minor absences (petit mal)   Spike and wave complexes at 3 Hz (Fig. 8.12), often with faster and slower complexes at the beginning and end of the attacks, constitute the EEG changes in this well recognised clinical entity. During classic minor absence attacks, the discharges have a clearly defined start and end abruptly, in association with some evidence of clinical change in the level of awareness. However, 3 Hz complexes, especially when present for less than five seconds, may occur without any clinical change and do not invariably signify petit mal attacks, while non-rapid-eye-movement (REM) sleep and hypoglycaemia are also facilitating factors.

Atypical minor absence attacks (Lennox – Gastaut syndrome)   Slow (2 Hz) complexes in prolonged runs, with a gradual rather than a sudden cessation, correlate with the occurrence of clinically refractory seizures. The discharges are enhanced in non-REM sleep, and in children have to be distinguished from the condition of electrical or non-convulsive status during sleep.

Hypsarrhythmia   High-amplitude mixed slow waves, usually delta, and multifocal spikes which tend to cluster to give an apparent burst-suppression appearance during sleep, constitute the 'chaotic' appearance of hypsarrhythmia. This is an EEG descriptive term in which there is a high correlation with the presence of clinical salaam spasms in the infant. Sometimes the spasms coincide with a brief flattening in the EEG activity.

Myoclonus   The EEG in association with myoclonic jerking can vary, depending on the aetiology of the myoclonus. There may be no EEG correlate

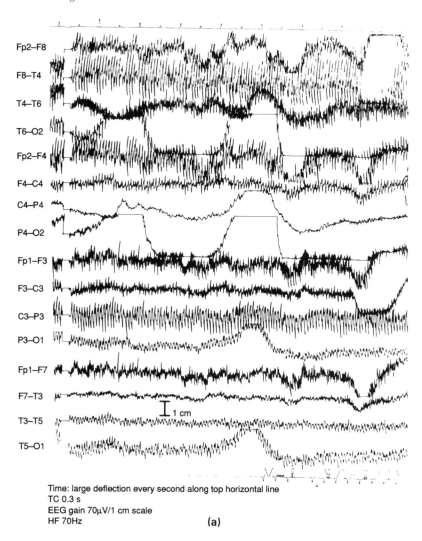

Fp2–F8
F8–T4
T4–T6
T6–O2
Fp2–F4
F4–C4
C4–P4
P4–O2
Fp1–F3
F3–C3
C3–P3
P3–O1
Fp1–F7
F7–T3
T3–T5
T5–O1

1 cm

Time: large deflection every second along top horizontal line
TC 0.3 s
EEG gain 70μV/1 cm scale
HF 70Hz   **(a)**

Fig. 8.11 (a) The EEG shows the trains of spikes occurring in the EEG during
the tonic phase of grand mal convulsion. (b) The subsequent clonic phase of this
epileptic attack is characterised by repetitive complexes in the EEG.

in benign myoclonus, or there may be polyspike and wave, or sometimes
spike and wave or sharp and slow waves.

Partial seizures

Complex partial seizures are associated with loss of consciousness.
Simple partial seizures are associated with no loss of consciousness.
    The various EEG correlates of differing focal seizures can be seen in
Table 8.1. Amplitude decrement between cortex and scalp, and discrete

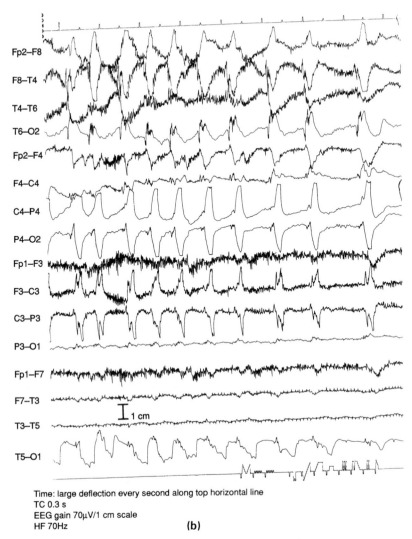

Fp2–F8

F8–T4

T4–T6

T6–O2

Fp2–F4

F4–C4

C4–P4

P4–O2

Fp1–F3

F3–C3

C3–P3

P3–O1

Fp1–F7

F7–T3

T3–T5

T5–O1

Time: large deflection every second along top horizontal line
TC 0.3 s
EEG gain 70µV/1 cm scale
HF 70Hz   **(b)**

Fig. 8.11 (b)

EEG discharges, at times over the inferior frontal or temporal areas of the cortex,
contribute to the negative scalp recordings in some patients with undoubted
focal epileptic seizures. Otherwise, in most major or generalised attacks, a
normal EEG during the episode should raise the suspicion of an alternative
diagnosis. An example of the serial changes occurring during a complex partial
seizure, here arising in the right frontotemporal area, is shown in Fig. 8.13a – d.

Complex partial seizures in adults may be associated with repetitive temporal
spikes. The discharges occur over the anterior or mesial temporal areas, so
that additional special electrodes may be needed to demonstrate the disturbance.
In children there may be runs of rhythmic slow waves during such an attack.

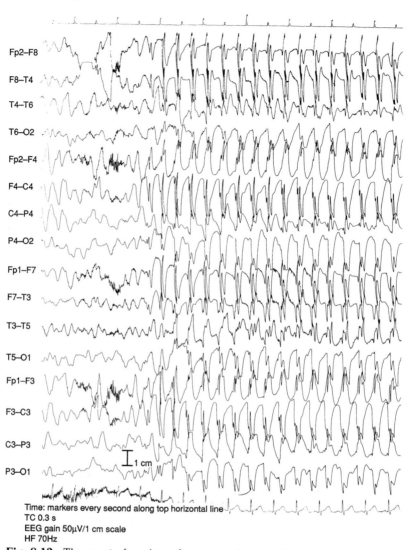

Fp2–F8

F8–T4

T4–T6

T6–O2

Fp2–F4

F4–C4

C4–P4

P4–O2

Fp1–F7

F7–T3

T3–T5

T5–O1

Fp1–F3

F3–C3

C3–P3

P3–O1

1 cm

Time: markers every second along top horizontal line
TC 0.3 s
EEG gain 50μV/1 cm scale
HF 70Hz

Fig. 8.12 The onset of a minor absence or classic petit mal attack is shown in this EEG, in which there are generalised 3 Hz complexes.

The focal discharges of epilepsia partialis continuans represent partial seizure activity originating in the motor area, and EEG discharges localised to the parasagittal region can sometimes be missed if adequate electrode placements are not included.

Seizures in infants

Seizures in premature and full-term infants usually comprise fragmentary clinical changes, such as deviation of the eyes, brief apnoea, cycling movements of the legs, or brief twitches of the limbs. The EEG changes also reflect the immature nervous system. Ictal discharges may consist only of runs of rhythmic activity, with a focal onset and spread or change of laterality as the seizure continues. Similar discharges also occur as interictal phenomena. While sharp transients may appear as ictal or interictal manifestations, such waveforms are less common in this age group than in the older child's or adult's EEG.

Interictal EEG abnormalities

'Epileptiform' or 'paroxysmal' EEG abnormalities are terms used to describe transient waveforms, particularly spikes and sharp waves, which can be distinguished from the background. A spike has a duration of 20 – 70 ms, and the main component is usually of negative polarity. A sharp wave is a similarly peaked waveform, but of a duration of 70 – 200 ms. These interictal transients may provide evidence to support a diagnosis of epilepsy. Similar waveforms can occur in association with disorders other than epilepsy, and must also be distinguished from physiological transients, such as vertex sharp waves of sleep.

Interictal generalised discharges

Discharges of 3Hz. The 3Hz discharges occurring ictally and interictally in minor absence attacks have already been considered. Long bursts, of more than 10 seconds, may be associated with automatisms, which may be incorrectly interpreted as manifestations of complex partial seizures.

Multiple spike and slow-wave discharges. 'Atypical spike wave activity' or 'multiple spike and wave discharges' occur in the EEG of patients with primary generalised epilepsy, including tonic – clonic and myoclonic seizures. The extent to which these deviate from the typical 3 Hz waveform reflects the probability that there are seizures other than typical absence or petit mal.

Slow spike and wave complexes. The slow spike and wave complexes described in atypical minor absence seizures, of Lennox – Gastaut type or childhood epileptic encephalopathy, can also be an interictal manifestation. In this syndrome there is significant disruption of the background EEG frequencies, usually due to additional pathology or degenerative process affecting cerebral function, and 80% of the children suffer from mental retardation.

Interictal focal discharges

Focal or local EEG discharges can indicate the possibility of focal attacks, and some discharges may have particular clinical significance.

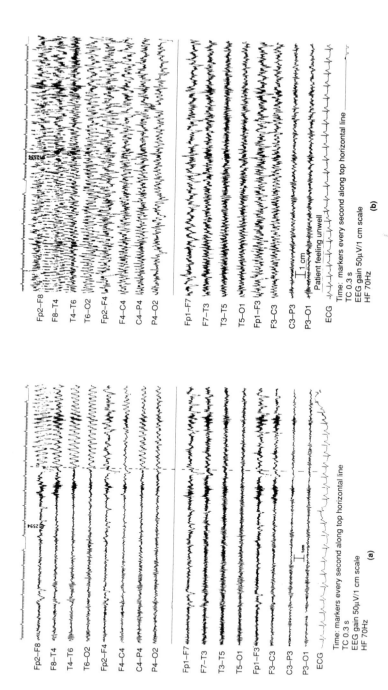

Fig. 8.13 (a) This EEG, recorded during hyperventilation, shows the onset of a complex partial seizure over the right hemisphere. Rhythmic waves are particularly marked over the temporal area. (b) The EEG during the continuation of the seizure shows spread of activity, and an increasing frequency. The activity is still more marked over the right than the left hemisphere.

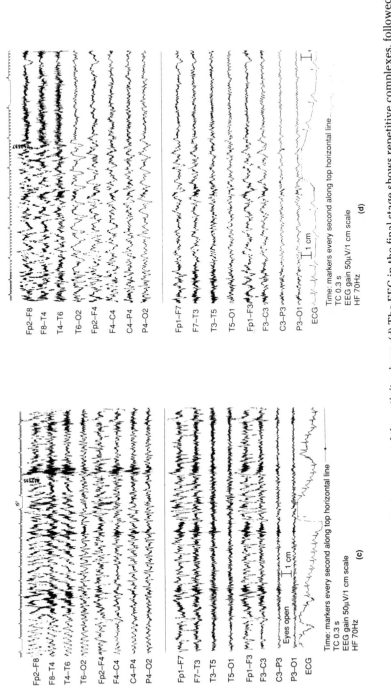

Fig. 8.13 (c) As the attack continues the frequency of the activity slows. (d) The EEG in the final stage shows repetitive complexes, followed by a resumption of relatively normal activity immediately after the seizure. The four EEG traces are a continuous record of this attack.

Patients with complex or simple seizures originating in the temporal lobes may show interictal temporal spikes. As with the ictal discharges, additional special electrodes may be needed to demonstrate the disturbance.

Stereotyped focal bi- or tri-phasic sharp waves over the central and mid-temporal areas occur over one or both hemispheres in the EEG of children with 'benign' or 'rolandic' epilepsy. This syndrome arises between the ages of 4 and 13 years, and remits spontaneously by late adolescence in 95% of patients. There are often generalised spike wave complexes and seizures during sleep, with focal manifestations particularly prominent in the waking state. A slightly less common but also benign variant has been described with occipital spikes in the EEG.

EEG activating procedures

A liability to epilepsy not clearly manifest in the routine resting EEG may be revealed by certain activating manoeuvres in patients with particular sensitivity. The production of photoconvulsive spike discharges by rhythmic stroboscopic light stimulation, particularly in the 20 – 30 Hz range, is the most common method, and an example was shown earlier in Fig. 8.5. The EEG discharges may not necessarily provoke any clinical change, or there may be myoclonic jerking, an altered level of consciousness, or even frank tonic – clonic seizures. The presence of asymptomatic discharges is reported to be approximately 1% in children, and of the order of 0.3% even in adults. However, the figures for this vary according to the exact conditions under which the test is carried out, and one study has quoted an incidence as high as 30% in children under the age of 18 years.

In some patients, the attacks can be triggered in a reflex manner by other stimuli, such as visual patterns or specific sensory stimuli such as music, movement, touch, reading, or mathematical calculations.

Fluctuations in the interictal EEG with time may mean that no abnormality is revealed during the relatively brief period over which a trace is usually recorded. In patients with focal seizures, of psychomotor type, Gibbs & Gibbs (1952) showed that a standard EEG would show relevant abnormality in only 30% of cases, whereas during sleep the trace was three times as likely to be helpful. Aimone-Marsan & Zivin (1970) found that less than 50% of patients with a clinical diagnosis of epilepsy, not restricted to any particular type, showed epileptiform activity in a single waking EEG. As many as 15% failed to do so in repeated EEGs on as many as ten separate occasions, while 60% showed such EEG features in some but not all their recordings. However, in 1983 Binnie reported that relevant EEG abnormalities can be detected in as many as 90% of patients with epilepsy if recordings under conditions of hyperventilation, photic stimulation, barbiturate sleep and sleep deprivation are included.

The limitations of the interictal EEG in the diagnosis of epilepsy has led to the development of various prolonged video monitoring techniques, in which the aim is to record a seizure. Additional polygraph traces of the electrocardiogram, eye movements, respiration, and muscle activity, for example, can help to differentiate alternative diagnoses.

In the small group of patients whose epilepsy is difficult to diagnose, such differential possibilities include non-organic pseudoseizures, as well as other organic episodes such as cardiac arrhythmias, migraine, vasovagal episodes, cataplexy, narcolepsy, hyperventilation, tetany, hypoglycaemia, or transient ischaemic attacks. Not infrequently there may be more than one type of attack. In one published series of patients with epilepsy admitted for observation and management of their attacks, 4.5% were found to have both real and pseudoseizures. This combination resulted in a 4.5-fold increase in their hospital stay compared with other patients.

For freely ambulant recordings, some form of telemetry is needed, but most departments can now make equal use of the miniaturised amplifier systems in the modern ambulatory EEG recording systems. Traces recorded on cassette tapes are replayed at increased speed for later analysis and evaluation. The importance of appropriate therapy for complex partial as opposed to minor absence (petit mal) seizures, for example, is one particularly useful clinical application of ambulatory monitoring of the EEG. Stalberg has shown that monitoring for about seven hours provides an answer for the referring physician in 65% of 180 investigations. Binnie (1983, 1989) obtained a similar proportion of 67% in a retrospective study, increasing to 81% in a rigorously controlled prospective investigation. In such patients, who often have a long history of difficult medical and drug management, with several hospital admissions, there are significant potential savings in economic terms if an early and unequivocal diagnosis can be achieved.

The failure of scalp records to reveal localised EEG rhythms originating deep within the brain has led to the introduction of mildly invasive techniques, with additional recording electrodes placed nearer the generator sites. These include nasopharyngeal, sphenoidal and foramen ovale electrodes, which are used to reveal inferior temporal spike activity. Their role is largely restricted to the detailed investigations necessary as a precursor to surgery for refractory seizures, when a combination of video and EEG investigations is generally regarded as essential.

Epilepsy, medication and the EEG

Medication should never be stopped in order to reveal EEG abnormalities, as status may be precipitated. It must be recognised that EEG abnormalities can be diminished by anticonvulsants, and benzodiazepines may similarly affect photoparoxysmal responses. However, the effect is not invariable, and there is only poor correlation between the EEG discharges and the control of fits, except for minor absence attacks of petit mal type. An increase in EEG complexes, accompanied either by deterioration or improvement in seizure control, has been reported in children with complex partial seizures. There are also limitations on the value of the EEG in the prognosis of seizure recurrence before anticonvulsant withdrawal. Nevertheless, such a course of action may need to be reconsidered if the EEG shows frequent and marked complex discharges.

Pseudoseizures

Delgado-Escueta & Mattson (1981) used monitoring to study 84 patients with apparent seizures, of whom 34 had pseudoseizures or psychogenic attacks, and found that coexistence with true seizures is not uncommon. The interictal EEG may show various minor sharp-wave abnormalities, especially if there is coexisting epilepsy. In major 'attacks' with considerable limb movement, the EEG may be partially obscured by the artefact. However, there is usually no more than brief attenuation of alpha activity, which may indeed continue throughout the episode. Additional help may be obtained from blood prolactin levels, which are usually raised after true but not pseudoseizures.

Refractory seizures and surgical treatment

Any preoperative evaluation of patients with refractory epilepsy must include an EEG during the seizure. Interictal discharges are insufficient and can be misleading. One series noted that 25% of patients admitted for consideration of surgery were found to have pseudoseizures accounting for their management problems. At least 12 and preferably 16 or more channels of EEG data should be available. Use of surface and sphenoidal electrodes should reveal whether the attacks are unifocal in at least eight to ten characteristic seizures. This should prevent false localisation where the attacks are of multifocal origin. The rate of false localisation on these criteria has been reported to be as low as 10%, although other estimates vary from 22% to 40%. Corroborative evidence for the EEG focus is usually obtained from other data such as CT, MRI, positron emission tomography (PET) and angiography. The final decision requires correlation of all the evidence, including that from the clinical findings and neuropsychology. Additional depth-electrode placements with prolonged EEG monitoring may then be required if there are striking inconsistencies in the results of these studies. One review, with a mean follow-up of 32 months, in which temporal lobectomy was undertaken in patients without malignant neoplasms, showed that 10 of 15 patients were subsequently seizure free, and 13 were having no more than one attack per month, compared with at least weekly preoperative seizures.

Violence, epilepsy and the EEG

Interictal violence

Early studies of EEG findings in violent individuals reported increased incidences of abnormalities in comparison with normal populations. In one study, interictal EEGs were abnormal in 55% of the habitually aggressive individuals, and 24% of those who had only committed a single violent crime. More recent studies, with additional video analyses, showed minimal or slight abnormality in 6.6% of EEGs, and none had 'epileptiform' features. It may be that the earlier studies were unduly biased by the inclusion of waveforms which are now regarded as normal variants. These include spike-like waveforms at 6 or 14 Hz, small sharp spikes, and mid-temporal bursts of drowsiness ('psychomotor variant').

Studies of interictal violent behaviour have tended to be unduly weighted by the inclusion of predominantly young males of low IQ who have personality disorders, a history of early and severe epilepsy, and associated neurological problems. If the contribution of patients with severe psychiatric disorders or low IQ is excluded, particularly in the reported studies on patients with temporal lobe epilepsy, there is no increased incidence of violence.

The findings of these and similar studies suggest that interictal violence is more frequently encountered in patients with epilepsy than in the normal population, but is probably due to associated factors such as brain damage or adverse social conditions rather than the epilepsy itself.

Ictal violence

The recent advances provided by continuous EEG monitoring with videometry have helped to clarify ideas where ictal violence is concerned. The most comprehensive study was reported by Delgado-Escueta *et al* (1981), in which 19 supposedly aggressive patients from several centres were reviewed by a workshop panel of experts (under the auspices of the Epilepsy Foundation of America – the EFA Study). Of seven patients finally judged to be aggressive, three were mentally retarded, and three had evidence of organic brain syndromes. In most cases spontaneous, non-directed, stereotyped acts of violence or aggression were observed during the height of the epileptogenic paroxysms. In two these occurred at the end or after a seizure, probably as a reaction to being restrained. Amnesia for the episodes was present on all occasions. The acts were never followed by purposeful movements, no weapons other than fists or hands were used, and there was no attempt at subsequent concealment.

Fenwick (1986) has concluded that even a very well documented diagnosis of epilepsy should not be considered relevant in the defence of criminal aggression, unless it can be established that the aggressive episode occurred as a part of an epileptic seizure. The fact that these are usually stereotyped, simple rather than complex, acts should also be borne in mind.

In a detailed review, Treiman & Delgado-Escueta (1983) found that evidence for ictal violence could only be upheld in an extremely small proportion of the reported relationships, when the temporal sequence of events was strictly examined. In an analysis of over 600 complex partial seizures (CPS), they drew two conclusions. Firstly, the violent act must have taken place in the context of one of the known patterns of CPS occurring in the appropriate sequence. Secondly, it is unlikely that organised directed aggression, especially if it involves complex motor activity such as using a gun, could be a manifestation of CPS. The EFA's study suggested that, rarely, moderately severe, directed aggression could occur in the later phases of a CPS, when the patient is partially responsive but amnesic. Sequential complicated acts such as homicide are nearly impossible. However, violent behaviour leading to severe injury does occur in reaction to restraint during the third phase of automatisms in CPS or after tonic – clonic seizures.

EEG and episodic behavioural changes

Modern technology, and particularly depth-electrode studies, have shed new light on the relationship between EEG discharges, epilepsy and behaviour. However, much of the work remains controversial in its interpretation. For example, episodic behavioural changes were at times noted to occur in association with focal depth discharges in the amygdala, hippocampus and septal region, but there were no simultaneous scalp EEG changes. This phenomenon, consisting of precipitous onset of symptoms, equally abrupt remissions, and frequent recurrences was designated 'episodic dyscontrol syndrome'. Less rigorous subsequent use of the term has confused the issue, and EEG evidence has so far not fully resolved the question as to whether these states are invariably due to seizures. The evidence has been reviewed in detail by Fenwick (1986).

Major psychiatric disorders and the EEG

Schizophrenia

The value of EEG in the diagnosis of any particular patient with this disorder is negligible, but analyses of group data are of interest. It has been suggested that familial cases tend to have normal EEGs, whereas sporadic cases often show abnormalities, perhaps reflecting dysfunction of the central nervous system. Patients whose EEGs before or during treatment are abnormal have more evidence of brain dysfunction than those with normal EEGs. Spectral frequency analysis of the EEGs of chronic schizophrenic patients has also shown distinctive regional differences, for example fluctuations with time affecting right/left hemispheric energy in mania and schizophrenia, was reported by Flor-Henry *et al* (1984). Further evidence for an organic cause may be suggested by these and other studies, especially with the newer quantitative methods. However, methodological deficiencies and variability in classification of disease entities throw doubt on the validity of some of the conclusions drawn.

Affective disorders

Similar reservations apply to the use of the EEG in this group of patients. It is important in all these patients to exclude organic brain disorder. The group studies again suggest that some patients may have underlying abnormalities of the central nervous system. Small *et al* (1975), for example, showed that both probands and family members had a 50% incidence of the small sharp-spike EEG variants. Flor-Henry *et al* (1983) reported right-sided EEG abnormalities during verbal cognitive activation tests in patients with psychoses, including those with psychotic depression.

Anxiety states

In patients with chronic symptoms of anxiety, the EEG is likely to show low-voltage fast activity, and relatively few alpha frequencies, as these are normally 'blocked' or diminished by alerting stimuli and mental activity. Acute anxiety states or panic attacks may be accompanied by overbreathing, which can induce slow-wave changes in the EEG. The latter effect occurs as a normal phenomenon in adolescence, but may still be apparent in adults when there is relative hypoglycaemia.

Sleep and the EEG

During drowsiness and sleep, the appearance of the EEG changes, the various levels of sleep being accompanied by specific alterations in the recorded waveforms. Table 8.2 describes the findings. The transition from stage to stage is somewhat imprecise, but the categorisation of sleep stages is not difficult for experienced electroencephalographers, who follow internationally recognised standard guidelines.

The major categories of slow-wave (non-REM) and REM sleep can be recognised by the EEG analysis. The EEG in REM sleep consists of relatively low-voltage mixed frequencies, and varying amounts of slow activity in the non-REM stages. The various stages are associated with differing physiological

Table 8.2 Sleep and the EEG

Stage	State	EEG
1	Drowsiness	Alpha spindles, to vertex sharp waves
2	Light sleep	Sleep spindles of fast activity, vertex sharp waves, K complexes
3	Deep sleep	Marked slow activity, K complexes, some spindles
4	Very deep sleep	Much slowing, some K complexes
REM	Rapid eye movement sleep	Desynchronisation with faster frequencies

and pathophysiological processes. For example, in children, release of growth hormone and night-terrors take place in slow-wave sleep, whereas dreaming and nightmares occur in REM sleep. Activation of epileptic seizures may take place during drowsiness and light sleep, or there may be significant alteration of the type of discharges during sleep, as for example the periodic appearance of sleep records in hypsarrhythmia. It is important to differentiate the normal vertex or parietal sharp waves of sleep from abnormal epileptiform discharges.

Sleep disorders

The use of EEG and polygraphic recordings of eye movements, electromyogram, electrocardiogram, respiratory movements (respitrace) and oxygen saturation levels (oximetry) can help to establish the diagnosis in a variety of sleep disorders, such studies being known as polysomnography. Four major categories of sleep disturbance are recognised (Table 8.3). Patterns of alternating REM and non-REM sleep can be displayed in histogram form, as a 'hypnogram'. Such graphical displays can more easily reveal altered periodic cycling between these states, or multiple brief arousals. Analysis of EEG activity may be essential in arriving at an accurate evaluation of the particular disorder involved. In some conditions there is a well recognised association with specific sleep stages, and in particular with REM or non-REM sleep. However, such studies often reveal that many patients suffer from a combination of medical conditions, making rigid classification difficult.

Insomnias

Polygraphic sleep studies may show greatly delayed sleep onset, and sleep fragmentation. The poor sleep, with delayed onset or early waking, of depression is well recognised. Stimulant drugs are a further cause, and sleep may be profoundly disturbed during withdrawal from many substances, including monoamine oxidase inhibitors and alcohol.

Narcolepsy

Monosymptomatic narcolepsy is characterised by inappropriate and virtually irresistible daytime sleep attacks as well as excessive daytime sleepiness.

Table 8.3 Disorders of sleep

Classification	Characteristics
Insomnias	Disorders of initiating and maintaining sleep
Hypersomnias	Disorders of excessive somnolence
Biorhythm disorders	Disorders of the sleep – waking cycle
Parasomnias	Disorders associated with sleep, sleep stages, or partial arousals from sleep

Polysymptomatic narcolepsy includes additional symptoms, such as cataplexy, sleep paralysis, vivid hypnogogic hallucinations, disturbed sleep, and terrifying dreams. Abnormally rapid onset of REM-stage sleep during an afternoon nap, or the abnormally rapid onset of stage 1 sleep during a multiple daytime EEG sleep latency test, can confirm the diagnosis. Combined EEG and polygraphic traces are necessary to determine the onset of stage 1 sleep, which is timed from the start of each of a series of recordings at intervals during the day, taken to stage 1 or continued for 20 minutes, whichever is the shorter. Abnormal night-time sleep cycles are also a feature of this condition.

Sleep and breathing disorders

Sleep apnoea

In these conditions it is often necessary to include night-time sleep, to obtain a recording during REM-stage sleep. It may be of peripheral (obstructive), central, or mixed central and peripheral origin. Use of polysomnography allows comparison of sleep stage, oxygen levels in the blood, and respiratory effort. In obstructive sleep apnoea or hypopnoea, the upper airway suddenly occludes during inspiration, leading to hypoxia and cardiovascular changes as well as sleep disturbance. It is to be differentiated from sleep-related central apnoea, when there is decreased respiratory muscle activity, but usually less effect on the cardiovascular system. However, the conditions may coexist. Oronasal obstruction and loss of oronasal airflow leaves the central drive intact, with continuing respiratory movements, whereas in central apnoea there is a failure of respiratory drive from the medullary centres. In mixed forms, central apnoea evolves into obstructive apnoea.

Obstructive apnoea

Massive obesity is associated with a condition of obstructive sleep apnoea, the 'Pickwickian syndrome'. Patients with thoracic deformities, or neurological and muscle disorders, causing compromised ventilation may become abruptly worse during REM sleep owing to the inhibition of intercostal and accessory respiratory muscles during this stage. Loss or diminution of the normal excitatory effect of arousal stimuli on respiration may be present in conditions which reduce the likelihood of arousal, for example alcohol, sleep deprivation, or drugs that depress the central nervous system. Where several factors are acting together, as in the elderly, there may be significant hypoxia during REM sleep. In turn this can lead to sudden cardiac arrhythmias.

Figure 8.14 shows examples from a polysomnographic recording in a patient with sleep apnoea. The nasal and oral air exchange is virtually nil, there is poor chest movement, but abdominal respiratory excursions are still present. The EEG shows slow waves of sleep.

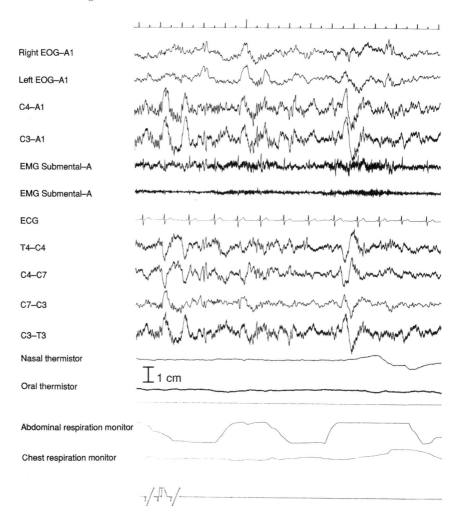

Right EOG–A1

Left EOG–A1

C4–A1

C3–A1

EMG Submental–A

EMG Submental–A

ECG

T4–C4

C4–C7

C7–C3

C3–T3

Nasal thermistor

Oral thermistor

Abdominal respiration monitor

Chest respiration monitor

Fig. 8.14 This combined EEG and polygraphic trace shows the slow and fast frequencies during sleep. In addition the use of themistors to record air exchange through the nose and mouth has revealed a period of apnoea. Simultaneous chest and abdominal respiratory monitors show that the respiratory excursions have continued during the period of apnoea, suggesting an obstructive cause.

Motor abnormalities

Repetitive stereotyped leg movements occurring in sleep, associated with repeated micro-arousals, can lead to excessive daytime sleepiness (EDS), and are very common. The movements are sometimes designated nocturnal myoclonus, but are not true myoclonus.

Hypersomnias

Idiopathic

This condition is characterised by a normal sleep cycle, prolonged night sleep and excessive daytime sleepiness, with lack of an early REM period in overnight sleep studies. Rarely, hypersomnia is related to the menstrual cycle and is a recurrent phenomenon.

Klein - Levin syndrome

This periodic hypersomnia is associated with compulsive eating, hypersexuality, loss of sexual inhibitions, and at times irritability or apathy. It is commonest in adolescent males, and is thought to be related to an episodic hypothalamic disorder.

Affective disorders and hypersomnia

In manic - depressive illness there may be episodes of hypersomnia during the depressive phases of the disorder. The EEG shows increased sleep duration, a short REM latency, and some reduction of slow-wave sleep.

Disturbed sleep - waking cycle

Three types of attacks occurring particularly in slow-wave sleep are confusional awakenings, sleep-walking, and night-terrors. They need to be distinguished from nocturnal confusion due to organic disease, automatisms, or fear in the context of nocturnal epileptic partial seizures. The EEG recordings can be valuable in the differentiation of the various causes, both by identifying the sleep stage involved and by revealing ictal discharges in epilepsy.

Of interest to the psychiatrist is the group of REM sleep behavioural disorders. There may be unusual aggressive episodes in the REM sleep of older patients without apparent daytime disturbances. Such behaviour can occur in patients with a variety of neurological pathology, including dementia. There are marked phasic REM bursts and myoclonic potentials. About 20 - 25% of patients with epilepsy have seizures exclusively or mainly at night. Grand mal seizures are activated in non-REM sleep, while absences or minor seizures may be seen in REM sleep.

Prolonged EEG recordings can be of particular value in distinguishing conditions such as nocturnal enuresis from epilepsy with incontinence, psychomotor automatisms of partial seizures from sleep walking, or partial seizure phenomena from night-terrors and anxiety dreams.

Sleep studies and impotence

Polysomnographic monitoring has also proved useful in distinguishing organic from non-organic causes of impotence, as erections are associated with REM sleep.

Studies of penile tumescence in relation to the sleep – wake cycles can evaluate the contribution of conditions such as vascular disease and diabetes compared with other, non-organic factors in the aetiology of this condition. However, it must be admitted that the demonstration of morning erections is equally informative in the differential diagnosis.

Sleep and violence

People who commit a criminal act while asleep are not conscious of their actions and cannot be held legally responsible. These events are called 'sane automatisms'. REM sleep may be associated with violent dreams, but rapid return of consciousness and body paralysis precludes action. Sleep walking and night-terrors, occurring in deep slow-wave sleep, may very rarely be associated with violent acts. Night-terrors allow a defence of sane automatism and possible acquittal following such acts. For most other violent automatic acts in a confusional state, following a plea of not guilty by reason of insanity, there is a mandatory referral to hospital, usually a secure one (Fenwick, 1986). Thus most automatisms, other than those related to hypoglycaemia or night-terrors, would be categorised as a disease of the mind if this plea were used.

Mapping

Various attempts have been made to quantify EEG data, and to use these to 'map' scalp distributions of the analysed activity. One example uses the frequency spectra, as shown in Fig. 8.15. Excess, mainly left frontal and temporal, slow waves are shown in the raw EEG. A simultaneous spectral map display, of 4.25 seconds of the EEG recording, shows the relative proportions of slow and faster frequencies in a spectrum extending up to 35 Hz. Computed neurophysiological topography uses voltage or power spectral analysed data, for example, derived from the raw EEG to provide coloured 'maps' of the scalp distribution, often with statistical deviations from a normal population (the examples shown are of course black and white reproductions of coloured originals). Considerable controversy still surrounds the use of this method, for a number of reasons. Unlike MRI and CT, which the 'maps' appear superficially to resemble, these are the result of measurement at only 16 to 32 points, with interpolation of intermediate points creating an illusion of higher resolution than actually exists. The mathematical techniques incorporate assumptions which can themselves lead to erroneous results, and the colour format tends to make artificial distinctions, because abrupt changes occur between data that are actually quite similar. The activity analysed is at all times only that which has been recorded from the scalp, and as such may well bear little or no relationship to activity occurring at or within the brain itself.

An example of a 'map' constructed from the results of frequency distribution analyses, the raw EEG, and the comparative histogram of the spectral components is shown in Fig. 8.16. Slow waves in the delta band are predominant over

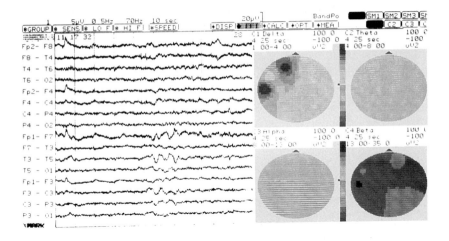

Fig. 8.15 The EEG recording shows a burst of delta slow activity over the left hemisphere. Frequency spectral analysis of a 4.25 seconds sample of the trace, which includes the slow waves, has been displayed on the 'maps'. Each map represents one of the four major EEG activities. There is generalised fast, beta activity, as shown by the darker areas over the head. Delta activity is maximal over the left frontal and temporal areas, as depicted on the delta 'map' of the head.

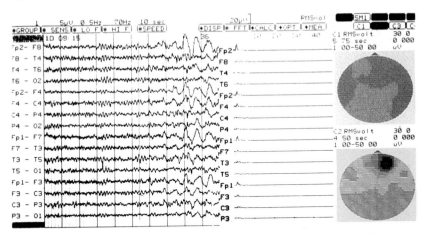

Fig. 8.16 The EEG recording shown on the left of the page has been subject to analyses of instantaneous voltages of activity present on two separate occasions. The first of these is at 5.75 seconds after the start of the recorded sample, and the second is 4.5 seconds later. The first sample, depicted on the upper map (a black and white reproduction of the colour original), shows no evidence of the frontal slow waves apparent in the lower map. The central part of the figure shows a histogram representation of the frequency spectra, and frontal delta waves are present on the Fp2 and Fp1 electrode traces.

the frontal areas, particularly on the right. It is important to remember that the display reveals information about physiology and has only a loose relationship to the underlying structures revealed by MRI and CT.

There have been many studies in which quantitative EEG and analysis of evoked potentials were used to characterise psychiatric disorders. Using a multivariate discriminant function, one such study claimed an ability to distinguish between unipolar and bipolar depressive patients, the most prominently contributing subsets being left medial alpha and occipital slow-wave asymmetry. Subgroups of patients with schizophrenia were also described on the basis of 'mapping', although when averaged together these could not be distinguished from normal subjects. This work awaits general confirmation with multicentre studies using the same method. Studies by other authors have concluded that it is not diagnostic in schizophrenia, and so far the data for schizophrenic patients have been conflicting.

Event-related potentials

Event-related potentials (ERPs) are the changes which affect the brain's electrical activity, recorded spontaneously as the EEG, in response to a variety of stimuli. They include motor potentials, and long-latency cognitive ERPs such as the long-latency potentials which accompany psychological activity, and slow potentials like the contingent negative variation (CNV). The responses following sensory stimuli (acoustic, somatic, or visual) are known as evoked potentials (EPs). Separation of the ERPs from the on-going EEG is effected by signal averaging, when the time-locked responses are retained, but random activity tends to zero with succeeding repetitive stimuli. The long-latency responses or slow potentials, that is those appearing more than 200 ms after the stimulus, are easily altered by physiological variables, but are of value in assessing cognitive function. They are related to expectancy, preparation and motor activity. Short-latency potentials are more stable and are of greater value in the evaluation of neurological than psychological changes.

Cognitive ERPs

Contingent negative variation

The use of two stimuli in an operant conditioning procedure, and recording with long time constants or direct-current amplifier, reveals a sustained negative shift of potential. Such a shift reaches its peak just before the second, or imperative stimulus, and returns to baseline when the response has been made. The phenomenon was given the name CNV by Grey Walter. Others have also noted that, when subjects are asked to press a button at intervals of their own choosing, the EEG reveals a slow negative potential shift peaking just before the initiation of the movement. This is termed the *Bereitschaftspotential* (BP), also called in English the readiness potential (RP). It has been shown that sustained negative shifts reflect states of increasing arousal or activation, and that positive shifts represent a decrease in such activation levels. Drugs which produce soporific or narcotic effects, such as barbiturates, tend to produce positive shifts. Those which act as stimulants, such as strychnine and caffeine, produced negative shifts. Adrenergic cortical activation results in a substantial negative shift, whereas drugs such as chlorpromazine, which are said to suppress adrenergic transmission at the synaptic level, induce a positive shift.

Memory, learning and the CNV   Early reports suggested that the CNV attained its maximum amplitude as the association between the two stimuli (S1 and S2) was 'learned', but this is no longer felt to be the case. The results of such experiments are complex, and in certain conditions the CNV is difficult or impossible to elicit, despite behavioural evidence for learning. Although methodological inadequacies in some of the reported work may have contributed to the confusion about this issue in the past, there is still no conclusive evidence that the CNV is a necessary concomitant of learning.

Hemisphere lateralities, psychological states and the CNV   Published work on this subject has been contradictory, but overall CNV lateralisation effects are small in amplitude, and at best only marginally reflect functional differences between the hemispheres. The correlation between slow potentials and psychological or behavioural states is equally complex, and shows no simple relationships. Variability and controversy affecting the conclusions so far reached hold no immediate hope of help in the clinical context.

The readiness potential

The RP depends on voluntary decisions and actions, but in common with the CNV is influenced by motivation, attention, carelessness and lack of concern. In theory it is therefore a further tool to explore psychological parameters, but experimental difficulties in obtaining reliable and reproducible data have so far prevented any major breakthrough in our understanding.

Slow potentials and clinical practice

Manipulation of the stimuli allows experimental paradigms to be designed which can test and evaluate cognitive functioning. The ERP components contain exogenous elements related to the stimuli, and endogenous components related to the reaction or attitude of the subject to the stimulus. Initially workers in this field recognised two potentials – the CNV, and the P3b (P3 or P300), a large positive wave maximal over the parietal cortex arising 280 – 1000 ms after the stimuli. The latter may be a marker for conscious thought, as the P3b can be recorded at intervals down to 300 ms, which is the limit of time separation for two or more conscious tasks performed in a row – known as the psychological refractory time.

In the last decade, numerous additional endogenous components have been described. Particular waveforms have been found to reflect, or to be mainly influenced by, different cognitive processes. The various components are elicited by altering the stimulus conditions in a selective manner according to the specific information required.

Children with developmental dysphasia have been shown to have an abnormal P3b recovery cycle, such that it is depressed when the acoustic information is presented too rapidly, but not when the intervals are greater than one second.

In patients with Down's syndrome, the topographic distribution of the P3b potentials differs from the normal (a result of maldevelopment rather than delayed maturation). The abnormality presumably reflects the known malformations affecting the position and size of the gyri and lobes in this condition.

Research using ERPs has revealed that the language disorder in autism is quite different from that of developmental dysphasia. Clinically it is thought that for the former there is a cognitive disorder which impairs attention, orientation, assigning importance to stimuli, and social interactions. Abnormal P3b amplitudes have been demonstrated in both conditions, but in autism the auditory response is smaller than normal, while in dysphasia it is larger than normal.

Impairment of cognitive function is part of many psychiatric disorders, and numerous workers have looked for alterations in ERPs in such patients. While the literature abounds with descriptions of these changes, there has been little evidence of specificity for particular conditions or syndromes. In schizophrenia, for example, most but not all reports describe a reduction in the amplitude of P3 compared with controls in the so-called 'oddball experimental paradigm', in which the subject must respond to a rare stimulus and ignore common stimuli. Unfortunately, similar findings apply to patients with Alzheimer's disease and other forms of dementia. Latency changes also occur, but the level of false negatives renders it valueless as a diagnostic tool.

Many psychiatric groups and subgroups have differed, usually significantly, from normals in waveform, amplitude, duration or variability of the potentials, but there has been a lack of specificity in the results obtained. Attenuated CNVs have been reported to be characteristic not only of schizophrenics, but also of patients with severe anxiety, depression and psychopathy. Part of the problem no doubt lies in the difficulty of accurately delineating the clinical conditions. Perhaps effects related to symptoms rather than to diagnostic categories should be sought.

Evoked potentials

These potentials reveal neuronal responses to sensory stimuli, and are directly related to the functional integrity of neurological pathways. For this reason they have been more use in medicine and neurology than in psychiatry. Yet a knowledge of the procedures, and their limitations, can be of inestimable value in the differential diagnosis of organic from non-organic brain syndromes. Unlike the slow potentials, there are well recognised age- and sex-related normal ranges, so that the information provides objective information relating to different neuronal systems. Once again, the tests rely on signal averaging, although some potentials may be of sufficient amplitude to be readily differentiated from the ongoing EEG activity, and single responses may be evident in the raw data. This is especially true for visual-evoked potentials and for studies in adolescents, whose EPs are generally of higher amplitude than those of adults.

Visual evoked potentials

Visual EPs (VEPs) to flash stimulation were recognised and documented many years before Halliday (1989) revealed that the wide variation of the flash responses did not apply to pattern-generated EPs. An alternating black-and-white checker-board pattern was noted to produce reproducible VEPs with minimal variability, and changes in the latency of the main positive wave correlated accurately with demyelinating damage to the optic nerves. Subsequently many workers have extended the database for EPs to a wide range of stimuli, and pathological variants have been well documented in many disorders.

The typical normal pattern VEP is shown in Fig. 8.17. A cardinal rule for good practice is the inclusion of data recorded from a peripheral or end-organ of the sensory system, as a lesion affecting the latter can also effect the EP. In the case of VEPs an additional channel records the electroretinogram (ERG) from the eye. Fig. 8.18 shows pattern VEPs and the small-pattern ERGs obtained with a surface flexible gold electrode.

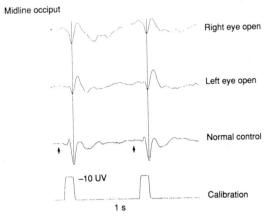

Fig. 8.17 Pattern visually evoked potentials seen in this binocular recording are elicited by alternating black-and-white checker-board patterns. The changes occur twice a second, and the calibration signal as well as the template obtained from a normal control population are displayed on channels three and four.

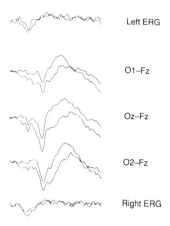

Left ERG

O1–Fz

Oz–Fz

O2–Fz

Right ERG

Fig. 8.18 In this figure the full-field binocular pattern-evoked potentials are displayed, together with the pattern electroretinograms (ERGs) for each eye on channels 1 and 5. The results of two separate test runs are traced, to show that there is reproducibility, and that the waveforms are not due to random noise or other signals. These are normal results. The sweep time is 256 ms.

A major application of the VEP technique has been the assessment of patients with multiple sclerosis (MS), when demyelination affecting the optic nerves or central pathways leads to a delay in the onset of the major positive wave (P100). Of particular value is the discovery of VEP abnormality in a patient whose clinical presentation involves areas other than the visual system. Such a finding then indicates damage in more than one area of the nervous system. The abnormalities are not pathologically specific, but alternative diagnoses can often be excluded from other evidence. The advent of MRI has superseded the VEP in some centres, but its lack of general availability and relative cost have not yet rendered it a universal alternative. The combination of multimodality EPs can be of help in the diagnosis of MS, but the rate of positive testing is maximum for the VEP, varying from 47% to 96% in different series, overall being of the order of 60 – 65%.

The VEP is abnormal in a wide variety of conditions, and has application in the differential diagnosis of some of these. However, being objective, it may provide decisive evidence whether a particular case of visual impairment is functional or organic. The uniocular traces shown in Fig. 8.19 are from the same subject as those depicted in the binocular studies of Fig. 8.18. This patient was found to have normal VEPs and ERGs, in spite of professing virtually total loss of vision. She had non-organic symptoms, and made a rapid and spectacular recovery over 48 hours while in hospital. The second trace for the left eye, in Fig. 8.19, shows some variation possibly due to lack of fixation in the final test, but this technical difficulty can be overcome with binocular studies. This patient subsequently made a rapid and complete recovery from her non-organic symptoms. The pattern VEP is very sensitive to a reduction of

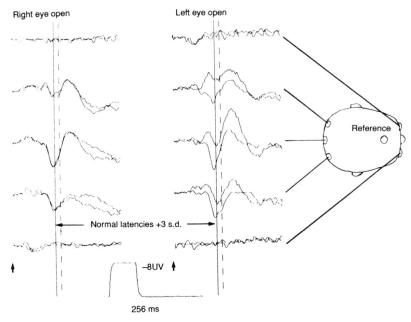

Right eye open   Left eye open

Reference

Normal latencies +3 s.d.

−8UV

256 ms

Fig. 8.19   These normal pattern visual evoked responses and electroretinograms were obtained from a patient who was claiming almost total loss of vision. She subsequently made a full and rapid recovery from the non-organic visual symptoms. The second trace from the left eye was the last test run, and affected by loss of fixation. This was corrected by use of binocular stimulation, as shown in Fig. 8.18, which was recorded subsequently from the same patient.

visual acuity, and the finding of a normal response in the presence of apparent gross visual impairment can allow a confident diagnosis of non-organic loss, especially if it is uniocular. It is important to be sure that the check size and contrast are adjusted to be sufficiently sensitive to avoid missing minor changes.

Lesions affecting part of the visual field can also be explored by the use of appropriate localised stimuli, and can confirm or refute apparent anomalies arising in the clinical examination. The VEP may be well retained with relatively limited cortical lesions, but when the lesion affects visual association areas, the patient's ability to comprehend and thus visualise the surroundings may be significantly impaired. In this situation other clinical features will usually clarify the situation. The converse use of EPs to demonstrate organic change in a patient thought to have a non-organic disorder is also of value.

In patients with myoclonic epilepsy there may be high-amplitude evoked potentials, sometimes seen in the raw EEG as a result of single or multiple flash stimuli. Some of these patients also exhibit sharp waves in the EEG when their limbs are gently tapped, or they tap their hands on a hard surface. A similar phenomenon may be demonstrated in patients with startle epilepsy, in whom it is thought these represent unusually enhanced somatosensory EPs.

Auditory evoked potentials

Brainstem auditory evoked potentials (BSAEP) arising less than 50 ms after the auditory stimulus are so-called 'far field' potentials which, although recorded over the scalp, arise from subcortical structures. A series of peaks can be detected within the first 20 ms of click or tone stimuli, and the EPs can be precisely categorised by the parameters of the stimuli.

An example is shown in Fig. 8.20. As the stimuli vary from one laboratory to another, it is important to refer to the particular laboratory normals for each patient. The test can help to quantify hearing thresholds, or localise dysfunction to specific portions of the auditory pathway. Thus lesions of the brainstem, as opposed to the eighth nerve, in MS will cause delays in the later waves, usually peaks III to V, while cochlear lesions also alter the early waves, I and II. An electrode in the meatus can record the electrocochleogram (ECoG) and aid the differentiation of lesions affecting the ear rather than the proximal pathways.

Figure 8.21 shows the complementary information obtained from traces recorded simultaneously using both meatal and surface electrodes to monitor auditory function during an operation on the posterior fossa. Where patients are very young, relatively uncooperative, or mentally handicapped, the BSAEP can be of help in determining auditory function, if necessary under anaesthetic, because the BSAEPs are retained under these circumstances. Later waves generated by auditory stimuli, including the middle and long-latency auditory EPs, are influenced by all the factors which affect cortical function. For this reason they are less helpful for the diagnosis of organic disorders.

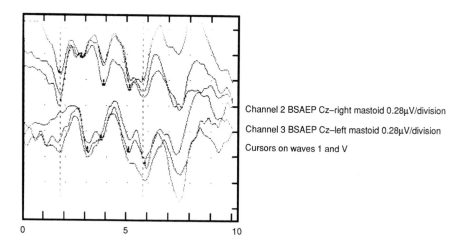

Channel 2 BSAEP Cz–right mastoid 0.28μV/division

Channel 3 BSAEP Cz–left mastoid 0.28μV/division

Cursors on waves 1 and V

0   5   10

Fig. 8.20   Normal click-induced brainstem responses to right-ear stimulation are shown. These reveal a clearer eighth-nerve-derived wave I for the right than the left-ear traces. The wave V responses, derived from the brainstem, are also marked with a cursor.

Click stimuli, right ear

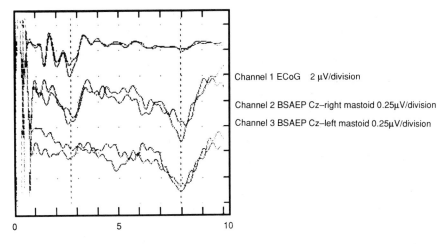

Channel 1 ECoG   2 μV/division

Channel 2 BSAEP Cz–right mastoid 0.25μV/division

Channel 3 BSAEP Cz–left mastoid 0.25μV/division

Fig. 8.21   In this recording the electrocochleogram, recorded from an intrameatal spring electrode (channel 1), is compared with the simultaneously recorded surface brainstem evoked potentials (channels 2 and 3). The ECoG is of greater amplitude (note the calibrations) than the surface potentials. Both were obtained as monitoring procedures to assess auditory function during a posterior fossa neurosurgical exploration.

Somatosensory evoked potentials

Somatosensory evoked potentials (SSEPs) arise as a result of sensory stimuli, usually brief repetitive electrical stimuli applied to a peripheral nerve or dermatomal skin area. Other sensory modalities, such as mechanical, can generate SSEPs but are technically more difficult to perform. The responses to electrical stimuli can be detected over the appropriate scalp areas and, under suitable recording conditions, may be seen with electrodes placed over distal sites such as the cervical and lumbar spine. An example is shown in Fig. 8.22.

Estimates of the latencies from stimulus to pick up at the different recording sites allows localisation of the neurophysiological changes. The SSEPs necessarily depend on the integrity of the distal sensory afferent nerves, and an assumption of their normality may lead to erroneous interpretation of SSEP abnormalities. All the major short-latency components, N9 to N20 (negative potentials recorded at the scalp), depend on the activation of peripheral nerve fibres conducting at approximately 70 m/s in the forearm. This corresponds to the faster group II fibres, the axons being largely concerned with transmission of cutaneous and proprioceptive information. The majority' pass directly into the dorsal columns to synapse in the dorsal column nuclei of the brainstem, but others send collaterals into the grey matter of the spinal cord. Localisation of proximal root or plexus lesions can be confirmed by correlating these results with peripheral nerve conduction studies (NCS) and electromyography (EMG).

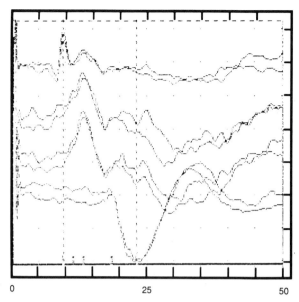

0   25   50

Fig. 8.22 The clavicular or Erb's point (channel 1), cervical spine CV7 (channel 2) and CV2 (channel 3), as well as scalp somatosensory responses (channel 4), recorded as a result of repetitive stimulation of the median nerve at the wrist. The scale is 5 ms per horizontal division, and 5 μV per vertical division, and 200 responses have been averaged. The cursors are placed on the brachial plexus potential, and the main positive component of the scalp potential.

Figure 8.23 shows an asymmetry between the responses obtained from the two sides in a patient who has a brachial plexus lesion due to infiltrating neoplasia from a breast primary. The asymmetry is apparent at the distal recording sites over the plexus and cervical spine, not merely at the scalp.

The technique has been particularly useful in defining neurophysiological damage affecting L5 and S1 nerve roots. This information can augment the clinical assessment of patients with possible non-organic back pain. It is now possible to obtain some objective estimate of the degree of neuronal loss which has been sustained in the relevant nerves and roots using a combination of EMG, NCS and SSEPs. For example, abnormalities consisting of delays or loss of scalp L5 and S1 dermatomal SSEPs can define the degree of organic neurophysiological damage in a patient who has had a previously operated and radiologically defined disc lesion, but whose symptoms may be inappropriately persistent. Conversely, the absence of such abnormality may guide the clinician to consider broader aspects of clinical management, leading to a careful consideration of other contributory factors in the person's lifestyle.

The differentiation of organic from non-organic symptoms and sensory signs may be helped by SSEPs, although it is important to realise that the procedure does not evaluate conduction in the small unmyelinated fibres, nor does it evaluate the presumed irritative phenomena affecting such nerves in the

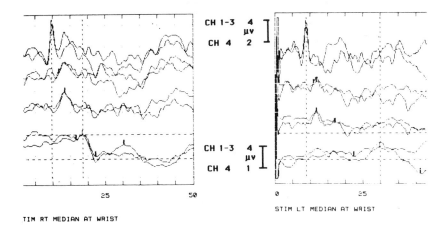

CH 1-3   4
         µV
CH 4   2

CH 1-3   4
         µV
CH 4   1

25   50

0   25

STIM LT MEDIAN AT WRIST

TIM RT MEDIAN AT WRIST

Fig. 8.23 In this dual tracing the right (presented on left) and left (presented on right) median nerve somatosensory responses have been compared. There is marked attenuation and a delay affecting the left-sided scalp responses, with a similar but less clearly defined asymmetry affecting the cervical potentials. This was due to a diffuse post-radiation lesion affecting the left brachial plexus. The upper calibration signals apply to the right, and the lower to the left median nerve traces. Note the difference in the signals for channel 4 on each side. The scalp trace for the left is barely 1 µV peak to peak for the later component, with practically no early response. The SSEP at the scalp for the right median nerve shows a 2 µV early response, the negative peak occurring approximately 18 ms after the onset of the stimuli.

production of pain. Some help from thermal sensitivity studies may indicate when small-fibre damage has occurred, but microelectrode recordings in healthy volunteers have now revealed neuronal discharges associated with the perception of pain, a phenomenon which is not measured by any of the clinically applicable techniques.

It is also important to recognise that the abnormalities are not pathologically specific. In addition to demyelinating disorders, such as MS, other conditions such as hereditary spastic paraplegia, Friedreich's ataxia, and subacute degeneration of the cord can produce abnormal SSEPs. In these diseases degeneration of the centrally directed axon from the first-order sensory neuron is the primary pathological process.

Degenerative disorders and evoked potentials

It is possible to assess neurophysiological changes in many degenerative disorders on the basis of their differential effect on white or grey matter in the central nervous system. In addition, some have characteristic involvement of peripheral nerves, as in the leukodystrophies, or of end-organs such as the retina as in conditions such as neuronal ceroid lipofuscinosis.

Damage to white matter in the central nervous system is likely to cause delays or abnormalities affecting a variety of EPs, depending on the site of the demyelination. The leukodystrophies often produce delayed or absent VEPs, BSAEPs and SSEPs.

In contrast, the degenerative processes primarily affecting grey matter may only alter the waveform of the EPs, often to a relatively minor degree, without producing significant delays in the latencies of the responses. However, damage to cortical grey matter is likely to cause significant changes in the EEG, with slowing of the dominant occipital rhythm and increased slow-wave activity.

A combination of EEG, multimodality EPs and studies of peripheral nerves or sense organs, such as the electroretinogram and electrocochleogram, can provide localising information about the distribution of the neurophysiological changes. This information may then help in narrowing the range of diagnostic possibilities for patients with degenerative neuropsychiatric disorders, especially children.

Rarely, carrier states can also be revealed, as in female carriers of adrenoleukodystrophy, confirmed by detection of elevated long-chain fatty acids, in whom multimodality EP studies have revealed results similar to those found in affected family members. In particular, there are increases in the N13 to N20 intervals for the SEPs, and I to V intervals for the BSAEPs.

Evoked potentials and psychiatric disorders

Apart from the applications noted above, the contribution of EPs to clinical psychiatry is limited. Various abnormalities of different EPs have been described in a variety of psychiatric disorders, including disturbances affecting early, middle, and late components. However, none of these has been found to be specific to particular conditions.

References

Aimone Marsan, C. & Zivin, L. S. (1970) Factors related to the occurrence of typical paroxysmal abnormalities in the EEG records of epileptic patients. *Epilepsia*, **11**, 361 - 381.

Binnie, C. (1983) Telemetric EEG monitoring in epilepsy. In *Recent Advances in Epilepsy* (eds T. A. Pedley & B. S. Meldrum), pp. 155 - 178. Edinburgh: Churchill Livingstone.

——— (1989) The monitoring of chronic epilepsy. In *Chronic Epilepsy, Its Prognosis and Management* (ed. M. Trimble), pp. 37 - 57. Chichester: Wiley.

Brazier, M. A. B. (1961) *A History of the Electrical Activity of the Brain.* London: Pitman.

Commission on Classification and Terminology of the International League Against Epilepsy (ILAE) (1981) Proposal for revised clinical and electroencephalographic classification of epileptic seizures. *Epilepsia*, **22**, 489–501.

Delgado-Escueta, A. V., Mattson, R. H., King, L., *et al* (1981) Special report. The nature of aggression during epileptic seizures. *New England Journal of Medicine*, **305**, 711 - 716.

Fenwick, P. (1986) Murdering while asleep. *British Medical Journal*, **293**, 574 - 575.

Flor-Henry, P., Koles, Z. J., Sussman, P. S., *et al* (1983) Multivariate EEG analysis of the endogenous psychoses. In *Advances in Biological Psychiatry. 13. Neurophysiological Correlates of Normal Cognition and Psychopathology* (eds C. Perris, D. Kemali & M. Koukkou-Lehmann), pp. 196 - 211. Basel: Karger.

———, ———, ———, *et al* (1984) Further observations on right/left hemispheric energy oscillations in the endogenous psychoses. In *Advances in Biological*

Psychiatry. 15. Neurophysiological Correlates of Mental Disorders (eds B. Saletu, C. Perris & D. Kemali), pp. 1 – 11. Basel: Karger.

Gibbs, F. A. & Gibbs, E. L. (1952) *Atlas of Electroencephalography, Vol. 2 (Epilepsy).* Cambridge, Mass: Addison-Wesley.

Halliday, A. M. (1989) Modern neurophysiology. Sensory evoked potentials. *British Journal of Hospital Medicine*, **41**, 50 – 59.

Small, J., Small, I., Milstein, V., *et al* (1975) Familial associations with EEG variants in manic–depressive disease. *Archives of General Psychiatry*, **32**, 43-48.

Stalberg, E. (1976) Experiences with longterm telemetry in routine diagnostic work. In *Quantitative Analytic Studies in Epilepsy* (eds P. Kellaway & I. Petersen), pp. 269-278. New York: Raven Press.

Treiman, D. M. & Delgado-Escueta, A. V. (1983) Violence and epilepsy: a critical review. In *Recent Advances in Epilepsy* (eds T. A. Pedley & B. S. Meldrum), pp. 179 – 209. Edinburgh: Churchill Livingstone.

Further reading

Burgess, R. C. (1990) Editorial: the scientific basis of computed neurophysiologic topography. *Journal of Clinical Neurophysiology*, **7**, 457 – 459.

Fenton, G. (1983) Epilepsy. In *Mental Disorders and Somatic Illness. Handbook of Psychiatry 2.* (ed M. H. Lader), pp. 147 – 185. Cambridge: Cambridge University Press.

——— (1986) Electrophysiology of Alzheimer's disease. *British Medical Bulletin*, **42**, 29 – 33.

Fenwick, P. (1986) Aggression and epilepsy. In *Aspects of Epilepsy and Psychiatry* (eds M. R. Trimble & T. G. Bolwig), pp. 31 – 57. Chichester: Wiley.

——— & Fenwick, E. (1985) *Epilepsy and the Law.* International Congress and Symposium Series No 81. London: Royal Society of Medicine.

McCallum, W. (1988) Potentials related to expectancy, preparation and motor activity. In *Human Event Related Potentials, EEG Handbook* (revised series vol. 3) (ed. T. W. Picton), pp. 427 – 534. Amsterdam: Elsevier.

Neary, D. (1990) Non Alzheimer's disease forms of cerebral atrophy. (Editorial) *Journal of Neurology, Neurosurgery and Psychiatry*, **53**, 929 – 931.

Niedermeyer, E. & Lopes da Silva, F. H. (1982) *Electroencephalography: Basic Principles, Clinical Applications and Related Fields.* Baltimore: Urban & Schwarzenberg.

Orwin, A., Wright, C. E., Harding, G. F. A., *et al* (1986) Serial visual evoked potential recordings in Alzheimer's disease. *British Medical Journal*, **293**, 9 – 10.

Roth, M. & Iversen, L. L. (1986) Alzheimer's disease and related disorders. *British Medical Bulletin*, **42**, 1 – 2.

Scott, D. F. (1982) The use of EEG in pseudoseizures. In *Pseudoseizures* (eds T. L. Riley & A. Roy), pp. 113 – 121. London: Williams & Wilkins.

Trimble, M. R. (1983) Interictal behaviour and temporal lobe epilepsy. In *Recent Advances in Epilepsy* (eds T. A. Pedley & B. S. Meldrum), pp. 211 – 229. Edinburgh: Churchill Livingstone.

——— (1985) Psychiatric and psychological aspects of epilepsy. In *The Epilepsies* (eds R. J. Porter & P. L. Morselli), pp. 322 – 355. London: Butterworths.

——— & Reynolds, E. H. (1987) *Epilepsy, Behaviour and Cognitive Function.* Chichester: Wiley.

Wolf, P. (1985) The classification of seizures and the epilepsies. In *The Epilepsies* (eds R. J. Porter & P. L. Morselli), pp. 106 – 124. London: Butterworths.

Weiner, R. D., Coffey, C. E. & Krystal, A. D. (1991) The monitoring and management of electrically induced seizures. *Psychiatric Clinics of North America*, **14**, 845 – 869.

9 Neuroradiology

John Bradshaw & Timothy Lewis

---

*Imaging the brain • Imaging the spine • Congenital lesions • Infection •
Vascular disease • Trauma • Neoplasia • Degenerative, metabolic
and toxic disorders*

Before the early 1970s, and apart from radionuclide imaging, the main investigation of patients with possible neurological disorders involved dangerous and uncomfortable invasive techniques, such as airencephalography and cerebral arteriography. Since the 1970s however, the introduction of computerised tomography (CT), and more recently magnetic resonance imaging (MRI), has revolutionised the evaluation of neurological disease. Their essentially non-invasive nature, their high sensitivity and good specificity for a wide variety of lesions, and their ever-increasing availability worldwide has ensured their success.

Recently there has been a resurgence of interest in radionuclide investigation of neurological disease. Whereas previous techniques merely gave static images of intracranial pathology, more recently exploited radionuclides, such as technetium-99 ml (used as a 'label' for HMPAO) and cyclotron-produced nuclides, have allowed us to look at cerebral function, providing useful insight in various groups of diseases.

The majority of serious neurological pathologies can be excluded or evaluated in psychiatric patients by the new techniques alone, and the non-invasive nature of modern scanning presents a temptation to scan large numbers of psychiatric patients in the hope of 'finding something'. This chapter endeavours to provide guidance about indications for imaging patients with psychiatric disorders. Furthermore, all imaging techniques have advantages and disadvantages, including risk to the patient, availability and cost. Clear understanding of these issues is essential if we are to do the best for our patients.

Further guidance on appropriate clinical indications for imaging investigations is given in Chapter 4.

Imaging the brain

Plain radiographs

Although plain-film radiography can demonstrate the changes of pituitary fossa enlargement, bone erosion and the secondary effects of raised intracranial pressure, the normal skull series does not rule out significant disease, and is thus often not indicated. In cases where more sophisticated techniques are not being considered, there may be a small place for plain films, but any determined approach to imaging will demand a CT or MRI scan.

Computerised tomography

Since its introduction in 1972, CT has quite rightly become the principal diagnostic modality in brain diagnosis. Using computerised reconstruction techniques to build up images from digital X-ray examination of slice-like samplings of the body, it can visualise the majority of intracranial pathology rapidly and non-invasively.

Computerised tomography does have some important limitations and should be used selectively, with an appreciation of its strengths and weaknesses. CT scanners are widely available in the UK, and many district general hospitals already have a CT scanning service. However, demand for time on these units is substantial because of the 'high yield' requirements in head injury, brain tumours, and so on, and access for psychiatric references is often limited. Increasingly, time on a CT scanner is also being taken up by orthopaedic, thoracic and abdominal indications. Straightforward unenhanced axial images will show most cerebral pathology, including hydrocephalus, infarction, tumours, old and recent trauma (Fig. 9.1), and some congenital lesions.

Images enhanced by intravenous iodinated contrast media greatly improve the visualisation of some intracranial lesions (see Fig. 9.2). Contrast enhancement occurs from a combination of increased radiodensity of the blood pool and the passage of contrast into the extravascular space in areas where the blood–brain barrier is deficient, as are seen with malignant tumours, inflammatory and infective lesions. A dose of contrast medium containing 15 g iodine is adequate for general purposes.

Computerised tomography has a limited ability to demonstrate early lesions in the posterior fossa and early white-matter disease, including demyelination. Sagittal reformatted images, or coronal images acquired directly, can improve the evaluation of lesions in the pituitary region or skull base.

Cerebral angiography

Cerebral angiography is invasive, unpleasant, and potentially dangerous. Nevertheless it is highly accurate in demonstrating vascular lesions such as atheroma, aneurysms and arteriovenous malformations, and it is vital in the pre-operative evaluation of these lesions and selected tumours. It is currently performed by introducing a catheter into either carotid or vertebral arteries, depending on the territory to be investigated. This is conveniently done by introducing the catheter into one of the femoral arteries under local anaesthetic and guiding it to the desired vessel under fluoroscopic control. Cerebral angiography should not be undertaken without good reason, and it should only be performed in centres with the experience and equipment to carry it out efficiently and safely. Prior neurological or neurosurgical referral is advisable.

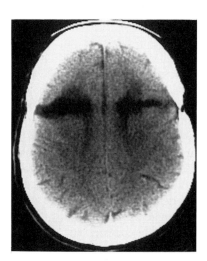

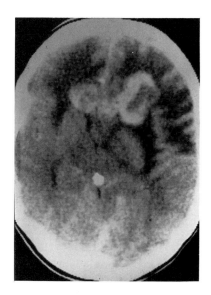

Fig. 9.1 A CT image through the upper hemispheres. Symmetrical bone defects in the frontal regions are associated with linear tracks running into both frontal lobes. This patient had undergone frontal leucotomy.

Fig. 9.2 A contrast-enhanced CT brain scan. This is an axial image at the level of pineal gland and frontal horns. An extensive low-density area is seen extending through both frontal lobes, with irregular central enhancement. The frontal horns are markedly compressed. This is a malignant glioma in the genu of corpus callosum.

Patients who are being considered for temporal lobe resection for epilepsy may require amytal angiography to determine the hemisphere specialised for language. Following catheter placement in the appropriate internal carotid artery, with radiographic confirmation, sodium amytal is injected into that hemisphere's arterial supply. This produces brief anaesthesia of the hemisphere, allowing psychological and neurological assessment of the location of function.

Magnetic resonance imaging

Magnetic resonance imaging (MRI) was introduced for clinical use during the mid-1980s. The patient is placed within the bore of a powerful magnet and the tissues interrogated by pulses of radiofrequency electromagnetic radiation. A resonant frequency is emitted by the body, permitting spatial localisation and slice-like images to be produced in any plane. This multiplanar facility is a major advantage over CT; also, the technique does not use potentially harmful ionising radiation, and is extremely sensitive to disease processes. These are particular advantages in the evaluation of the central nervous system.

Unlike CT, MR images are not degraded by bone artefacts, and MRI resolves structures within the posterior fossa particularly well. It can detect the early changes of infection, tumours, infarction and white-matter disease, even when CT scans appear normal.

Recent advances have produced an intravenous contrast medium appropriate for MRI. The availability of these paramagnetic contrast agents, which have pharmacological properties similar to those of iodinated radiographic contrast agents in CT, has increased the diagnostic accuracy of MRI by demonstrating abnormalities of the blood–brain barrier.

Unfortunately, MRI is not yet widely available in the UK. The number of scanners is slowly rising, but its versatility is such that demand for access for scanning of the central nervous system, joint derangements, and other body regions will ensure that the resource will remain relatively scarce for several more years.

Radionuclide imaging

The value of nuclear medicine in neuroradiology is now in the demonstration of function. This can be accomplished by the use of single photon emission computerised tomography (SPECT) or positron emission tomography (PET). SPECT is readily available and relies on the activity of HMPAO labelled with Technetium-99 ml for images; the technetium-labelled HMPAO accumulates relative to blood flow and thus demonstrates regional cerebral blood flow (rCBF). PET scanning relies on the dual-energy emission of positron-emitting nuclides. These nuclides are produced in a cyclotron and have short half-lives. PET scanning is only available in a few centres located close to a cyclotron and requires dedicated scanning facilities. PET scanning has the great advantage of high spatial resolution.

Patients with temporal lobe epilepsy will show increased rCBF at the focus if radionuclide is injected during an attack. In the resting state there may well be focal reduction of rCBF, and the information thus available from SPECT is helpful for corroboration before surgical excision.

Imaging the spine

Plain radiographs

The main indications for plain films are now in the initial investigation of trauma and for the exclusion of systemic disease (metastases, osteoporosis, ankylosing spondylitis) in those with low back pain. It is not possible to diagnose disc protrusion on the basis of plain films alone.

Radionuclide scanning

Radionuclide scanning is sensitive for infective and metastatic disease of the spine, but recent work suggests MRI, where available, is superior.

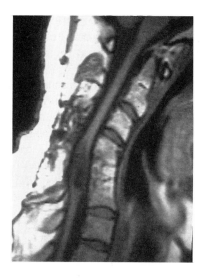

Fig. 9.3 Sagittal T_1-weighted MR image of cervical spine. The fourth, fifth and sixth cervical vertebrae are fused as a consequence of a previous severe spinal injury. The cord behind these vertebrae is seen to be expanded by a cystic lesion – post-traumatic cord syrinx.

Computerised tomography

Bony structures are well visualised on CT. Lumbar disc protrusions are also detected in most patients. The cord and nerve roots are not satisfactorily visualised on CT however without the presence of contrast medium to opacify the cerebrospinal fluid (myelography).

Myelography

Myelography has been the mainstay of spinal diagnosis for many years. This unpleasant procedure may also be associated with chemical meningitis or simply troublesome headaches in some patients. Rarely, deaths have been recorded. Properly carried out it is a highly sensitive and accurate examination, and where followed by CT of suspicious areas, is usually the definitive imaging examination of the spine. It is rapidly being replaced, however, by MRI for all but the most complex spinal problems.

Magnetic resonance imaging

The non-invasive nature of MRI, its multiplanar capacity and ability to demonstrate the interior of the cord make it ideally suited to the investigation of all kinds of spinal disorders (Fig. 9.3).

Congenital lesions

Congenital abnormalities of the skull, brain and spine are common and varied (see Table 4.3, p. 140). All of these abnormalities may present in many different ways, including seizures, mental handicap and intellectual or behavioural changes. While many can be adequately demonstrated by CT (and the spinal lesions by myelography), MRI is quite outstanding for these conditions (Figs 9.4, 9.5), and should certainly be the procedure of choice for neural tube defects, neurofibromatosis and diseases of neuronal migration. The ability to differentiate grey and white matter clearly, without contrast, is extremely valuable in the assessment of hemispheric dysplasias.

Vascular abnormalities can now be adequately investigated by MRI but if operative intervention is contemplated, then conventional angiography remains the definitive investigation.

While most cases of hydrocephalus will be adequately demonstrated on CT, a few, especially new, cases where the cause is unclear, may require MRI, which can demonstrate an underlying cause such as aqueduct stenosis, Chiari malformation, and so on.

Congenital cysts take many forms. Porencephaly usually occurs in the hemispheres and their communication with the ventricles is elegantly demonstrated by MRI in the coronal plane. Arachnoid cysts occur in the cerebellopontine angle, suprasellar cistern, Sylvian fissure and dorsal spine. Local pressure effects in these areas lead to appropriate clinical presentations. Again, MRI shows these lesions well but they can be adequately evaluated with CT or myelography as appropriate.

Birth infarcts show the characteristic vascular territorial distribution seen in adult-onset infarction, but with the added consequences of hemiatrophy in most instances. More generalised hypoxia leads to a variety of destructive or cystic manifestations throughout the hemispheres. Both these processes are well seen on CT.

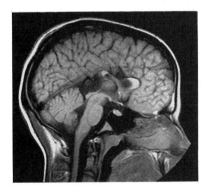

Fig. 9.4 Sagittal T_1-weighted MR image showing absence of most of the corpus callosum except genu – agenesis of corpus callosum.

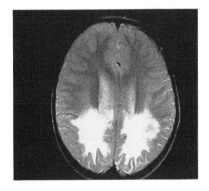

Fig. 9.5 Axial T_2-weighted MR image through the upper parts of the lateral ventricles. The striking symmetrical high signal intensity in the white matter of the posterior hemispheres suggests white-matter disease – adrenoleucodystrophy.

Infection

Most acute cerebral infections present with fairly dramatic symptoms and signs. Headaches, fever, neck stiffness and focal neurological signs are usually prominent features, and psychiatric elements are also quite common. Meningitis is not usually evident on brain scanning unless hydrocephalus or infarction has developed. Psychiatric presentations in patients with previous meningitis may be associated with complications such as hydrocephalus, ischaemia or atrophy; these can be detected with CT or MRI.

Encephalitis can usually be demonstrated as an area of oedema, particularly after a few days and especially on MRI. Abscesses are more readily identified because of their evolving mass effect and contrast-enhancing capsule. The demonstration of intracranial infection is greatly improved on CT with the use of intravenous contrast, and an unenhanced scan is not an adequate investigation to exclude subdural empyema.

Chronic infections are often granulomatous in type and are usually demonstrated on enhanced CT or MRI. However, their mass-like nature frequently causes them to be mistaken for neoplastic lesions (e.g. metastases). While tuberculosis and sarcoid are the most important causes of these chronic lesions, cerebral toxoplasmosis in immune-compromised patients (AIDS) may also present with non-specific masses. AIDS patients may also present with deteriorating intellectual function due to direct infection of the brain substance by HIV virus. These manifestations are shown on CT or MRI, but the pattern is often non-specific.

Most cases of suspected infection of the brain are adequately assessed with contrast-enhanced CT.

Spinal infections may involve the disc space or epidural tissues. Pain is a prominent feature and radionuclide, CT or MRI scanning show lesions well. Plain films may also be helpful.

Vascular disease

The various manifestations of vascular lesions represent the commonest cause of disease in the older population. Most of those with neurological manifestations will present with the physical results of infarction or haemorrhage. These will usually be manifest as unilateral weakness or other results of discrete focal loss of brain function.

Computerised tomography has been the mainstay of diagnosis for such patients for many years. Infarction and haemorrhage are both well shown by this technique. Angiography may be required if a local cause for haemorrhage needs to be excluded. Vascular lesions in the posterior fossa, however, are not often well shown on CT, and MRI is distinctly superior here. Lesions such as aneurysms, arteriovenous malformations and venous occlusion can be detected by CT and confirmed by angiography. Giant aneurysms present a

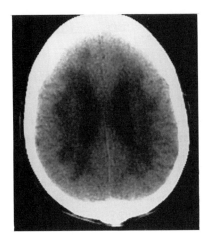

Fig. 9.6 A CT image through the upper hemispheres. The patchy areas of low density in the white matter around the lateral ventricles in older patients are highly suggestive of small-vessel cerebral ischaemia or Binswanger's disease.

slightly different clinical picture from small aneurysms. Although they not infrequently produce subarachnoid haemorrhage, their common presentation is as an intracranial mass lesion, often associated with dementia. They show on CT as mass lesions with marginal calcification and brisk enhancement of some portion of the aneurysm, often with a laminated surrounding structure. MRI is being used increasingly for the demonstration of these lesions. Small aneurysms as a cause for subarachnoid haemorrhage however require high-quality angiography for their demonstration. Planned surgery or other intervention will also demand a full angiographic assessment.

Many patients with vascular disease present in other ways, however. Intellectual deterioration, psychosis and dementia may all be the result of brain ischaemia. Binswanger's disease (Fig. 9.6) and multi-infarct dementia (see Chapter 6, pp. 188–193) are well recognised. CT and MRI may show multiple, small, discrete wedge-shaped cortical infarcts, but more commonly ill-defined patchy changes are seen in the white matter of the upper hemispheres adjacent to the lateral ventricles and are thought to be the result of small-vessel ischaemia. Hypertension is commonly present. On the other hand a large proportion of apparently healthy people over the age of 55 years will show evidence of similar lesions on MRI.

Trauma

Most patients suffering an acute head injury will have obvious cerebral or spinal signs. Psychiatric presentations are less common and are more likely to be seen as the result of the delayed effects of trauma.

Cerebral trauma is well demonstrated in the acute stages by CT. In some instances, however, widespread shearing injuries or diffuse lesions

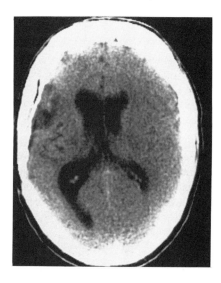

Fig. 9.7 A CT image through lateral ventricles. The right lateral ventricle is dilated, and this is associated with focal atrophy in the frontoparietal area of the right hemisphere. The patient had sustained a previous severe head injury as evidenced by the irregularity of the overlying skull vault. What is seen is post-traumatic atrophy. (The image is displayed as if the slice were viewed from below. The right hemisphere is therefore on the left of the picture.)

are not evident on CT but may cause generalised atrophy in later life. Recent evidence suggests MRI may be able to show such lesions in the acute phases, but what its role may be in predicting long-term disability is, as yet, unclear.

Chronic cerebral trauma resulting in repeated small haemorrhages can lead to generalised cerebral atrophy, with numerous tiny clefts in the hemispheres. Such changes, typically associated with professional boxing, can be demonstrated with MRI.

Those who survive major cerebral trauma and its consequences of intracranial haemorrhage may well require further investigation at a later stage. Either CT or MRI will provide good diagnostic images of focal encephalomalacia, hydrocephalus or diffuse atrophy (Fig. 9.7). Changes seen are commonly in the temporal poles or inferior parts of the frontal lobes. If MRI is available it will provide images superior to CT.

Some patients with previous spinal trauma present with deteriorating function or spinal pain. Before MRI, detection of possible delayed cord damage was difficult. Cord cavitation or syrinx formation (Fig. 9.3) and increasing bony deformity are well shown by MRI and may be amenable to surgical relief. CT myelography may show these changes but would certainly be less sensitive for lesions inside the cord.

Neoplasia

Intracranial tumours present in a variety of ways, including: headache, nausea, dysfunction of the visual or other cranial nerves, unilateral weakness, seizures and disturbances of intellect, thought or consciousness.

Broadly these lesions can be divided into:

(1) those that arise outside the brain substance, including meningioma, neuroma, epidermoid, glomus jugulare and chordoma; these are mostly benign, although complete resection is often difficult
(2) intrinsic brain tumours, including the various grades of glioma, oligodendroglioma, medulloblastoma, lymphoma and ependymoma.

Detection of these lesions by imaging techniques is highly successful. Both enhanced CT and MRI have a high measure of success in the detection and elucidation of these lesions. Angiography is normally only required where the diagnosis is in doubt, or when vascular anatomy needs to be delineated for surgical planning. Although the additional anatomical information provided by angiography is not often required by surgeons, it may be possible to occlude the feeding vessels of tumours and angiomatous malformations by the introduction of particulate emboli or tissue adhesive at superselective catheterisation. The reduction in vascularity thus achieved can be a major help to surgeons in difficult cases.

The vast majority of intracranial tumours, whether intra- or extra-axial in type, can be demonstrated on CT, especially if contrast enhanced. Visualisation in the lower part of the posterior fossa is suboptimal, however, and small lesions in this location are easily missed. Overall a good assessment of the presence, location and likely histological possibilities can be made in most instances.

Magnetic resonance imaging adds a further dimension to the diagnosis of intracranial tumours. Its high sensitivity, excellent rendering of anatomy and posterior fossa structures, provide a unique range of advantages over CT. The addition of paramagnetic contrast enhancement in selected cases further refines this remarkable imaging tool. MRI also has some limitations, particularly its inability to discriminate between specific disease processes and failure to detect calcification. Recent technical developments and refinement of pulse sequences show promise that these limitations may shortly be overcome, at least in part.

At this time CT should be the technique of choice for supratentorial tumours. MRI would be the first technique for suspected lesions in the posterior fossa and pituitary.

Spinal tumours can be broadly divided into those that lie inside the cord itself, such as gliomas and ependymomas; those that lie outside the cord but within the dura, such as meningioma, lipoma and some metastases; and those that lie outside the neural axis and its coverings, mostly within bone or the extradural space, such as metastases, lymphoma and bony tumours.

All these lesions give rise to pain and/or limb weakness or sensory changes, with the manifestations being dependent on the spinal level involved. Objective physical signs such as reflex or motor loss, or a definite sensory level, make further investigation mandatory. MRI is now the technique of choice for those lesions, frequently with contrast enhancement. CT/myelography is also successful, but early lesions within the cord are less easy to detect. Plain films may show bone destruction or enlargement of the spinal canal but are frequently normal in the early stages. Consequently normal plain films do not exclude these lesions.

Degenerative, metabolic and toxic disorders

Modern imaging techniques have brought a new understanding to generalised diseases of the brain. Both CT and MRI can detect a wide variety of degenerative, demyelinating and other conditions, and monitor their natural history or response to treatment.

The demonstration of white-matter disease is difficult using CT, and MRI is the investigation of choice. Multiple sclerosis is the commonest cause of demyelination, and MRI (Fig. 9.8) will show evidence of plaques in well over 90% of cases. The demonstration of small foci of increased signal on some (T_2-weighted) sequences is supportive evidence of demyelination, but the appearances are non-specific and similar changes are seen in vascular and inflammatory conditions such as Behçet's disease and sarcoid. Similar changes are also found in those with cerebrovascular disease without evidence of focal cortical infarction. An additional restriction on the value of MRI is the identification of small foci of high signal in normal elderly individuals. The demonstration of such lesions in patients over the age of 60 cannot be used to diagnose multiple sclerosis.

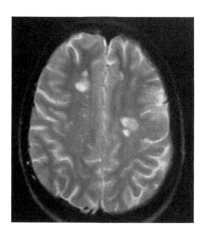

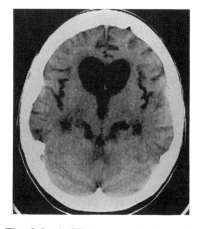

Fig. 9.8 A T_2-weighted axial MR image through the upper hemispheres. Numerous areas of high signal intensity are seen throughout the white matter of the upper hemispheres. In a young patient these changes are almost always due to multiple sclerosis.

Fig. 9.9 A CT image at the level of the frontal horns. The frontal horns are markedly enlarged and this is associated with prominent sulci over the frontal lobes and in the Sylvian fissures. The posterior part of the brain is relatively spared in this predominantly frontal atrophic process – Pick's disease.

A large number of separate entities are now recognised in the group of leucodystrophies. CT shows evidence of white-matter changes in many cases, but MRI demonstrates abnormalities at an earlier stage. The symmetrical pattern of white-matter involvement is usually fairly characteristic, and progress of the condition can be monitored.

A group of conditions under the general heading of mitochondrial cytopathy is being increasingly recognised. Leigh's disease is often characterised by symmetrical necrosis manifested on CT or MRI as abnormal areas in the basal ganglia.

Primary brain degeneration in such conditions as Alzheimer's, Pick's (Fig. 9.9) and Parkinson's disease usually shows normal appearances on CT and MRI. Some patients however will show excessive generalised or focal atrophy. The assessment of focal atrophy by CT or MRI appears to be less reliable than at post-mortem, and caution should be exercised in the interpretation of scans in support of focal atrophy, as is seen in Alzheimer's disease. SPECT scanning has demonstrated that patients with Alzheimer's disease show reduced regional cerebral blood flow in posterior temporal and parietal regions. This pattern can be helpful in diagnosis. Focal atrophy of the caudate nuclei can often be shown on CT or MRI in Huntington's disease (Fig. 9.10). Abnormal iron deposition in the basal nuclei can also be seen on MRI in Huntington's or Hallervorden–Spatz diseases, characteristic areas of low signal being the principal feature.

Substance abuse, including alcohol, may lead to generalised atrophy (Chapter 6, p. 207). Long-term alcohol abuse may lead to specific atrophy of the cerebellum.

The syndrome of normal-pressure hydrocephalus and dementia appears to be a well defined clinical entity, and some patients with significant ventricular dilation will respond to ventricular shunting. Others however do not.

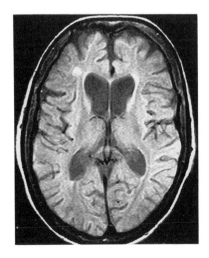

Fig. 9.10 A proton-density MR image through the lateral ventricles at the level of the caudate nuclei. These latter structures are markedly atrophic in this patient with Huntington's disease.

Unfortunately, the appearances of normal-pressure hydrocephalus and central atrophy are similar on both CT and MRI, and the distinction remains difficult. Differences in the shape of the anterior horns of the lateral ventricles may help. It has recently been suggested that MRI's ability to show flow in the aqueduct may help to indicate which patients may benefit from therapy.

Most patients with epileptic seizures do not require imaging investigation. This should be reserved for: patients whose epilepsy starts in later life or has distinctly focal characteristics; and those where seizures are associated with neurological deficit or following trauma. In these cases CT or MRI may well reveal an underlying structural cause such as tumour or arteriovenous malformation. Patients with intractable epilepsy in whom surgery is being contemplated should have MRI to evaluate the temporal lobes fully, as this technique can demonstrate mesial temporal sclerosis in many cases. Amytal angiography may be indicated, as described above.

Degenerative diseases of the spine are common, and almost inevitable with advancing age. Disc degeneration is the commonest manifestation, but facet-joint arthropathy is also a frequent cause of symptoms. Pain in the back with referral down the leg or arm are the usual presentation for these conditions and there may be objective alterations in sensation, power or reflexes in the affected limb. These usually constitute sound indications for further investigation. Lumbar disease is frequently adequately assessed by plain CT alone; myelography or MRI are usually reserved for those cases where CT is normal, equivocal, or where there has been previous surgery and in the 'failed back syndrome'. Plain CT is of limited value in the cervical region. Where this region is under suspicion, MRI or CT myelography will be the procedure of choice in the first instance.

Further reading

Kirkwood, J. R. (1990) *Essentials of Neuroimaging*. New York: Churchill Livingstone.
Moseley, I. F. (1986) *Diagnostic Imaging in Neurological Disease*. London: Churchill Livingstone.
Stevens, J. M., Valentine, A. R. & Kendall, B. E. (1988) *Computed Cranial and Spinal Imaging*. London: Heinemann.

Appendix. Cutaneous innervation and a summary of reflexes

Peripheral distribution

Segmental or radicular distribution

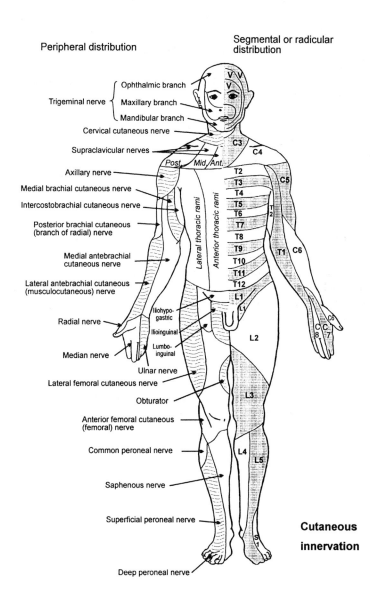

Ophthalmic branch

Trigeminal nerve — Maxillary branch

Mandibular branch

Cervical cutaneous nerve

Supraclavicular nerves

Axillary nerve

Medial brachial cutaneous nerve

Intercostobrachial cutaneous nerve

Posterior brachial cutaneous (branch of radial) nerve

Medial antebrachial cutaneous nerve

Lateral antebrachial cutaneous (musculocutaneous) nerve

Radial nerve

Median nerve

Iliohypo-gastric

Ilioinguinal

Lumbo-inguinal

Ulnar nerve

Lateral femoral cutaneous nerve

Obturator

Anterior femoral cutaneous (femoral) nerve

Common peroneal nerve

Saphenous nerve

Superficial peroneal nerve

Deep peroneal nerve

Post. Mid. Ant.

Lateral thoracic rami

Anterior thoracic rami

Cutaneous innervation

Segmental or radicular
distribution

Peripheral distribution

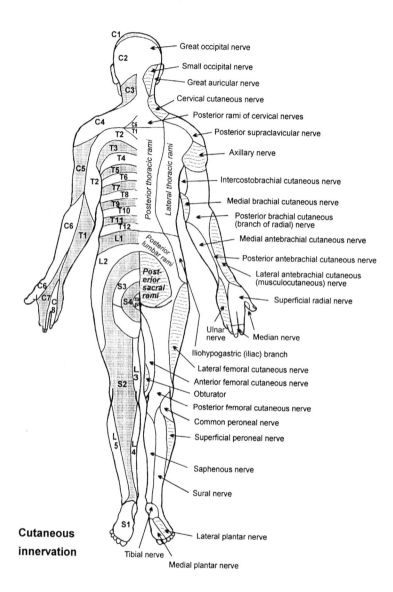

**Cutaneous
innervation**

The material in this Appendix is reproduced from J. G. Chusid's *Correlative
Neuroanatomy & Functional Neurology* (Lange Medical, 1985); 'Principal postural
reflexes' first appeared in W. F. Ganong's *Review of Medical Physiology* (Lange Medical,
1983).

Summary of reflexes

Reflexes	Afferent nerve	Centre	Efferent nerve
Superficial reflexes			
Corneal	Cranial V	Pons	Cranial VII
Nasal (sneeze)	Cranial V	Brainstem and upper cord	Cranials V, VII, IX, X, and spinal nerves of expiration
Pharyngeal and uvular	Cranial IX	Medulla	Cranial X
Upper abdominal	T7, 8, 9, 10	T7, 8, 9, 10	T7, 8, 9, 10
Lower abdominal	T10, 11, 12	T10, 11, 12	T10, 11, 12
Cremasteric	Femoral	L1	Genitofemoral
Plantar	Tibial	S1, 2	Tibial
Anal	Pudendal	S4, 5	Pudendal
Deep reflexes			
Jaw	Cranial V	Pons	Cranial V
Biceps	Musculocutaneous	C5, 6	Musculocutaneous
Triceps	Radial	C6, 7	Radial
Periosteoradial	Radial	C6, 7, 8	Radial
Wrist (flexion)	Median	C6, 7, 8	Median
Wrist (extension)	Radial	C7, 8	Radial
Patellar	Femoral	L2, 3, 4	Femoral
Achilles	Tibial	S1, 2	Tibial
Visceral reflexes			
Light	Cranial II	Midbrain	Cranial III
Accommodation	Cranial II	Occipital cortex	Cranial III
Ciliospinal	A sensory nerve	T1, 2	Cervical sympathetics
Oculocardiac	Cranial V	Medulla	Cranial X
Carotid sinus	Cranial IX	Medulla	Cranial X
Bulbocavernosus	Pudendal	S2, 3, 4	Pelvic autonomic
Bladder and rectal	Pudendal	S2, 3, 4	Pudendal and autonomics

Principal postural reflexes

Reflex	Stimulus	Response	Receptor	Integrated in:
Stretch reflexes	Stretch	Contraction of muscle	Muscle spindles	Spinal cord, medulla
Positive supporting (magnet) reaction	Contact with sole or palm	Foot extended to support body	Proprioceptors in distal flexors	Spinal cord
Negative supporting reaction	Stretch	Release of positive supporting reaction	Proprioceptors in extensors	Spinal cord
Tonic labyrinthine reflexes	Gravity	Extensor rigidity	Otolithic organs	Medulla
Tonic neck reflexes	Head turned: (1) to side (2) up (3) down	Change in pattern of rigidity (1) extension of limbs on side to which head is turned (2) hind legs flex (3) forelegs flex	Neck proprioceptors	Medulla
Labyrinthine righting reflexes	Gravity	Head kept level	Otolithic organs	Midbrain
Neck righting reflexes	Stretch of neck muscles	Righting of thorax and shoulders, then pelvis	Muscle spindles	Midbrain
Body on head-righting reflexes	Pressure on side of body	Righting of head	Exteroceptors	Midbrain
Body on body-righting reflexes	Pressure on side of body	Righting of body even when head held sideways	Exteroceptors	Midbrain
Optical righting reflexes	Visual cues	Righting of head	Eyes	Cerebral cortex
Placing reactions	Various visual, exteroceptive, and proprioceptive cues	Foot placed on supporting surface in position to support body	Various	Cerebral cortex
Hopping reactions	Lateral displacement while standing	Hops, maintaining limbs in position to support body	Muscle spindles	Cerebral cortex

Index

Compiled by Linda English

319